Se

MAN AND THE
CHEMICAL ELEMENTS

Man's most notable achievement in the investigation of the elements

The trial explosion in New Mexico of the first atomic bomb may well prove
to be one of the most significant events in Man's history. The photographs
were taken respectively 0·016 second and 8 seconds after the initiation of
the explosion. (See page 320.)

Reproduced by permission of the Directorate of Atomic Energy, Ministry of Supply

MAN
AND THE
CHEMICAL
ELEMENTS

*from stone-age
hearth to the
cyclotron*

J. NEWTON FRIEND
D.Sc. (B'ham), Ph.D (Würz.), F.R.I.C.

NEW YORK
CHARLES SCRIBNER'S SONS

Published in London, England, by
CHARLES GRIFFIN & COMPANY LTD

First American Edition 1953

PRINTED IN GREAT BRITAIN BY CHORLEY AND PICKERSGILL LTD LEEDS

PREFACE

Some ten years ago I wrote a series of articles on "The Historical and Industrial Discovery of the Elements". They were published in *Chemistry and Industry* and the many kind letters I received encouraged me to write a comprehensive book on the subject — incorporating most of the original material, augmenting it with much information of equal academic importance and of no less general interest, and including accounts of recent developments.

There can be little doubt that one of the best approaches to a science is through its history, and no doubt at all that the story of man and the chemical elements is of great fascination. That the first of these is widely recognised is adequately demonstrated by the frequent appearance of historical questions in academic and professional examination papers; and the second I have tried to show in these pages.

My information has been culled from many and various sources; I believe that all the important ones are acknowledged in the text. My sincere thanks are due to the Society of Chemical Industry for permission to make full use of my earlier articles, and to the publishers who have done all in their power to facilitate the work.

J. NEWTON FRIEND

July 1951

CONTENTS

CONTENTS

CONTENTS

PLATES

CHAPTER 1

PREAMBLE

What is an element?

At the outset let us be mutually agreed as to the meaning we propose to assign to the word "element".

The term is usually taken to indicate something fundamental, something simple, with the aid of which more complex systems or bodies can be produced. Thus the child goes to school to learn his ABC — the elements or the rudiments of his mother-tongue. To the chemist, however, the word "element" has a special significance. He has long realised that the matter by which he is surrounded is often extremely complex; it is built up in some mysterious way from simpler bodies, just as words may be built up from letters. These simpler bodies came to be known as the chemist's LMN's. Pronounce these letters quickly and it is not difficult to arrive at our word "element".

The so-called Aristotelean elements, Fire, Air, Earth, and Water, were postulated by Empedocles (490 to 430 B.C.) at least half a century before Aristotle (384 to 322 B.C.) saw the light. They were regarded as simple, material bodies; but in later years, largely as the result of Aristotelean philosophy, the terms were used in an abstract sense to denote essences or qualities of bodies. Thus hot substances and combustible materials were rich in the element Fire, whilst liquids owed their fluid properties to Water.

A nearer approach to the present conception of an element was that of Anaxagoras (500 to 427 B.C.) who assumed as many elements as there were "simple" substances. Thus sand and salt were simple substances, since the latter could be extracted from a mixture by dissolution in water and recovered by evaporation. But the number of these "simple" substances was inordinately large.

The word element was first used in its more modern sense by

1

Boyle about 1662, and was clearly defined by Lavoisier in 1789 as implying —

A substance that cannot be split up by any known means into something simpler

or, an element is —

Matter in its simplest form.

For over a century this definition sufficed. It was, nevertheless, unsatisfactory, being neither more nor less than a confession of ignorance and impotence. Thus it demanded that caustic potash should be regarded as an element until Davy succeeded in decomposing it by electrolysis in 1807. Similarly lime was regarded as an element and when Charles Tennant chlorinated slaked lime in 1799, the product was perforce called chloride of lime, a name that clings to it even to-day.

Lavoisier's definition is now no longer true. With the aid of fast-moving projectiles, such as α-particles, protons, deuterons and neutrons, under the influence of high potential differences, or in some cases ejected from radio-active matter, it is possible to effect the artificial transmutation of what are regarded as true elements into new ones of higher or lower atomic weight. Thus in 1919 the late Lord Rutherford bombarded nitrogen with α-particles from Radium C and obtained evidence of the liberation of protons or hydrogen nuclei as the result of "head on" collisions between nitrogen atoms and the α-particles. Similarly, in 1932 Cockcroft and Walton effected the disintegration of several elements by using, as projectiles, protons and deuterons, moving under potential differences up to one quarter of a million volts. In 1934 Curie and Joliot obtained radio-elements of even higher atomic weight than the parent by exposing the latter to bombardment with α-particles from polonium. Thus boron (at. wt. 10) yielded radionitrogen (13), whilst aluminium (27) was converted into radiophosphorus (30).

More recently still, it has been found possible, not only to synthesise elements of atomic weight higher even than that of uranium, but to break down these elements or effect their "fission", as it is now termed, into elements of only about half their own atomic weights (p. 318). It has now been found possible to convert mercury into gold — but the gold is radioactive, and the process is costly (p.221). Thus the dream of the early alchemists has come true, but not quite in the way they had hoped.

The atomic number

Many years ago, therefore, it became evident that Lavoisier's definition would have to be replaced by a new one more in harmony with the known facts of the case. Fortunately chemists had not far to turn. In 1895 Röntgen, professor of physics in the University of Würzburg in Bavaria, discovered that when matter is bombarded with cathode rays it emits new rays of extraordinary penetrating power. These rays, often now called Röntgen rays, were termed X-rays as their nature was then unknown, just as iodine was referred to as substance X at the time of its discovery (p. 48) before it was recognised to be an element.

X-rays are invisible but their presence may be shown by the fluorescence produced on, for example, a screen of barium platino-cyanide when placed in their path. They also travel in straight lines, they ionise gases so that their presence can readily be de-tected electroscopically; indeed the electroscope can be used to measure their intensity. They are regarded as pulsations in the ether of space, similar to light waves, but of very much shorter wave-length. X-rays cannot be examined with an ordinary prism or diffraction grating, such as may be used for an optical spectrum, because their wavelengths are too small. But the orderly arrangement of the atoms in a crystal enables the latter to function as a grating and to produce an X-ray spectrum. For this purpose Iceland spar is largely used.

In 1913 Moseley made a remarkable observation. He was a young scientist of unusually brilliant promise working at Man-chester University under the guidance of the late Lord Rutherford. Unfortunately for science he felt it imperative to obey the call of his Country during the first World War, and perished at the Dardanelles in 1915. Moseley discovered that the X-rays, emitted by an element when bombarded with cathode rays, yield on analysis with a crystal grating a characteristic spectrum consisting of groups of lines. The three principal groups belong to what are known as the K, L and M series. These spectra are fortunately very simple. Thus, in the K-series the spectrum of an element consists of but two well-marked lines, and what is more remarkable still is Moseley's observation that the wave-numbers of these lines shift in stepwise manner with great regularity from one adjoining member in the Periodic Table to another. Mathematically expressed

$$w \propto (z - b)^2$$

w being the wave number, z the positive charge on the nucleus of the atom, and b a constant. If $\sqrt{w}$ is plotted against z the relationship is linear, and measurement of w enables us to calculate z. Each element yields only one value for z, so that if we arrange the elements in the serial order of their z charges, beginning with hydrogen as unity, we can give to each a serial number known as the *Moseley number* or the *atomic number*. Isotopes of any one element all have the same atomic number.

As in general z rises with the atomic weight, the above arrangement of the elements is almost identical with Mendeléeff's periodic scheme; indeed it is the modern interpretation of the Periodic Law, and yields the *Ideal Periodic Table*, for there are no exceptions to it. Thus argon and potassium, nickel and cobalt, iodine and tellurium, now fall into line with the periodic scheme although consideration of their atomic weights, as in Mendeléeff's scheme, throws them out of gear.

We may therefore define an element as —

A substance possessing one atomic number and one only.

Thus ammonium, NH_4, would, if it could be tested, yield two atomic numbers, namely those of hydrogen and nitrogen. Despite its resemblance in combination to an alkali metal, it is not an element. Radium, on the other hand, yields only one atomic number, despite the fact that upon disintegration other elements are obtained from it; it is an element, therefore, and not a compound.

Moseley's researches have given us a method of ascertaining the maximum number of elements that can possibly exist in serial order between any two known elements. Thus between barium (atomic number 56) and hafnium (72) exactly 15 elements are possible; all of these are known and all occur in Nature with the exception possibly of No. 61. They are the rare-earth elements and resemble one another very closely; Mendeléeff's system gave no indication as to their number. In early days, therefore, considerable confusion existed, some of the elements being known under two or more names and regarded as separate entities; on the other hand mixtures of two or more elements were frequently regarded as single elements, as for example *didymium*, which

Periods	Group O	Group I	Group II	Group III	Group IV	Group V	Group VI	Group VII	Group VIII
	2 He 4·003	1 H 1·0080							
First short period	10 Ne 20·183	3 Li 6·940	4 Be 9·013	5 B 10·82	6 C 12·010	7 N 14·008	8 O 16·000	9 F 19·00	
Second short period	18 A 39·944	11 Na 22·997	12 Mg 24·32	13 Al 26·97	14 Si 28·06	15 P 30·98	16 S 32·06	17 Cl 35·457	
First long period — Even series		19 K 39·096	20 Ca 40·08	21 Sc 45·10	22 Ti 47·90	23 V 50·95	24 Cr 52·01	25 Mn 54·93	26 Fe 55·85 / 27 Co 58·94 / 28 Ni 58·69
First long period — Odd	36 Kr 83·7	29 Cu 63·57	30 Zn 65·38	31 Ga 69·72	32 Ge 72·60	33 As 74·91	34 Se 78·96	35 Br 79·916	
Second long period — Even series		37 Rb 85·48	38 Sr 87·63	39 Y 88·92	40 Zr 91·22	41 Nb 92·91	42 Mo 95·95	43 Tc [99]	44 Ru 101·7 / 45 Rh 102·91 / 46 Pd 106·7
Second long period — Odd	54 Xe 131·3	47 Ag 107·880	48 Cd 112·41	49 In 114·76	50 Sn 118·70	51 Sb 121·76	52 Te 127·61	53 I 126·92	
Third long period		55 Cs 132·91	56 Ba 137·36	57 La 138·92	58 Ce 140·13 / 59 Pr 140·92	60 Nd 144·27 / 61 Pm [147]	62 Sm 150·43 / 63 Eu 152·0	64 Gd 156·9 / 65 Tb 159·2	
(rare earths)		66 Dy 162·46 / 67 Ho 164·94	68 Er 167·2 / 69 Tm 169·4	70 Yb 173·04 / 71 Lu 174·99					
Fourth long period		79 Au 197·2	80 Hg 200·61	81 Tl 204·39	72 Hf 178·6 / 82 Pb 207·21	73 Ta 180·88 / 83 Bi 209·00	74 W 183·92 / 84 Po [210]	75 Re 186·31 / 85 At [210]	76 Os 190·2 / 77 Ir 193·1 / 78 Pt 195·23
Fifth long period — Even series / Odd	86 Rn 222	87 Fr [223]	88 Ra 226·05	89 Ac ..	90 Th 232·12	91 Pa 231	92 U 238·07	93 Np [237]	94 Pu [239] / 95 Am [241] / 96 Cm [242]

Based on the Report of the Commission of Atomic Weights of the International Union of Chemistry at its meeting in Amsterdam in September 1949. Values in brackets [ ] denote the mass numbers of the most stable known isotopes.

Welsbach showed in 1885 to consist of two elements which he named neodymium and praseodymium.

Between hydrogen and uranium a maximum number of 90 elements is indicated and all of these are known to occur in Nature with the exception, possibly, of elements 61, 85 and 87. The search for an element of higher atomic number than uranium for long proved abortive; indeed theoretical reasons were adduced to show that such an element would be too unstable to exist more than momentarily. But elements 93 (neptunium) and 94 (plutonium) are now known to occur in Nature; they have also been synthesised together with 95 (americium) and 96 (curium)*.

Relative abundance of the elements

Numerous estimates have been made of the relative amounts of the various elements that occur in the Earth's crust. They vary considerably, as is to be expected when we bear in mind the limitations of our experience; apart from the atmosphere and ocean a limited portion only of a thin shell of solid on the surface of the Earth constitutes all that we can examine. For the atmosphere and ocean our information is fairly good, though still subject to minor corrections. For the solid crust we must select some arbitrary depth and that of 10 miles is usually chosen as this clears the lower depths of the oceans. The average composition of the lithosphere (Greek *lithos*, stone) must approximate closely to that of the igneous rocks alone, some of which were the earliest to be formed; the sedimentary rocks represent altered igneous material from which some of the soluble salts have been leached into the oceans and to which oxygen, carbon dioxide and water have been supplied, mainly from the atmosphere. The thin film of organic matter on the Earth's surface can be neglected; even coal beds are negligible; the ocean itself comprises about 6·8 per cent of the Earth's 10-mile crust.

The estimated figures are as follows —

	10^{12} tons
Total weight of the Earth	6,000,000,000
Solid 10-mile crust	17,418,000
Oceans	1,276,000
Atmosphere	5,260

*To these have recently (1950) been added berkelium (97) and californium (98).

In the following table* are given the approximate percentages of the more abundant elements in the Earth's 10-mile crust, including the air and the ocean.

	Per Cent			Per Cent
Oxygen	50·0	Fluorine		0·10
Silicon	26·0	Barium		0·08
Aluminium ..	7·30	Manganese ..		0·08
Iron	4·18	Nitrogen.. ..		0·03
Calcium	3·22	Copper		0·02
Sodium	2·36	Strontium ..		0·02
Potassium ..	2·28	Nickel		0·016
Magnesium ..	2·08	Cerium		0·009
Hydrogen ..	0·37	Tin		0·008
Titanium ..	0·37	Lead		0·003
Chlorine	0·20	Silver ..		2×10^{-5}
Carbon	0·18	Gold ..		2×10^{-7}
Sulphur	0·11	Radium ..		$1·4 \times 10^{-12}$
Phosphorus ..	0·11	All other elements		0·874

It will be noted that oxygen and silicon are overwhelmingly abundant; amongst the metals, aluminium, iron and calcium are the most plentiful. It may be a surprise to note that lead is less common than tin, despite the much higher price of the latter in the metal market; the so-called rare-earth metal cerium is more plentiful than either. Silver is 100 times as plentiful as gold and the latter at 248s. per oz. troy would appear to be much under-valued with silver standing round 5s. Although nitrogen is more than three times as abundant in the atmosphere as oxygen, there are only 6 parts of nitrogen to 10,000 of oxygen in the Earth's crust.

The ages of man

It is often convenient to divide the history of man's progress into epochs or ages, according to the nature of the materials he commonly used in his daily life. Thus in the various stone ages his weapons were mainly of flint, in the bronze age of bronze, and so on. These ages represent stages of civilisation rather than time intervals and were not necessarily co-eval for different races. Thus the ancient Philistines, mentioned in the Old Testament, were in their iron age whilst the Hebrews were still in their bronze age.

---

*This list is essentially that given by F. W. CLARKE, "Data of Geochemistry" (Washington, 1916) p. 34, down to strontium. The remaining data are culled from various sources.

The stone ages

At first man's weapons would be of the simplest and crudest types; oft-times ordinary stones, branches of trees, horns of animals would be used for hunting down his quarry. But as stones suitable in shape and size might not always be at hand at the critical moment it would occur to him to collect them beforehand and improve them by fracture, chipping or rubbing. In this way shapes would be evolved that were particularly suitable for special purposes, such as axes, arrow and spear heads, knives, scrapers and so on. The rude flaking of the earliest periods would gradually be improved upon until implements were ultimately produced exhibiting the most beautiful workmanship. Some of the finest specimens were produced in Egypt just prior to the First Dynasty, some 3,500 B.C.

At an early date man became acquainted with fire and learned how to produce it at will. This was an event of stupendous importance. His camp fire added both to his comfort and to his safety at night, keeping the wild beasts at a distance; it guided his friends to camp after dark; it enabled him to harden clay into pottery and eventually to reduce metals from their ores.

Virtually co-eval with the knowledge of fire would be the recognition of charcoal, so that this form of carbon was one of the very earliest elements to be known.

A second epoch-making event was the invention of the bow and arrow. When this took place we do not know; possibly some 50,000 B.C. This gave man an immense superiority over the animal; it was no longer necessary to go close up to wild beasts to spear them; birds could be caught on the wing at much greater distances than with a stone, skilful though primitive man must have been in the art of stone throwing. Man thus became more secure in his home, and his food supply was more certain than ever before. He now had time on his hands; what should he do? He began to adorn his cave-dwelling with pictures or frescoes such as those found in 1875 in the famous rock-shelter "La Madelaine", in 1879 at Altamira in Spain, and in the Dordogne in 1895. As pigments he used various earths such as chalk for a background, oxides of iron for red and brown colours, and charcoal produced in his fires for sharp outlines.

Meanwhile he certainly became acquainted with metals; he was familiar with gold, and prized it because of its intrinsic beauty and freedom from tarnish. He also knew copper, silver, and any other metals that perchance occurred native. This does not mean, however, that he was in any sense a metallurgist; that was to come later. He would regard a metal merely as a stone, though a very useful one withal, because it could be hammered into shape, rubbed to a sharp edge, or made into pretty ornaments for his women-folk.

The age of metals

It is generally held that the metallurgical discovery of metals, as products of ores, was brought about in a commonplace and humble manner, namely, in the domestic hearths of stone-age man (p.90). This was another of the real epoch-making events of human history. The possession of metal weapons gave men decisive advantage in battle and the chase over those who relied upon stone alone. A courage, born of security or a sense of superiority, coupled with a desire to find new sources of the metal, was one of the factors leading to the exploration of new lands.

The discovery that bronze is not obtained from a single pure ore, but from a mixture of at least two ores, followed in due course; by this time man had acquired a very substantial degree of metallurgical skill and knowledge. At the zenith of the bronze age some of the workers appear even to have regulated the percentages of tin in their alloys to suit particular purposes.

As time progressed, bronze gradually gave way to iron. For many years the two metals were used side by side; in certain prehistoric remains, such as those at Hallstadt in the Austrian Tyrol, implements of bronze and iron have been discovered lying together, indicative of contemporary use.

Elements known to the ancients

Seven metallic and two non-metallic elements were known to man before the Christian Era. The metals include those popularly called the "coinage" metals, gold, silver and copper, together with lead, tin and iron; to these quicksilver or mercury was added about the fourth century B.C. The two non-metals were carbon in its various forms as diamond, graphite and charcoal, and brimstone or sulphur. Six of the metals are mentioned by name in the Old Testament, together with the diamond and brimstone. As will be explained later, the "tin" of Holy Writ was not the pure metal as we know it to-day, but a rich tin-copper alloy. It is uncertain if the "diamond" was our stone (p. 55); the Biblical "brass" was usually a bronze, for zinc was unknown to the ancients, and only occasionally would brass be produced as a "natural alloy". According to the Old Testament, gold, iron and "brass" were known before the "Flood", that is prior to about 4000 B.C. Silver, lead and "tin" are not mentioned until after the Flood. Homer, writing *circa* 880 B.C. knew of the six metals; he was, of course, familiar with charcoal and was moreover aware of the disinfectant properties of brimstone.

There is an old Canaanitish legend, to which reference is made in the book of *Genesis* iv. 22, in which the humanised god, Tubal Cain, son of Zillah, is described as "an instructor of every artificer in brass and iron". The word *Tubal* is believed to be Babylonian and connected with *Gibril*, the god of Solar Fire. The suffix *Cain* is missing from the Greek version and means artificer. It was perhaps added to Tubal to explain why the hero was regarded as the father or instructor of smiths. Possibly in the earliest form of the Hebrew legend Tubal was the instructor of men in the art of making fire, probably by rubbing two pieces of wood together, for this is an old Arabian method and appears in later times in connection with ritual. Enoch* recalls the general tradition that the first metal worker was supernatural, the fallen angel Azāzel being a teacher of the art. Azāzel was the leader of the evil angels who are stated in *Genesis* vi. 2, 4, to have formed unions with the daughters of men and taught them various arts. Their offspring were the giants who filled the earth with unrighteousness.

In later years the Egyptians became wonderfully skilful in the working of metals, so much so that when the Greeks conquered Egypt in the fourth century B.C. they were greatly impressed. Egypt is watered by the longest river of the old world. Every autumn the Nile rises in flood, bringing down with it a fine mud which fertilises the soil. The black appearance of the land after flooding caused the country to be known as *Khem* or Black Land. In referring, therefore, to the skill of the natives in working metals, the Greeks spoke of the *Art of Khem*. This word descended to us through the Arabic as *Alchemy*. Later the prefix *al*, which is merely the Arabic definite article, was dropped and to-day we speak of *Chemistry*. In its original meaning, therefore, chemistry was more akin to metallurgy; but the world has moved on since then — so has science, and chemistry with it.

It is customary to divide the elements into three groups, namely non-metals, metals and metalloids, the last named being inter-

---

*See "The Book of Enoch" written *circa* 105 to 64 B.C.

mediary (p. 68). The word metal comes from the Greek *metallon*, which is believed to have originated in a verb meaning to seek or search for. The metallurgist was thus the one who prospected for ores, mined them when found and worked the ore for metals; he was at once a prospector, a miner and a metal worker.

Problems

It is often difficult to ascertain, from the study of the literature alone, what particular metals or alloys were used for specific purposes in the past. For this there are several reasons.

(1) Although the early workers could usually distinguish without much difficulty between gold, silver and copper or bronze, they often confused other base metals and alloys with one another. Their statements are thus apt to be misleading.

Thus, for example, lead and tin do not appear to have been distinguished before Roman times, and even in Pliny's day they seem to have been regarded more as varieties of the same metal than as entirely different species.

(2) As knowledge grows, words gradually change their meanings. For example, the Mexicans called their own copper or bronze *tepuztli*, a West Indian word that is said to have originally meant "hatchet". Later the same word was used for iron, with which metal the Mexicans were already familiar at the time of the Spanish Conquest. Tepuztli then became a general term for metal, and in order to distinguish copper from iron the former was termed *red* and the latter *black* tepuztli*.

Similarly the Greek word *chalkós* at first referred to copper or bronze and we use the word *chalcolithic* to indicate that stage or era of human culture in which copper was the predominant metal. But as iron gradually supplanted copper, so chalkós came to mean iron, and *chalkeus*, the copper smith, became the "worker in iron" in Homer's Odyssey. As the smith had worked in copper and bronze long before he had ever beaten iron on his anvil, he and his smithy derived their name from these early metals; but *chalkeus* and *chalkeion* continued to designate blacksmith and forge throughout all classical Greek literature, when iron was the metal that was worked†.

We moderns have done the same thing. The washerwoman's "copper", though made of iron, still retains its old designation;

---

*TYLOR, "Mexico and the Mexicans", 1861, p. 140.
†RIDGEWAY, "The Early Age of Greece" (C.U.P., 1901) Volume 1, p. 295.

and who is not familiar with fire-"irons" made of brass, "tin"-tacks of iron and sealing "wax" of shellac?

In the Torres Strait Region an earth oven or hole in the ground in which food is baked is commonly called a "copper" and many have erroneously supposed the name to have been borrowed from the "copper" cooking vessels of New Zealand whalers. The word is really, however, a form in pidgin English of the native term *kŏpa*, an earth oven*.

Somewhat similar difficulties have arisen in the interpretation of the words brimstone (p. 22) and quicksilver (p. 16), owing to their having been used in a spiritual as well as a material sense.

(3) Finally, it should be mentioned that, in the past, the antiquary has not always possessed the requisite chemical or metallurgical knowledge, with the result that relics have not infrequently been most incorrectly described. Copper objects have been classed as bronzes and *vice versa*, whilst, to the present author's own knowledge, hæmatite arrow-heads have been described as made of iron of such excellent quality that it had resisted corrosion throughout the ages!

The alchemists

From the earliest times gold has been regarded as the perfect metal; the medieval alchemists denoted it symbolically by a circle, the hall mark of mathematical perfection. It was also identified with the sun in accordance with the practice of associating metals with celestial bodies. How this practice originated we do not know, but it may have been connected with the holy number seven. There were seven metals or alloys known to the ancients and there were also seven dominating celestial bodies, these latter including the sun, moon and five planets, namely Mercury, Venus, Mars, Jupiter and Saturn, revolving, as was then believed, round the Earth. Man is slow to realise his own insignificance. Aristarchus some 250 B.C. had already explained, though much in advance of his time, that the Earth must be travelling round the Sun. But for almost another two millenia man preferred to believe that his world was the hub of the universe. Uranus was not known to the ancients, being discovered by Sir William Herschel in 1781; this was a great achievement for, counting the Earth as one, there were now seven planets known. The discovery of Neptune in 1846 upset this holy number and matters were made even worse when Pluto was observed in 1930.

*SMYTHE PALMER, "The Folk and their Word-lore" (Routledge, 1904), p. 15.

For the ancients there was thus one metal for each heavenly body. Gold was naturally associated with the sun in virtue of its bright yellow colour and dominant position among the metals. Indeed some alchemists spoke of gold as "condensed sunbeams", much in the same way as quartz or rock crystal was regarded by Albertus Magnus, round A.D. 1250, as a form of ice so hardened by Alpine frosts that it refused to melt. Silver, the less perfect metal, was allowed only half a circle, its symbol thus resembling the crescent moon; this, coupled with its pale colour, clinched the connection with that luminary.

Symbols of the alchemists

Gold	○	Sun	Lead	.. ♄	Saturn
Silver	☽	Moon	Iron	.. ♂	Mars
Copper	♀	Venus	Quicksilver	☿	Mercury
Tin	♃	Jupiter			

Iron, the warrior's metal *par excellence*, came under the ægis of Mars, the god of war; it was appropriately symbolised by a shield and spear. The symbols of the remaining elements bore a cross signifying the close connection between alchemy and religion. Tin and lead were given somewhat similar symbols because they were sometimes regarded as mere variants of one and the same metal. In either case they were debased forms of silver, hence the curved portions. The lead symbol suggests a sickle or scythe. As lead was heavy, dense and dull it came under the influence of Saturn, the farthest known planet from the Earth, and apparently therefore moving the most sluggishly. From this originated the "scythe of Saturn" and the idea of spiritual density or moroseness associated with the word saturnine.

Some authorities see in the symbol for tin the *Zeta* of Zeus or Jupiter; others the arabic 4 or *arbah* ち, indicating the fourth planet — again Jupiter. Copper with its orange colour more closely resembles gold than the other metals and was awarded a disc plus the inevitable cross. The symbol thus bore a fanciful resemblance to a hand mirror and was hence called the looking-glass of Venus. The Egyptian symbol *ankh*, ♀, the "handled cross", denoting the sun's gift of life to the world, is closely similar.

Quicksilver, as its name implies, is alive and active corresponding to Mercury the nimble messenger of the gods. Its symbol, regarded as the caduceus or wand of Mercury, embodied the sign of the cross, surmounted by the circle of perfection and the crescent of silver which latter metal it so closely resembles in colour and brightness. As the supposed constituent of all metals (p. 15) and by virtue of its incorrodibility, quicksilver had earned the circle of perfection.

In early days apothecaries were wont to have with them bottles containing coloured liquids and labelled with appropriate signs, as badges of office, so to speak. These included yellow solutions, indicative of gold, marked with a circle; red solutions signifying iron and marked with the shield and spear of Mars; and so on. As the years rolled by and the profits increased it was appropriate that the size of the bottles should also increase until they reached the dimensions now familiar to us in the shops of our wealthy pharmacists.

It is of interest to recall that the seven days of our week are associated through the celestial bodies with the seven metals known to the ancients. Thus the sun and moon are clearly perpetuated in Sunday and Monday, the gold and silver days. Tuesday is the day of *Tiw*, the Anglo-Saxon equivalent of Mars. *Woden*, the Saxon counterpart of the Scandinavian *Odin*, gives us Wednesday; the Romans early identified Wodin with Mercury; the French use the word *mercredi*, that is *mercurii dies*. Thursday is *Thor's* day, Thor being equivalent to Jupiter, whence the French *jeudi* or *Jovis dies*. Frigg was the wife of Woden and corresponds to Venus, the goddess of love; whence Friday and the French *vendredi*, the *veneris dies*. Saturday is clearly *Saturn's* day. The French name for Sunday, *dimanche*, departs from this scheme: it is a corruption of *domini dies*, the Lord's Day.

In this connection it may be noted that the order of the days of the week is not random, as at first sight it appears to be. In times when astrology was an important branch of science, day and night were each divided into twelve planetary or unequal hours (unequal because day and night vary in length throughout the year). The hour of one planet succeeded that of another in the order of diminishing planetary distance from the earth according to the Ptolemaic* system of astronomy—

Saturn	Jupiter	Mars	Sun	Venus	Mercury	Moon
♄	♃	♂	○	♀	☿	☽

*The geocentric Ptolemaic system was superseded by the heliocentric system of Copernicus (1473–1543) principally owing to the work of Galileo, Kepler, and Newton in the seventeenth century. The planets are now known to revolve about the sun in elliptical orbits of small eccentricity at the following mean distances (in millions of miles)—Mercury, 36; Venus, 67·2; Earth, 92·9; Mars, 141·5; Jupiter, 483·3; Saturn, 886·1; Uranus, 1783; Neptune, 2793; Pluto, 3666.

The day took its name from the hour with which it began. "Understonde wel", says Chaucer*, "that these houres inequales ben clepid [called] houres of planetes ... The firste houre inequal of every Saturday is to Saturne, and the seconde to Iupiter, the thirde to Mars, the fourthe to the sonne, the fifte to Venus, the sixte to Mercurius, the seventhe to the mone. And then ageyn the 8 is to Saturne, the 9 to Iupiter ..." Continuing in this way, the twenty-fifth hour (or the first hour of the next day) is found to be "the houre of the forseide sonne". So the day after Saturday is Sunday — and so on through the week.

Transmutation

The idea that the metals could undergo transmutation under natural conditions with the lapse of time was widespread for many centuries. Plato (427 to 344 B.C.) believed this. The ancient Chinese philosophers believed that arsenic, in the course of 200 years in the ground became converted into tin (p. 19). Even as late as the eighteenth century miners believed that lead was gradually converted to silver and that bismuth was lead half-way on the road thither (p. 87). The alchemists believed it might be possible to hurry up or catalyse this transmutation in the laboratory, and if so, why not make it profitable by converting a base metal direct into gold? At first blush this might appear but a foolish dream; it was however a logical conclusion from the then current ideas of the constitution of matter.

The sulphur-mercury theory

Geber†, the famous Arabian chemist, regarded the six metals gold, silver, copper, lead, tin, and iron, as compounds of quicksilver with sulphur in different proportions. Gold was composed of the purest mercury and sulphur. The base metals contained the same essential ingredients as gold, but were contaminated with various impurities. If, therefore, these latter could be removed pure gold must result; the base metals would thus be transmuted to gold. The name Geber is the Westernised form of Jabir, the full name of this famous chemist being Abu Musa Jabir ibn Hayyan. He was born at Tus, near Meshed, A.D. 721 or 722, the son of a

---

*"A Treatise on the Astrolabe". The quotation is from "The Works of Chaucer", Globe edition (Macmillan, 1910).
†"The Works of Geber". Translated by R. Russell, 1678. Introduction by Holmyard (Dent, 1928).

druggist. Losing his father at an early age* he was sent to Arabia to study the Koran and ultimately became *persona grata* at the court of Harun al-Rashid, at Baghdad; this Harun was the Caliph of the "Arabian Nights". Later he retired to Kufa in Iraq, which had been his father's home, and remained there in seclusion until the time of his death early in the ninth century. Some 200 years later a street in Kufa, known as Damascus Gate, was rebuilt and in the course of necessary demolitions Geber's laboratory was uncovered. In it were found a mortar and a large lump of gold which, says the chronicler, "the King's Chamberlain took possession of". It was assumed of course, that the gold was the product of transmutation.

The word "gibberish" is derived from Geber and refers to the unintelligible jargon used by alchemists of whom Geber was regarded as the typical representative. Sylvester, writing in 1621, says of the builders of the tower of Babel: "som howl, som halloo, sum do stut and strain. Each hath his gibberish." We are reminded of Isaiah's reference to a people who speak with "a stammering tongue, that thou canst not understand" (*Isaiah* xxxiii. 19). Alchemists were sometimes nicknamed "Geber's cooks" and Camden, writing in 1637, referred to alchemy as "Geber's cookery".

It is evident that Geber's quicksilver and sulphur were not the material elements known by those names, for he mentions that on heating the material elements together "the red stone known to men of science as cinnabar" was produced. The constituents of gold were thus hypothetical or idealised substances to which material quicksilver and sulphur were the nearest known approach (p. 71). The European alchemist, Albertus Magnus, who became Bishop of Ratisbon in 1259, is believed to have subscribed to the quicksilver–sulphur theory, although the authenticity of the alchemistic works attributed to him has been queried. It was he who introduced the word "affinity" to indicate the reason why sulphur united with quicksilver — a term that is widely used and appreciated by chemists to-day.

Sir Isaac Newton appears to have believed in the possibility of transmuting base metals into gold and to have kept furnaces going for many weeks with this end in view, sitting up at nights to attend to them. But after his appointment as Master of the Mint in 1699 it would hardly have been wise for him to allow his name to be associated with alchemy. The less said the better. At his death in

---

*He was a druggist and was beheaded by the Caliph for political intrigue.

1727 the catalogue of his library contained many works on alchemy.

Numerous stories were current in alchemistic days of base metals being transmuted to gold. All were told by "reputable witnesses" and were "undeniably true".

Jean Jacques Manget who, from 1669 until his decease in 1742, was "first physician" to the Elector of Brandenburg relates one such story in his "Bibliotheca Chemica Curiosa". He says that in 1650 a young cleric who spoke fluent Italian was asked to show an Italian visitor to Geneva the "sights" of that beautiful city. After a couple of weeks the stranger ran short of money and asked his guide to introduce him to a goldsmith who would be willing to lend him some crucibles and allow him the use of a furnace. This being duly arranged, the stranger melted some tin in a crucible and to it added mercury that had been heated in a second crucible together with a red powder in a wax capsule. The mixture became greatly agitated and evolved copious fumes. When these had cleared away the stranger poured the still molten contents of the crucible into moulds and obtained thereby six bars of pure gold. One of these he gave as recompense to the goldsmith and the others he sold to the Master of the Mint, who thereby guaranteed the genuineness of the metal. Being now in funds the stranger paid his hotel bill, handed the cleric 20 gold coins as honorarium for his services and to these added a further 15 for joint entertainment with the goldsmith during the next few days. He then left, promising to return and have supper with them that evening. But he failed to return and was not heard of again —another mysterious disappearance.

Most of the stories end like that just as they are becoming interesting.

Many alchemists, like Paracelsus (1490 to 1535) and Basil Valentine (p. 84), published recipes for making the Philosopher's Stone, the magic wand, with the aid of which base metals may be converted to gold. But why such generosity? We look askance at these recipes, remembering the words of Alfred C. Lewis —

> It's not the man who knows the most
> That has the most to say;
> It's not the man who has the most
> That gives the most away.

In general this is true, and human nature has not altered much with the lapse of centuries.

17

It is perhaps worth noting that alchemy has several times received the serious attention of legislature in this country. In 1404, during the reign of Henry IV, the making of gold and silver was forbidden by Act of Parliament; to transmute metals was to compound a felony. The authorities feared that a successful alchemist might become a menace to the state. On the other hand the feeble-minded Henry VI (1422 to 1461) granted several patents to people who imagined they had discovered the philosopher's stone and could thus transmute metals.

The miner

Miners have been proverbially superstitious. Working underground, deprived of the stimulating rays of the sun, they were apt to cherish a belief in the supernatural that most of us who labour above ground hesitate to share.

The Welsh mines were believed to house "knockers", little fellows about 18 inches in height, good-natured and willing to assist the miner by drawing his attention to the richest veins of ore. These knockers were not generally to be seen, but guided by knocks the miners who followed in the direction of the sounds. Other inhabitants of mines have not always been quite so friendly. Christopher Merret*, writing in 1677 of the Cornish tin mines, stated that the miners were wont to tell stories of sprites or "small people" as they called them, who terrified them by causing horrid knockings and fearful hammerings. Many German mines were similarly peopled by sprites or goblins known as "kobalds". These pestilential gnomes placed poisonous ores in the path of the miners and on the sabbath it was customary to pray for deliverance from their machinations when attending church. This belief is perpetuated in the name *cobalt* (p. 291).

The growth of minerals

Miners have long cherished the idea that metals and minerals, like plants and animals, can grow and breed. Pliny, writing at the beginning of the Christian Era†, refers to certain lead mines

---

*C. MERRET, *Phil. Trans.*, 1677, **12**, No. 138, p. 949.

†PLINY, "Natural History", translated by Bostock and Riley (Bohn, 1857), Book 34, Chap. 49. Pliny was probably born at Novum Comum, A.D. 23, on the south shore of Lake Larius in N. Italy. He died at the age of 56 in A.D. 79 when Herculaneum and Pompeii were overwhelmed by the eruption of Vesuvius. Pliny is famous for his enormous literary production "Historia Naturalis", the only one of his works that has survived to our times. It was completed A.D. 77.

which "when they have been abandoned for some time, become replenished and are more prolific than before." Even to-day the Tibetan miners will collect and export gold dust; they refuse, however, to touch the nuggets as these are believed to breed the dust. In effect the nuggets are the geese that lay the golden eggs.

Many circumstances contributed to these beliefs. Take, for example, the bog iron ore which "grows" in the Swedish lakes. It consists essentially of hydrated ferric oxide, probably oxidised from dissolved ferrous salts and thrown out of solution by lowly organisms. The ore once removed from the lake bed is gradually replenished. In Cumberland and in Lancashire there are places where limestone has been replaced molecule by molecule with ferrous carbonate from percolating waters charged with ferrous salts in solution. Oxidation and heat have converted the ferrous carbonate to hæmatite; the rocks thus possess the appearance of having "grown together" as the miners say, the hæmatite gradually passing into the limestone and possessing similar stratifications and dip. Casts of mollusca and other fossils characteristic of carboniferous limestone have been found in the hæmatite as well as crystals of hæmatite pseudomorphic with calcite.

In the Middle Ages mines were frequently closed in order that the supply of metals might be renewed.

Merret* mentions that a "white sparr" found along with tin-stone in Cornish mines was locally regarded as the "mother" of the ore. Even as late as the middle of the nineteenth century the country folk in Berkshire believed that the stones in the fields grew. "They could prove to you" wrote John M. Bacon† "that stones grew from year to year, even as cabbages grow, though of course much more slowly; since did they not pick the 'big-uns' off the field every season for road mending, yet their number never diminished, showing beyond doubt that the 'little uns had growed'."

Early Chinese philosophers believed that arsenic would regenerate itself after 200 years and after a like period would be transmuted to tin (p. 15).

---

*MERRET, loc. cit., p. 951.
†GERTRUDE BACON, "The Record of an Aeronaut" (London, 1907), p. 52.

CHAPTER 2

THE PERMANENT GASES

THE permanent gases included in this chapter comprise oxygen, nitrogen, hydrogen, deuterium and tritium.

The ancients recognised only two forms of matter, to which we give the names solid and liquid. The rustling of the leaves of the trees in the woods was due to nymphs dancing from bough to bough; the waves of the sea during a tempest were lashed into fury by Neptune's god-like wrath. But gradually it was realised that these conceptions created many insoluble problems; it was better to assume that matter was not destroyed when wood burned and water evaporated, but was converted into an invisible spirit-like substance which was still in existence even if it could not be seen. We owe the word "gas" to that erratic genius van Helmont (1577 to 1644) who probably derived it from the Dutch *Geest*, ghost or spirit, in view of its elusive nature*.

Faraday, who resumed his earlier work on the liquefaction of gases in 1845 found himself utterly unable to liquefy hydrogen, nitrogen, oxygen, nitric oxide and carbon monoxide, no matter what pressure he applied, and concluded that they were un-liquefiable; they came to be known, therefore, as *permanent gases*. We now know the reason for this. For every gas there is a temperature, known as the critical temperature, above which a gas cannot be liquefied no matter how great the pressure. Above its critical temperature any gas is permanent; below it the gas is a vapour. The critical temperatures of the above-mentioned gases lie well below the ordinary temperature of the atmosphere; that was why Faraday was unable to liquefy them; they have all since been liquefied; liquid air and oxygen are now commercial commodities.

We shall now proceed to discuss the following gases—oxygen, ozone, nitrogen, hydrogen with its isotopes, and, in the next chapter, the inert gases. Although fluorine and chlorine are also permanent gases, it is convenient to consider them later along with the other halogens.

---

*An alternative derivation from the Greek *chaos*, space, accepted by many authorities appears to the present Author to be less probable.

Oxygen

So much has been written from time to time about the early history of this element that the barest outline will now suffice. Oxygen is the most abundant element in the earth's crust of which it constitutes some 50 per cent if we include the ocean and the atmosphere. The last named alone holds approximately 1218 billion tons of the gas. Leonardo da Vinci (1452 to 1519), the famous artist whose painting of "The Last Supper", in Milan, is world famous, appears to have been the first European to state that air is not completely consumed during respiration or combustion. Boyle showed in 1660 that air was necessary for life, and in 1670 an Italian naturalist wrote that if the air holes of an insect were covered with oil or syrup, the insect would die in convulsions while one might say a Paternoster — a monkish method of measuring time.

Although Harvey discovered the circulation of the blood in 1619, he believed the object of the air in entering the lungs was merely to cool the heart. Hooke, in 1665, knew that nitre contained a constituent similar to the active principle of the air, and in 1728 Stephen Hales, Vicar of Teddington, actually heated nitre, collected the oxygen and measured its volume. But he did not examine the gas. A great discovery was thus narrowly missed.

In the early seventies of the eighteenth century the Swedish chemist Scheele and Presbyterian minister Joseph Priestley* discovered oxygen independently. Both investigators obtained it, probably as early as 1773, in several ways, including the heating of mercuric oxide. The Priestley statue in Birmingham represents Priestley heating the oxide in a tube with the sun's heat concentrated by a lens held between his thumb and second finger. Poetic licence! The actual lens was twelve inches across! Legend hath it that Priestley discovered the gas on 1st August 1774; this is apparently due to a misreading of his laboratory notes. He prepared the gas on that day, but *not for the first time*. He had been familiar with it for at least a year. His first public announcement was at the Royal Society on 23rd March 1775, and in most cases that would now be taken as the date of the discovery.

Scheele embodied an account of his researches in a book entitled "Air and Fire", the manuscript of which was completed in 1775; but publication was delayed by the printer until 1777, much to

---

*See his "Memoirs" edited by his son in 1805.

the chagrin of Scheele, for, in the meantime, Priestley had announced his discovery of oxygen. Scheele called the gas *empyreal* or *fire air*, the term "air" being synonymous with the present use of our word gas. These names reflected the ease with which substances burned in the gas. So did Priestley's term *dephlogisticated air*, but to appreciate this and the importance of the discovery of oxygen it is necessary to appreciate also the then current views on combustion. It is safe to say that neither Scheele not Priestley realised the important part played in combustion processes by the gas they had discovered.

The theory of phlogiston*

Why do substances burn? This is a problem that exercised the curiosity of man from the earliest times. Colour, shape, hardness, opacity — none of these properties appeared to have anything to do with it. Surely the explanation must be that substances burn because they possess the essence of combustibility; in 1697 Stahl, professor of Chemistry and Medicine at Halle University, coined the name "phlogiston" for this essence, deriving it from the Greek *phlox*, flame, or *phlogistein*, to set on fire. Substances burning in air gave up phlogiston to the air which was regarded as not yet saturated with it; as soon as it became saturated no further combustion could occur, for phlogiston could not escape from matter unless it had somewhere to go. The idea was much like that of a sponge which until it is saturated can absorb water; but once it is saturated it no longer functions.

The new gas of Scheele and Priestley allowed unusually vigorous combustion to occur. It was a really dry "sponge"; it could mop up the phlogiston in which it was perhaps entirely deficient. Hence Priestley's name for it — dephlogisticated air.

The substance we are familiar with under the Latin name of "sulphur" was for a long time known as "brimstone" or burning stone, the stone that burned completely away and, unlike wood, left no ash. Brimstone thus became the personification of combustibility, and the words brimstone and sulphur developed a double meaning, spiritual and material. This has naturally led to some confusion of thought. In Holy Writ we read, for example, in *Rev.* xxi. 8, that the wicked "shall have their part in the lake which burneth with fire and brimstone". From statements like this the

---

*This theory has been exhaustively studied by PARTINGTON and McKIE, *Annals of Science*, 1937, **2**, 361; 1938, **3**, 1, 337; 1939, **4**, 113.

conception of hell, which continued down to recent times, was that of a place where the wicked were exposed eternally to intense heat aggravated by fumes of burning sulphur; in other words hell was a heated poison-gas chamber. Such, however, was by no means the original idea, for material sulphur was not in the mind of the writer. The expression meant "fire and the essence of fire" a typical eastern duplication so common in languages that have no comparatives, to indicate great intensity, like our expressions, "out and out" or "through and through". The wicked were thus to be exposed to intense fire. But even this is not quite the real meaning. The early Hebrew tongue had relatively few words and practically none to represent abstract moral ideas. Thus when a man was angry he was said to be "hot", and the lesson the sacred writer wished to convey was that hell is a place or state where the wicked are exposed to the intense wrath of God — after all, a very modern conception.

In 1640 Albaro Barba wrote a book entitled "The Art of Metals" in which occurs one of the earliest known references to American Petroleum. It runs*—

"La Naphte is a *sulphurous* liquor, sometimes white, and sometimes black also, and is that which is called Oyl of Peter, of admirable vertue to cure old pains, proceeding from cold causes. It will draw fire to it (as the loadstone does iron) . . . "

Clearly there was no suggestion of material sulphur here. We need not laugh at our ancestors for giving material and spiritual meanings to the same words. We do the same to-day. When we are told that a man is full of good spirits we do not infer that he has just polished off a bottle of whisky. There is no confusion in our minds; neither was there in the minds of our forefathers. With the introduction of the conception of phlogiston many came to regard the spiritual sulphur and phlogiston as the same essence.

When metals are calcined in air, oxides are usually produced. This was explained by Stahl on the supposition that the metal, on being heated, parted with its phlogiston leaving a residue of calx. In the light of this idea the calx was of simpler composition than the metal itself. Thus —

$$metal = calx + phlogiston$$

A substance such as charcoal was regarded as being rich in

*This quotation is from the English translation of 1669 by the EARL OF SANDWICH.

phlogiston and could reverse the above process by restoring the phlogiston to the calx when heated with it and so reproduce the metal. Thus —

$$calx + charcoal = metal + charcoal\ ash$$

Paracelsus (p. 85) at the beginning of the sixteenth century, had already described metals that had undergone oxidation as *dead*. Thus a calx was a dead metal; verdigris was dead copper. He mentioned that metals could be brought to life again or "reduced to the metallic state" by heating with charcoal; he was the first to use the word reduce in this sense.

The theory of phlogiston was during the eighteenth century very popular amongst chemists despite the fact that it was full of anomalies. For example, if phlogiston were a material body, it is evident from the equation given above that a metal must weigh more than its calx. If phlogiston were merely an immaterial essence, the two would weigh the same just as a hot body weighs the same as when it is cold within the error of experiment. Now Jean Rey had already in 1630 shown that lead and tin actually *increase* in weight when calcined; but trifles of this kind were not allowed to interfere with so convenient a theory!

In 1766 Cavendish identified hydrogen and distinguished it from carbon monoxide, marsh gas, and other inflammable gases. Priestley, on hearing of this, immediately identified hydrogen with phlogiston and, as hydrogen was so much lighter than air, he found here an explanation for the gain in weight of a metal when converted to calx. Evidently a gross confusion of thought.

Lavoisier's theory of combustion

In 1774 Priestley was in Paris and met Lavoisier, already at the age of 31 the foremost chemist in France. Unfortunately his brilliant career was doomed to end with his execution in 1794, a victim to the blood-lust of the French Revolution. Of him Legrange said "It required but a moment to strike off his head and probably 100 years will not suffice to reproduce such another."

Priestley gave an account of his experiments to Lavoisier who then realised that the theory of phlogiston could not be true. He explained combustion as due to union of the combustible material with this new gas, which evidently now required a new name. At first he called it "eminently pure air"; later he changed the name to *oxygen* or *acid producer* (Greek *oxus*, sharp or acid; *gennao*, I produce) in his belief that the element was an essential constituent of all acids. The German name *Sauerstoff* embodies the same idea. This is one of the few instances in which the name given to an element by its discoverer has not been retained. Nitrogen and hydrogen, the two next elements to be considered, are further examples, as are also chlorine, iodine, tellurium and beryllium.

Isotopes

In 1929 spectroscopic examination of the absorption bands of oxygen led Giauque and Johnston to conclude that it is not a simple gas but contains three isotopes of atomic weights (16), (17) and (18). The two latter are present in only small amount, nevertheless their existence has been confirmed by the mass spectrograph. Atmospheric oxygen contains these isotopes in the proportions of 99·76 of isotope (16), 0·04 of (17) and 0·20 of (18).

This discovery of the complexity of ordinary oxygen was one of great importance. Since 1906 the atomic weight of ordinary oxygen gas has been standardised at 16·000, all other atomic weights being expressed relatively thereto. This mean value of 16·000 is really 1·000275 times as great as that of the single isotope (16). When, therefore, atomic weights are determined by the mass spectrograph relatively to the physical isotope (16), the values are relatively too high for the chemical standard and must be divided by 1·000275, termed the *conversion factor*, in order to render them comparable with purely chemical data. As will be seen shortly, this was the source of the clue to the discovery of deuterium (p. 36).

Applications of oxygen

An important modern use to which oxygen is put is to enrich the air supplied to aeronauts at high altitudes and to certain invalids, and to resuscitate persons who have been suffocated or are suffering from carbon monoxide poisoning, etc. The "iron lung" has become quite a feature in modern medical practice. In conjunction with hydrogen and acetylene the gas is used to attain high temperatures for metal cutting and welding. Oxygen is used in bleaching, in the oxidation and thickening of oils, etc, and in the preparation of ozone.

The isotopy of oxygen has proved valuable in certain academic studies. For example using water containing the O (18) isotope, namely $H_2{}^{18}O$, it has been shown that, in the hydrolysis of esters with caustic soda, fission occurs at the C atom. Thus —

$$RC\begin{smallmatrix}\diagdown O\,Et\\[2pt]\diagup\\O\end{smallmatrix} \qquad \text{and not} \qquad RC\begin{smallmatrix}\diagup O + Et\\[2pt]\diagdown\\O\end{smallmatrix}$$

Ozone

Ozone is a "condensed" form of oxygen containing three atoms in the molecule. In 1785 van Marum drew attention to the fact that the air in the neighbourhood of an electrical machine in action possesses a peculiar odour. This "electrified air" was used shortly afterwards by Cavallo as a remedy for fœtid ulcers, its power of removing unpleasant smells being thus early recognised. Schönbein*, in 1840, concluded that the odour was caused by the presence of a new gas which he called ozone from the Greek *ozo*, I smell.

It was at first thought that ozone was a compound of oxygen and hydrogen, but this was negatived when Marignac obtained it from dry oxygen. In 1845 Marignac and de la Rive† suggested, therefore, that ozone was a peculiar or allotropic form of oxygen. In 1848 Hunt suggested that it was an oxide of oxygen, of formula $O.O_2$, analogous to SO_2 and SeO_2. This was supported in 1860 by the observation of Andrews and Tait‡ that, when ozone was formed from oxygen, a contraction occurred, so that the new gas possessed a higher density. Odling§ in 1861 suggested that the reaction involved might be most easily represented by the equation —

$$3\,O_2 = 2\,O_3$$

and the correctness of this was experimentally proved by Soret in 1866 and confirmed by Brodie in 1872. The reaction may be pictured as follows. Three molecules of oxygen approach as indicated by (i) in the scheme shown (Fig. 1). When they are sufficiently close the attraction of the two central atoms for each other in the unstable complex (ii) counterbalances that of the two external pairs. Circumstances will decide whether the complex shall dissociate to oxygen again or to ozone.

On account of its powerful oxidising properties ozone exerts a marked bactericidal effect. It is frequently employed therefore in

---

*Schönbein, *Pogg Annalen*, 1840, **50**, 616; 1843, **59**, 240; 1844, **63**, 520.
†Marignac and de la Rive, *Compt. rend.*, 1845, **20**, 1291.
‡Andrews and Tait, *Phil. Trans.*, 1860, **150**, 113. *J. Chem. Soc.*, 1860, **13**, 344.
§Odling, "Manual of Chemistry", 1861, p. 94.

improving the atmosphere of buildings that are likely to be crowded, such as underground passages, and the stations and tunnels of electric tube railways; care must of course be taken that the concentration of the gas shall always be well under the danger limit.

Another extensive application is in the sterilisation of water. As early as 1886 experiments were carried out on the ozonisation of water to effect the removal of organic matter and bacteria. Eight years previously Pasteur had introduced his germ theory of disease and the danger of transmitting diseases such as typhoid and cholera by vitiated waters was beginning to be realised. In 1885 Percy Frankland had shown that almost all the bacterial content of water

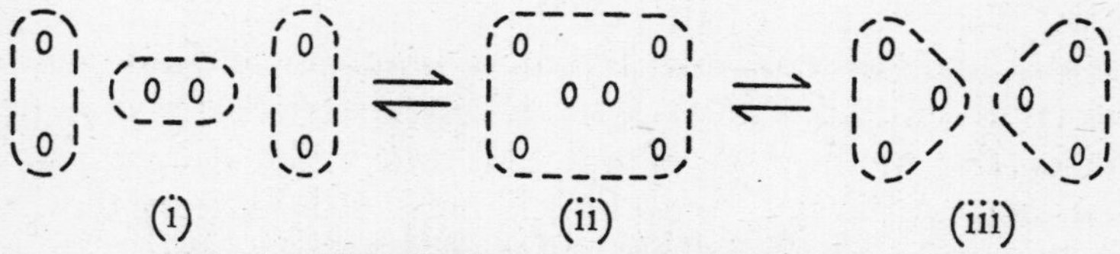

Fig. 1 — Formation of ozone from oxygen

could be removed by sand filtration. By the use of ozone after filtration it was hoped that complete removal might be achieved. It was not until the development of more efficient types of large ozonisers had been effected that the process could become one of industrial importance. Many such systems were eventually installed, mostly on the Continent; but the advantages of the use of chlorine for this purpose are so obvious that, at any rate in this country, sterilisation by chlorination is now largely adopted.

Small ozone sterilisation plants are made for sterilising water, etc, used in the manufacture of beverages and foods generally.

Ozone is used as an oxidiser in bleaching such substances as starch, flour, oils, wax, delicate fabrics, etc. It has also been used to aid the "ageing" or maturing of wines, spirits and tobacco. The action of ozone on unsaturated organic substances provides a convenient general method for the preparation of aldehydes and ketones; it has been applied to the production of vanillin for flavouring purposes and heliotropin for perfumery. An ozoniser of the silent discharge type is used and air is treated to emerge from the apparatus with an ozone content approximating to 2 or 3 grams per cubic metre. The "ozone water" of commerce contains no ozone; its activity is due to such substances as hypochlorites, etc.

Nitrogen

The discovery of nitrogen in 1772 is usually credited to Daniel Rutherford, pupil of Joseph Black who held the Chair of Chemistry at Edinburgh University*; he happened also to be uncle to Sir Walter Scott. As has been mentioned, it was already known to Leonardo da Vinci that air was a mixture; at the suggestion of Black, Rutherford investigated the gas left after the oxygen of the air had been used up either chemically or by animal respiration, the carbon dioxide in the latter case being removed with alkali. As the residual gas would not support combustion, it was regarded as saturated with phlogiston, whence its name *phlogisticated air*. Priestley was the first to show quantitatively in 1772 that one-fifth of the air disappeared when charcoal was burnt in a closed vessel and the residual gas shaken with milk of lime. Scheele independently discovered it and called it *foul air*. Lavoisier in 1776 definitely recognised this residue as a simple gas and called it *azote* from the Greek *a*, not, and *zōos*, living. This name is still used by the French and is retained in our "azo" and "diazo".

With the fall of the phlogistic theory, however, the term "dephlogisticated air" became untenable and Chaptal in 1791 suggested *nitrogen*, since it is a constituent of nitre.

Active nitrogen

When an electric discharge is passed through nitrogen at low pressures, *circa* 2 mm, a yellow glow is seen which persists for some time after the discharge has ceased. Although this had been known for some time, it was left for R. J. Strutt†, the late Lord Rayleigh, to examine the physical properties of the after-glow and the chemical reactions of the active form, which differ widely from those of ordinary molecular nitrogen.

It was at first thought that the activity was due to triatomic nitrogen analogous to triatomic oxygen or ozone, but later work showed that view to be untenable.

The view now held is that active nitrogen contains at least two distinct species, namely —

(i) Metastable, activated molecules, N_2^*, mainly responsible for the chemical activity and

---

*PROFESSOR BLACK'S name is well known to chemists for his researches on "Fixed Air", that is, carbon dioxide. He lived 1728 to 1799.

†STRUTT, *Proc. Roy. Soc.*, 1911, A**85**, 219.   R. J. Strutt was the fourth Baron Rayleigh.

(ii)   A much smaller proportion of nitrogen atoms, responsible for the glow.

Uses of nitrogen

Nitrogen exists almost exclusively in the atmosphere which holds some 4041 billion tons of the gas — over every acre are some 31,000 tons.

About 1913 Langmuir invented the gas-filled electric lamp bulb, and at first nitrogen was used. This gas has now been super-seded by certain of the inert gases, such as argon and krypton. Nitrogen is used in flushing petrol refuelling tubes for aeroplanes in mid-air to prevent firing, and in various "fixation" processes, for the production of ammonia, nitric acid, cyanamide, cyanides, etc. The main industrial use of nitrogen is in the form of its com-pounds, into which it is converted by natural processes as well as by artificial.

In 1784 Cavendish showed that nitrogen will combine under the influence of the electric spark with oxygen to form oxides. This occurs in nature during thunderstorms and, in temperate climes it is estimated that in this way 11 lb. of nitrogen are "fixed" per acre per annum. In the tropics the amount will be much greater. In 1897 Lord Rayleigh[*], describing his experiments in which argon was isolated from the atmosphere (p. 41), pointed out the possibilities of utilising the electric arc for the industrial fixation of nitrogen. The first technical attempt to utilise this reaction was made in 1902 at Niagara but was not a commercial success. The following year, however, the Birkeland–Eyde process was started at Notodden in Norway and proved successful.

Nitrogen may also be fixed as ammonia, by passing the mixed gases, nitrogen and hydrogen, in the proportion of 1 to 3 by volume over a heated catalyst under pressure. The Haber process was the first to achieve technical success. It was devised by Haber during World War I to enable the Germans to produce explosives, as our navy had cut off their Chilean supplies of nitrate. Had Haber not succeeded, the war would have been over in our favour several years earlier than it was. Haber was a Jew, and a grateful Fatherland showed its appreciation of his services many years later by his expulsion. He died brokenhearted in 1934.

In Serpek's process (1919) atmospheric nitrogen is fixed as

---

[*] J. W. STRUTT, third Baron Rayleigh.

aluminium nitride, AlN, which is subsequently hydrolysed yielding ammonia and pure aluminium hydroxide.

In 1784 Scheele observed that, by heating a mixture of potassium carbonate and carbon in an atmosphere of nitrogen, potassium cyanide is produced. In 1835 Dawes observed that potassium cyanide is a product of the blast furnace, and in 1924 the suggestion was made by Franchot* that about one per cent of the nitrogen of the air blast could be recovered as cyanide from the blast furnace. In the Bucher Process (1917), potassium carbonate is replaced by the sodium salt; numerous other modifications have been introduced. Mention should also be made of the fixation of nitrogen as calcium cyanamide, CaN.NC, the process being patented by Frank and Caro during the years 1895 to 1898. In 1866 Hellriegel showed that the bacteria in the roots of leguminous plants can "fix" atmospheric nitrogen.

The Egyptian national god Amen was known by the Romans when they conquered Egypt as Ammon, and identified by them with their god Jupiter. Outside the Egyptian temples the refuse from the sacrifices, etc, gradually disintegrated and parts were converted into mineral salts, which became known as "salts of Ammon". In course of time it was found that these salts were mixtures, part being volatile. The name Ammon was retained for these volatile portions which are now termed ammonia or ammonium salts.

The atomic clock

A new use for ammonia, NH_3, has been found†. The mean solar day is not absolutely constant. Owing to variations in the rate of rotation of the earth on its axis there is a fluctuation of 1 second in every 20 to 30 million seconds. In addition to this there is a slight lengthening of the solar day due to a slowing down of the earth's rotation, through tidal action mainly, which amounts to about 1 second per day every 120,000 years. This has raised the question as to whether or not it might be possible to check time intervals by some absolutely constant wave motion on the lines adopted for measurements of length (p. 308). This problem is in course of solution by the invention of the "atomic clock", as it is

---

*FRANCHOT, *J. Ind. Eng. Chem.*, 1924, **16**, 235.
†See *Scientific American*, 1949, p. 28; 1948, p. 23. *Electronics*, 1949, **22**, 82. *Tech. Bull. Nat. Bureau of Standards*, 1949, **33**, 17. *Radio-Corporation Amer. Review*, 1948, **9**, 38.

called, the first of which was unveiled in January 1949 at the National Bureau of Standards, U.S.A. This is based on the molecule of ammonia which consists of three hydrogen atoms situated in a plane at the corners of an equilateral triangle with the nitrogen atom above or below as shown in Fig. 2. The molecule is capable of absorbing radio-energy at a sharply defined frequency, the N atom vibrating from position N to N' and back. An absorption line is produced in the spectrum of the incident radiation and

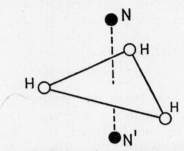

Fig. 2 — The ammonia molecule

this is utilised to stabilise the frequency of a microwave oscillator and thus to check the passage of time. To put the position popularly, the oscillator corresponds to the pendulum of an ordinary clock.

The ultimate accuracy of such a clock depends upon a variety of factors. Theoretically it should be possible to obtain a permanent accuracy of 1 part in 10 billion (10^{13}). At present 1 part in 10 million has been achieved. Such a clock can be used to improve our astronomical time standards; being entirely constant and independent of the earth's movement it could be used, for example, to determine if the sidereal day is more constant than the mean solar day, as some authorities believe may be the case. Conversely it may be of great use to the radio-engineer as it could be used to control more rigidly the frequency of the waves emitted from various stations and thus make more efficient use of the available radio spectrum. This is very necessary if overlapping is to be avoided, because the present crowding has imposed severe limitations both nationally and internationally on the expanding use of radio for industry and communications.

Hydrogen

Several combustible gases occur in nature and have been observed by man for ages. At the time of Cavendish they were known as *inflammable air* and were not distinguished from each other. Cavendish, *circa* 1766, was the first to examine hydrogen and determine its physical properties so that it could be recognised again. He called it *inflammable air from metals* as he thought it came from the metals and not from the acids he used.

Cavendish had observed that hydrogen exploded with air, and Priestley called attention to the dew condensing on the glass walls of the containing vessel after an explosion. Cavendish investigated the matter and proved that water was a compound of oxygen and hydrogen. His paper was published by the Royal Society on 15th January 1784. James Watt had almost simultaneously arrived at the same conclusion. His letter was laid before the Royal Society on 29th April 1784. He was deeply chagrined to find that Cavendish had forestalled him.

Both Cavendish and Priestley thought hydrogen was pure phlogiston. When the phlogistic theory was shown to be untenable Lavoisier revised the nomenclature and suggested the name *hydrogen* (Greek *hudor*, water), that is, *water producer*, in place of inflammable air. The German name *Wasserstoff* carries the same idea.

On hearing about Cavendish's experiments Pilatre de Rozier filled his lungs with hydrogen and set fire to the gas as it escaped from his mouth. On repeating the experiment with a mixture of hydrogen and air there was a terrific explosion and de Rozier thought for a moment that all his teeth had been blown out.

Spin isomerism

The change in specific heat of hydrogen with temperature is abnormal if the gas consists of only one kind of simple molecule. The new quantum theory involving wave mechanics led*, in 1927, to the belief that two different types of diatomic hydrogen molecule exist, namely *ortho*-hydrogen, in which the directions of the protonic spins are the same, and *para*-hydrogen, in which they are opposite as shown in Fig. 3. This is not an atomic phenomenon, as all the atoms are alike. It is purely molecular and concerns the two possible ways in which spinning protons can link up. In 1929 the existence of these two types of molecule was proved experimentally†.

---

*HEISENBERG, *Z. Physik*, 1927, **41**, 239
†BONHOEFFER and HARTECK, *Zeitsch. physikal. Chem.*, 1929, **134**, 113.

Ordinary hydrogen is a mixture of approximately three of ortho to one of para. The two forms behave alike chemically but differ very slightly in their physical properties, for the ortho possesses more energy than the para. Low temperature favours the production of para, and the transformation is catalysed by charcoal at low temperatures enabling pure para-hydrogen to be obtained; hitherto it has not been found possible to obtain the pure ortho. The para melts and boils at only 0·03° and 0·13° C respectively below ordinary hydrogen so that there is little hope of separating them by purely physical fractionation. Similar spins occur with molecules other than hydrogen but their effect is negligible except for deuterium.

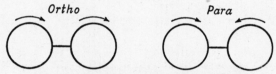

Fig. 3 — Ortho- and para-hydrogen

Balloons

One of the earliest uses of hydrogen was for filling balloons, and Joseph Black*, the well known Edinburgh Professor (p. 28), appears to have been the first to make this suggestion. Soon after the appearance of Cavendish's paper in 1766, in which attention was drawn to the unusually low density of hydrogen, Black invited a party of his friends to supper informing them that he had something mysterious to show them. After the party had assembled he liberated the bladder of a calf filled with hydrogen which immediately rose to the ceiling. The company fully believed that the bladder had been attached to a black thread and drawn up to the ceiling through a minute hole by a confederate operating in the room above. An equally neat experiment illustrating the buoyancy of hydrogen was that of Cavallo, a Neapolitan long domiciled in London, who in 1772 filled soap bubbles with the gas and watched them rise into the air with boyish enthusiasm. Matthew Boulton of Birmingham called hydrogen the "goddess of levity".

The first hydrogen-filled balloon† of practical importance was

---

*W. RAMSAY, "Life and Letters of Joseph Black" (Constable, 1918) p. 78.

†Earlier in the same year a hot-air balloon had been sent aloft by the Montgolfier Brothers; it was 35 ft. in diameter and reached a height of 1500 ft. Its cargo included a sheep, a duck and a cock. Paris was thrilled and fire-balloons became known as montgolfieres.

D

released in August 1783 from the Champs de Mars in Paris by M. Charles, the famous engineer known to all students of chemistry in connection with the fundamental law of the expansion of gases with rise of temperature (1787). The balloon was 13 ft. in diameter, rose rapidly to a considerable height and then fell at Gonesse, 15 miles from Paris, about an hour later.

The peasants who witnessed its descent were filled with superstitious terror at the appearance of so "monstrous and foul a bird", for the smell of the escaping hydrogen, owing to impurities, was anything but pleasant. Indeed, the French Government found it necessary a little later, as interest in ballooning gained ground, to issue a proclamation throughout the country explaining what a balloon was and warning people not to be alarmed if they happened to see one. A century or so later the Russian Government followed suit.

No human beings went aloft in Charles's first balloon. The earliest pioneers to rise above their fellow men in this way were the Marquis d'Arlandes and the afore-mentioned Pilatre de Rozier on 21st November 1783. The King, Louis XVI, had expressed a wish that, if human beings were to take part in balloon trips, criminals should be selected, as their lives were less important to the state. But de Rozier was indignant "that vile criminals should have the glory of being the first to rise in the air" —and he carried his point.

The following month M. Charles went aloft with M. Robert. The trip was so successful that Charles decided to go aloft again, this time alone. In his excitement he forgot to adjust the ballast with the result that upon release the balloon shot up with great rapidity to a height of at least two miles which nearly proved fatal to the bewildered engineer.

In 1836 Charles Green showed that coal gas could be used in place of the more expensive hydrogen, but having less buoyancy, larger balloons were necessary. He passed away at the ripe age of 85 in 1870, having made no fewer than 1400 ascents and earned for himself the title of "Father of Modern Balloonists".

Unfortunately for the balloonist, both hydrogen and coal gas are inflammable and many accidents have resulted from the gases catching on fire in mid air. When the properties of helium were investigated it was realised that this was an ideal gas for the purpose in view of its chemical inertia. Although twice as dense as hydrogen, it was still much less dense than air. In 1925 the

U.S.A. prohibited export of the gas as it was needed for home consumption. As British sources of helium are negligible, we had perforce to continue using the inflammable gases. This was the indirect cause of the tragic loss of the ill-fated British Airship R101, which was filled with hydrogen obtained by passage of steam over heated iron. On its way to India it caught fire over France and 48 of its occupants were killed. This happened on 5th October 1930.

At the close of the eighteenth century we British were not on the best of terms with the French who conceived the idea that ballooning might afford them an opportunity of invading us from the sky, as our "wooden walls" made any sea attempt too hazardous. Actually, however, the boot was on the other leg, for the first balloon to cross the channel left Dover on New Year's Day 1785 to travel in the opposite direction.

The first occasion on which a balloon was used for military purposes was at the Battle of Fleurus, near Charleroi in Belgium, in 1794. The balloon was captive and remained up all day, signalling the dispositions of the enemy to Jourdan's army, enabling them to achieve victory.

In 1798 Napoleon, after taking Cairo, sent up a fire balloon with the object of impressing the Egyptians, but he was singularly slow to appreciate the military value of balloons. Had he but used them as "eyes" at Waterloo in 1815, he would not have mistaken Blucher for Grouchy, and that page of history might have been different.

It was early appreciated by scientists that balloons might be used to obtain invaluable information on meteorological and other kindred problems. Probably the first chemist to take to the air with this object in view was Gay-Lussac, whose name is perpetuated in his Law of Combining Volumes of Gases (1808) and the Gay-Lussac Tower used in the Chamber Process for the manufacture of sulphuric acid. On 23rd August 1804, in company with M. Biot, he ascended from Paris with the object of studying, amongst other things, the behaviour of the magnetic needle at high altitudes, and the composition of the atmosphere. At a height of some 11,000 feet they liberated a bird; for a moment it rested upon the edge of the car, then directed its course in gradually extended circles towards the earth, thus refuting an old idea that a bird could not fly in a rarefied atmosphere.

On another occasion, when by himself, Gay-Lussac attained a height of some 22,000 feet, and wishing to ascend still higher, he threw overboard a chair as ballast*. It apparently did not occur to him that someone below might be injured; however, a shepherdess saw this wooden chair fall from the skies into some bushes and ran to tell her friends of the marvel. The simple country folk gathered round to hear her story and then examined the chair. One thing puzzled them. If heaven were the beautiful place they were taught to believe, how was it that the workmanship of the chair was so crude?

During the siege of Paris† in the course of the Franco-Prussian war of 1870 to 1871, balloons were used by the French to make contact with the outside world. As many as 64 balloons, averaging 2000 cubic metres of gas, were released from Paris carrying a personnel of 161 and something like 3 million letters. Of these balloons 57 fulfilled their purpose, two only being lost at sea whilst five were captured by the Germans.

Besides freights of letters the majority carried also baskets of pigeons and five carried dogs, destined to return with news to the beleaguered city. As a result no fewer than 50,000 messages were sent to Paris by pigeon-post. On one voyage a balloon carried two cases of dynamite, the intention being to drop them on to the enemy; fortunately for the latter no suitable opportunity presented itself and Paris capitulated in March 1871.

Deuterium

In 1927 Aston, with his mass spectrograph, compared the masses of hydrogen and oxygen atoms and obtained the ratio 1·00778 : 16. This physical value was in excellent agreement with the chemical one accepted at the time. As already mentioned, however, Giauque and Johnston two years later showed that ordinary oxygen consists of three isotopes so that the mean atomic weight is 1·000275 times greater than that of the pure isotope (16) used as standard by Aston‡. As compared with chemical oxygen, therefore, Aston's value was 1·000275 times too high. Dividing by this conversion factor gives the value 1·00753 for the chemical atomic weight of pure hydrogen, which is too low to be satisfactory. Birge and Menzel§ suggested in 1931 that ordinary hydrogen might contain

*This amusing story is told by MISS WEEKS "Discovery of the Elements" (*J. Chemical Education*, 1945) Fifth Edition, on the authority of Bugge, "Das Buch der grossen Chemiker" (Berlin, 1929) Vol. 1, pp. 386 seq.

†Nature, 1872, **6**, 88; 1870, **3**, 115, 134, 175.

‡The more recent value for the conversion factor is here used.

§BIRGE and MENZEL, *Physical Review*, 1931, **37**, 1669.

a heavy isotope, and this was confirmed in December of the same year by Urey and his co-workers*, who found two faint lines near the ordinary Balmer lines of a sample of hydrogen taken as a residue from the evaporation of a considerable bulk of liquid hydrogen. The intensity of these lines was increased if fractionation was continued and the heavier fraction examined. Calculation showed this "heavy hydrogen" to possess twice the normal mass of ordinary hydrogen. It was called deuterium, from the Greek *deuteros*, second.

Like hydrogen, deuterium yields ortho and para forms. At room temperature the ordinary gas comprises 66·6 per cent of ortho. Low temperature favours the production of para-deuterium, and the transformation of ortho to para is catalysed by charcoal at low temperatures exactly as for ordinary hydrogen. For comparative purposes, some constants may be noted —

	Hydrogen	Deuterium
Atomic weight	1·0080	2·0135
Boiling point ° abs.	20·39	23·5
Molar latent heat in gm.-calories per mole	183	276
Trouton's Constant, L/T	9·1	11·8

Tritium

Another isotope of hydrogen, with an atomic weight 3 was reported in 1935 as present in natural waters. It occurs only in very minute quantities to the tune of 1 part in 10^{17} parts of water; to this the name tritium was given, with symbol T. It is a short-lived element, with a half life of about 30 years†.

Chemistry is now becoming very complicated. With three isotopes each of hydrogen and oxygen it is possible for no fewer than 18 different molecules of so simple a substance as water to exist. As two natural isotopes of carbon are also known, one shudders to think of the number of varieties of the starch molecule that can exist, starch being $(C_6H_{10}O_5)_n$, where n is a large number.

General uses of hydrogen and deuterium

Hydrogen is used in the fixation of atmospheric nitrogen as ammonia by the Haber process; the manufacture of hydrochloric

---

*UREY and CO-WORKERS, *Physical Review*, 1932, **39**, 164, 864.
†SELWOOD, TAYLOR and BLEAKNEY, *J. Amer. Chem. Soc.*, 1935, **57**, 580.

acid by direct combustion in chlorine; the hardening of oils; production of "oil from coal" by hydrogenation of coal; the oxy-hydrogen flame — now largely superseded by the oxy-acetylene, but still used in making mercury vapour lamps and fusing platinum. Air-hydrogen mixtures are used in autogeneous soldering of lead and an atomic hydrogen blowpipe is used in certain welding processes.

Deuterium has proved extremely useful as a tracer in following metabolic changes in the animal body. Many experiments have been carried out on mice. It has been shown, for example, that fat may be stored in the body even at a time when the body needs it for conversion into energy. Butyric acid is rapidly consumed to produce energy, from which it appears that butter may be expected to relieve exhaustion more rapidly than other fats. Deuterium oxide, D_2O, often called "heavy water" is used as a moderator in atomic piles to slow down fast moving neutrons to the speed desired. Most substances either absorb neutrons or are otherwise unsuitable; neither deuterium nor oxygen absorbs them.

The question as to whether or not small amounts of deuterium are essential to the animal organism has not been solved. There *may* be some connection, for it has been found that dilute solutions can accelerate the growth of micro-organisms.

The hydrogen bomb

Another use to which hydrogen or deuterium may be put in due course is in the construction of the H-bomb, the principle of which is as follows —

If, during the course of any reaction, matter is destroyed, it reappears as energy. The relation between the mass, dm, in grams destroyed and the energy, dE, in ergs produced is given by Einstein's Equation (1905)

$$dE = u^2 dm = 9 \times 10^{20} dm$$

Where u is the velocity of light, namely 3×10^{10} cm per second. That is, for every gram of matter destroyed, the energy produced

$$= 9 \times 10^{20} \text{ ergs}$$
$$\equiv \frac{9 \times 10^{20}}{4 \cdot 185 \times 10^7} \text{ or } 2 \cdot 15 \times 10^{13} \text{ gm-calories}$$

At the high temperature of the sun, which attains some 20 million °C near its centre, hydrogen atoms condense to helium, some 10,000 helium atoms being produced in every c.c. of the sun per second. During this condensation matter is lost and reappears as energy. This is the source of the sun's heat.

Let us try to gain some idea of its magnitude. For every 4 gram-atoms of hydrogen of atomic weight 1·0080 that condense to yield 1 gram-atom of helium (at. wt. 4·003) the amount of matter lost

$$= 4 \times 1\cdot008 - 4\cdot003 = 0\cdot029 \text{ gm}$$
$$\equiv 0\cdot029 \times 2\cdot15 \times 10^{13} \text{ or } 6\cdot24 \times 10^{11} \text{ gm-calories.}$$

Big figures like these do not convey much to us. We can perhaps appreciate them better if we remember that 1 gram of coke on combustion to carbon dioxide evolves 8080 gm-calories of heat.

The quantity of heat liberated, therefore, when each gram-atom of helium is produced from 4 grams of hydrogen is equal to that obtained by the complete combustion of

$$\frac{6\cdot24 \times 10^{11}}{8080} \text{ or } 7\cdot7 \times 10^7 \text{ gm of coke}$$
$$= 76 \text{ tons of coke.}$$

This condensation can only take place, however, at very high temperatures and it would be necessary to use a uranium or plutonium bomb as detonator. At the moment of the explosion there would be a sufficiently high temperature and pressure to initiate the condensation which could then, under favourable conditions, become self-supporting, as in the sun.

It might perhaps be found preferable to use deuterium instead of hydrogen, although the heat liberated per gram-atom of helium produced would be slightly less, namely

$$2 \times 2\cdot0135 - 4\cdot0030 = 0\cdot024 \text{ gm}$$
$$\equiv 5\cdot16 \times 10^{11} \text{ gm-calories}$$
$$\equiv 63 \text{ tons of coke}$$

Even so it is unlikely that the free gas would be used. Probably a deuteride would be, such as that of lithium, LiD, or beryllium, BeD_2. In any case it would be necessary to ensure that the deuterium was not dissipated by the force of the explosion before condensation could occur. Unless fairly complete condensation were effected, the bomb might not be any more powerful than a comparable plutonium bomb. Such a bomb, however, would leave less radio-matter behind. The problem as to whether or not the H-bomb is worthwhile has yet to be decided. Any work and money expended in its production are of little value to the world at peace. Unlike the uranium bomb it offers no promise as a source of industrial energy or of new products like radio-isotopes of economic or scientific value.

CHAPTER 3

THE INERT GASES

THE inert gases dealt with in this chapter include argon, helium, neon, krypton and xenon. Radon is discussed later (p. 324).

The discovery of the inert gases reads like a romance*. The first of these gases to be discovered terrestrially was *argon*. In 1894 Lord Rayleigh observed that the density of atmospheric nitrogen was greater than that of the chemical gas, and in 1894 asked chemists to suggest a reason. Sir William Ramsay asked if he might collaborate. After searching the literature, they found that Cavendish in 1785 had already noted that, after sparking with excess oxygen, atmospheric nitrogen yielded an inert residue that could not be made to combine with oxygen. Was this a new gas? Rayleigh and Ramsay accordingly passed atmospheric nitrogen over magnesium to remove the nitrogen as solid magnesium nitride, Mg_3N_2, and introduced the residual gas into a Plücker tube and examined its spectrum. To their joy, although the characteristic lines of nitrogen were present, there were also new red and green lines suggesting the presence of a new element. As this new gas was present in the atmosphere the story goes that the authors decided to call it *aeron*, but they received so many letters asking when Moses would turn up, that they decided in view of its remarkable chemical inactivity to christen it *argon*, a Greek word meaning inert. Although at the British Association Meeting in Oxford in 1895 the announcement was received with scepticism, truth ultimately prevailed.

A word *Argon* has been known for a long time. Marco Polo (p. 55), in his travels in the second half of the thirteenth century, visited the kingdom of a prince named Argon, who would undoubtedly have objected to the derivation of the modern word as applied to himself.

The scene now shifts to India. In 1868 there was a total eclipse of the sun, visible in that country, and the Danish astronomer

---

*A detailed history is given by RAMSAY, "The Gases of the Atmosphere" (Macmillan, 1902). Full references to the original literature are given in FRIEND'S "Textbook of Inorganic Chemistry" (Griffin, 1914) Vol. 1, Pt. 2 by H. V. A. BRISCOE, and in "Helium" by KEESOM (Amsterdam, 1942).

Janssen went thither and examined the sun's corona spectroscopically for the first time in history. He detected a prominent yellow line close to, but not identical with, the sodium lines which, however, did not correspond with any known element. Bunsen and Kirchhoff in 1860 had concluded that every element has its own characteristic spectrum and could be detected by it. Frankland and Lockyer* therefore suggested, in 1868, that this new line was due to an element present in the sun, but not present terrestrially. As alkali metals were known to give line spectra it was thought the new element would be a metal. They therefore suggested it be called *helium* from the Greek *helios*, sun. The same line, designated as D_3, was later detected in the spectra of certain stars, and in 1882 Palmieri found it in Vesuvian gases.

In the latter part of 1894, when searching for new sources of the newly discovered argon, Ramsay received a letter from Miers, the eminent mineralogist, at that time connected with the British Museum, suggesting that it might be worth while examining pitchblendes. Ramsay gratefully took the hint and obtained a specimen of cleveite, a variety of uraninite, essentially $UO_2 . 2UO_3$, for which it is said he paid 3s. 6d. — a small sum for so vast a return. He treated the powdered mineral with dilute sulphuric acid, sparked the resulting gas with oxygen over soda, removed excess oxygen with alkaline pyrogallol, washed, dried and transferred to a vacuum tube. The light given by the passage of electricity through this tube was examined visually in a spectroscope alongside that from a Plücker tube containing argon, for comparison. It so happened that this second tube, owing to impurities in the electrodes, gave the spectra of hydrogen and nitrogen as well as of argon. It was at once evident that the cleveite gas contained both argon and hydrogen, but it also gave a brilliant line in the yellow, nearly but not quite coincident with the yellow sodium lines. The wavelength of this line was measured by Crookes† and proved to be the solar D_3 line. It thus became known that helium could now be regarded as a terrestrial element. About the same time Cleve also independently found helium.

In 1889, Hildebrand‡ had noticed that uraninite, when dissolved in acid, evolved a gas which he believed to be nitrogen. He noticed

---

*A full account was given by SIR NORMAN LOCKYER in *Nature*, 1896, **53**, 319, 342, also FRANKLAND and LOCKYER, *Proc. Roy. Soc.*, 1868, **17**, 91.
†CROOKES, *Proc. Roy. Soc.*, 1895, **58**, 69.
‡HILDEBRAND, *Bull. U.S. Geol. Survey*, 1889, No. 78, 43.

that the spectrum contained lines not usually attributable to nitrogen; he knew however that gaseous spectra are profoundly affected by changes in pressure and although he and his assistant jocularly suggested that they might be dealing with a new element, the matter was allowed to drop. Many a true word is spoken in jest; a great discovery was narrowly missed.

Before long both the elementary nature of helium and its identity with the solar element were called into question; but these doubts were soon set at rest. The homogeneity of the gas was confirmed by Ramsay and Travers[*] who showed that spectral anomalies were due to contamination with argon. The identity of the celestial and terrestrial spectra was confirmed by Huggins[†] and Hale[‡].

In 1903 Ramsay and Soddy made a sensational discovery, namely that helium is a disintegration product of radium.

After many fruitless attempts had been made by Dewar and others to liquefy helium, that difficult task was achieved by Onnes in 1908 in his famous cryogenic laboratory at Leyden University. It was not until 1926, however, that the gas was solidified by Keesom, the pupil and worthy successor of Onnes. Solid helium melts at $- 271 \cdot 5° $ C or $1 \cdot 5°$ abs.

The two elements argon and helium suggested the need for a new vertical group in the periodic table. If so, elements were required to precede sodium, rubidium and cæsium. Ramsay and Travers[§] searched for these. They examined many possible sources, but were most successful with liquid air residues, and in 1898 they discovered successively three more gases which they christened *krypton* (Greek *kryptos*), the hidden one; neon (Greek *neos*), the new one; and *xenon* (Greek *xenos*), the stranger. The last member of the series, *radon*, was not discovered spectroscopically. It is a radio-element first detected by Dorn in 1900, and is discussed later.

Helium ought logically to be called *helion*. This was suggested by the author to the Chemical Society in 1926, but the Publication Committee was not in favour of the change.

---

[*]Ramsay and Travers, *Proc. Roy. Soc.*, 1897, **60**, 206; 1898, **62**, 316. Travers, *ibid.*, 1897, **60**, 449.
[†]Huggins, *Chem. News*, 1895, **72**, 27.
[‡]Hale, *Astronom. Nachrichten*, 1895, **138**, 227.
[§]Ramsay and Travers, *Proc. Roy. Soc.*, 1898, **62**, 316; 1898, **63**, 405, 437; *Phil. Trans.*, 1901, **197**, 47. See Moore, *Chem. News*, 1911, **103**, 242.

Applications of helium

Helium is used for air-ships, blimps, etc, its non-inflammability rendering it particularly suitable for these purposes although its lifting power is only half that of pure hydrogen. To a limited extent helium is employed in thermometry and in lamps for yielding the D_3 line in optical work. When inhaled with oxygen, helium is used as a cure for asthma and other ailments, such as croup and diphtheria, in which the windpipe is obstructed.

Helium is of great assistance to the diver and in caisson work. After prolonged exposure at great depths much time is absorbed in bringing the diver to the surface; every 33 feet of depth gives an extra atmosphere of pressure. Helium is also used in the manufacture of zirconium by Kroll's process.*

The average man carries about 1000 c.c. of nitrogen gas dissolved in his body under ordinary atmospheric conditions. If the pressure is increased the volume of dissolved nitrogen increases proportionately, though it takes several hours for equilibrium to be reached. If, therefore, the diver is decompressed too rapidly by being brought swiftly to the surface, nitrogen is released from solution and bubbles collect in the blood stream; the diver becomes black in the face due to oxygen shortage for the heart cannot drive the bubbles through the blood vessels owing to their enormous resistance. The remedy is to lower again when the bubbles redissolve. As helium is much less soluble in the body there is less danger of bubble formation and decompression may be effected in a mixture of oxygen and helium (usually 1 to 4 by volume) in one-twenty-third of the time required with air. This may be of supreme importance in cases of accident or of attack by, say, sharks. Hydrogen appears to be equally effective.

J. B. S. Haldane used a mixture of 9 volumes of hydrogen to 1 of air, which is not explosive and may be safely stored in cylinders under pressure. It contains only 2 per cent of oxygen by volume, but under a pressure of 10 atmospheres it has as much oxygen per c.c. as ordinary air. Argon behaves similarly to nitrogen. Neon may be intermediate.

By way of contrast it may be mentioned that xenon is *more* soluble in the body even than nitrogen, and causes dizziness and numbness. It has been suggested that xenon may be the cause of air-sickness at high altitudes.

---

*G. L. MILLER, *Industrial Chemist*, 1950, **26**, 435.

Argon is used in gas-filled incandescent electric lamps, being more efficient than nitrogen. Efficiency increases with the molecular weight of the gas, and before World War II krypton and xenon were being used for the purpose. Special plants had been erected at Ajka in Hungary and at Boulogne in France to separate these gases from the atmosphere to render them available in sufficient quantities to meet the needs of the lamp industry.

Neon is used extensively for various types of lighting such as shop signs, street lighting and illumination of airfields.

CHAPTER 4

THE HALOGENS

THE halogens (Greek *hals* salt, *gennao* I beget) constitute a group of four or possibly five closely allied elements, namely fluorine, chlorine, bromine and iodine with possibly alabamine or astatine. Their name was coined by Berzelius (1779 to 1848), since the various members known in his day were to be found as salts in seawater resembling sea salt or halite. Before fluorine was isolated, the three remaining elements formed a typical example of the "Doebereiner triads". In 1829 Doebereiner pointed out that a determination of the atomic weight of bromine by Berzelius effected the previous year, supported his prediction that it would probably be the arithmetic mean of the atomic weights of chlorine and iodine.

Chlorine

The first halogen to be discovered was chlorine, by that indefatigable Swedish pharmacist Scheele who also discovered oxygen. In 1774 he studied the action of muriatic acid (Latin *muria*, brine), the name given to an aqueous solution of "marine acid air", our hydrogen chloride, on pyrolusite and observed that, upon warming, the mixture smelled like aqua regia, a greenish-yellow, choking gas being evolved.

Scheele had been brought up on the phlogistic theory already outlined in connection with oxygen and in consequence regarded the new gas as marine acid air deprived of its phlogiston by the pyrolusite. He accordingly baptised it in the name of *dephlogisticated marine acid air*. This cumbersome name obviously could not be retained and with the passing of the phlogistic theory a more suitable name had to be found*.

For many years chlorine was regarded as a compound of oxygen†. Its method of preparation appeared to suggest this, the gas being obtained by the oxidation of muriatic acid. Lavoisier therefore called it *oxymuriatic acid*; under such a name it fitted into Lavoisier's

---

*For full discussion of discovery of chlorine and proof of elementary character see CHATTAWAY, *Chem. News*, 1910, **101**, 25, 37, 50, 73.

†BERTHOLLET suggested this in 1785, *Mem. Acad. Sci., Paris*, 1785, p. 276.

scheme, according to which all acids, even muriatic acid itself, contained oxygen, the "acid producer". Oxymuriatic acid thus bore the same relation to muriatic acid as sulphuric to sulphurous. It was Davy* who, in 1810, showed conclusively that chlorine is an element. He passed hydrogen chloride over metallic potassium and found that only the metal chloride and pure hydrogen were produced. He therefore suggested the name chlorine (Greek *chloros*, greenish yellow) in allusion to its colour. Thus arose another example in which the name given to an element by its discoverer came to be changed (p. 25).

Chlorine is used for various purposes on an enormous scale by civilised communities. In 1910 it was used at Reading during an epidemic to sterilise the water, and since then this has become a usual practice; the process received great impetus during the 1914–1918 war, when water supplies for the troops were chlorinated, and again in 1940 when the authorities urged the adoption of chlorination by all of the larger water undertakings in view of the war risks. Chlorine is used in the sterilisation of sewage; extraction of bromine from carnallite and seawater; de-tinning of scrap tin-plate; removal of objectionable odours from gasoline, etc. At one time considerable quantities were used in the extraction of gold, but this process has now been largely superseded by the cyanide and amalgamation processes. Much chlorine is used in the manufacture of chemicals; it is burned with hydrogen to yield hydrochloric acid; with lime it gives bleaching powder; it is consumed in preparing chlorides, chlorates and hypochlorites, etc.

Wool is chlorinated to increase its resistance to "felting" during laundering. It is easier to wash as the surface after chlorination is hydrophilic and is readily cleansed by soap.

Chlorine finds an enormous demand in the preparation of various chlorinated organic derivatives. Amongst these may be mentioned carbonyl chloride or phosgene, $COCl_2$, used in the dye industry and as an asphyxiant in chemical warfare; 200 ppm in air constitute a fatal dose in 2 minutes. Carbon tetrachloride or "CTC", CCl_4, and pentachlorethane, $CHCl_2.CCl_3$, are used for extinguishing fires, the former also as a solvent and degreaser; trichlorethylene, $CHCl:CCl_2$, known commercially as triklone or simply tri, is a degreaser and an anæsthetic; chlorpicrin, CCl_3NO_2, has been used in the extermination of rats by the Russians in the Caucasus, to effect the elimination of bubonic plague communicated

---

*Davy, *Phil. Trans.*, 1811, pp. 1 and 32. The Bakerian Lecture for 1810.

to humans by rat fleas; DDT., $(ClC_6H_4)_2.CH.CCl_3$, is an invaluable insecticide. These will suffice.

Gaseous chlorine was first used as an asphyxiant in chemical warfare in April 1915 when the Germans launched a cloud attack against the Africans, Canadians and French in the Ypres salient. There were 20,000 casualties of which 5000 were fatal, whilst many others were damaged for life. Very small amounts of chlorine in the air help to ward off colds and to relieve them when once they have gained a hold. After the first world war chlorine chambers were used in America and the custom received a fillip when President Coolidge himself in May 1924 received treatment in one and was able to state afterwards that he felt considerable relief from his cold. The maximum safe concentration is 1 ppm in air for more or less prolonged inhalation; 32 ppm constitute a lethal dose in 30 minutes.

Iodine

Iodine was the second halogen to be discovered*. It was first observed by Courtois, a manufacturer of nitre, in 1811, but this was not announced until two years later by Clément and Desormes. Like so many other important discoveries that of iodine is what is popularly called "accidental". That is to say it was not the result of a specific search for the element, but of a chance observation by an intelligent observer.

In the preparation of nitre from seaweed or wrack (French *varech*) the dried plants were burned and the ashes leached for the sodium and potassium salts. Upon concentration sodium chloride separated first, followed by potassium chloride and sulphate, other salts of these metals, such as sulphites and carbonates, being left in solution. These were destroyed by addition of sulphuric acid. On one occasion the acid was probably more concentrated or in larger quantity than usual and a violet vapour arose with an irritating odour not unlike that of chlorine. This condensed to a solid crystalline deposit on cold objects without formation of liquid. For a time this new substance was referred to as X, an appellation used many years later to designate the unknown rays discovered by Röntgen in 1895 and nowadays often employed in cases of blackmail. As Courtois had insufficient laboratory facilities he

*A valuable compilation of data in connection with iodine is published by the *Iodine Educational Bureau,* maintained by the Chilean Nitrate and Iodine Producers under the title "Iodine Facts".

asked his friends Clément and Desormes to undertake the study of X. Its analogy to chlorine suggested its elementary nature and this was subsequently demonstrated by Gay-Lussac in 1814 and independently by Davy. Gay-Lussac suggested the name *ione* (Greek *ion*, the violet) whilst Davy proposed *iodine* from Greek *ioeides*, violet coloured as being more analogous to chlorine and fluorine and less likely to lead to confusion with other terms.

Iodine in minute quantity is a normal constituent of the human body and the average person requires a daily dose of 0·000,017 gm. Absence of the requisite amount leads to general debility and in more severe cases to goitre or "big-neck". In very severe cases mental weakness develops known as cretinism, from Latin *creta*, chalk, because of its prevalence in Alpine districts. In Switzerland sodium iodide is added to table salt by legal regulation to ensure that everybody receives his necessary "ration" of iodine. In Britain there are several areas of iodine deficiency in the soil and addition of iodides to the feeding-stuffs of cattle, etc, effects an enormous improvement in the herds.

Iodine is used largely in medicine owing to its powerful germicidal action. The brown solutions of iodine in alcohol or aqueous potassium iodide applied as "paints" to wounds, etc, are familiar to all. Iodine is the main constituent of iodoform; it is also used in photography and in chemical laboratories.

Bromine

In 1825 Löwig, one of Gmelin's students at Heidelberg, began to study a red liquid obtained by chlorination of the concentrated waters from a salt spring at Kreuznach. Before, however, he could complete his study Balard* announced the discovery in 1826 of a new element extracted with chlorine from the Montpellier brines after first removing the sodium chloride. This element was a dark red liquid identical with that of Löwig and to it he gave the name *muride* in view of its presence in brine. But this name was not acceptable to chemists in view of probable confusion with muriatic acid and the name was changed to *bromine*, from Greek *brōmos*, a stench.

Liebig† had narrowly missed the same discovery. A German firm had asked him to examine a red liquid which he regarded as chloride of iodine and not worth further attention. Upon the

---

*BALARD, *Ann. Chim. Phys.*, 1826, (II), **36**, 377.
†SHENSTONE, "Justus von Liebig, His Life and Work" (Cassell, 1901), Chap. 3.

E

announcement of Balard's bromine Liebig realised the mistake he had made; on his shelves this very element had been standing unrecognised.

Bromine is used as a disinfectant; *bromum solidificatum* is merely kieselguhr saturated with bromine. Bromine is a valuable raw material in the manufacture of dyestuffs and drugs. A recent use is in the preparation of ethylene dibromide, $C_2H_4Br_2$, required for anti-knock motor fuel. The simpler methyl bromide, CH_3Br, finds application as a fire extinguisher. Bromine has been used, generally in conjunction with other gases, as an asphyxiant in warfare. Some 31 ppm in air are usually fatal within 30 to 60 minutes.

Fluorine

Fluorine was the last halogen to be isolated. Fluorspar* has been known for many centuries. Georgius Agricola†, who earned for himself the title of "Father of Metallurgy", referred to the use of fluorspar as a flux in his work "Bermannus", *circa* 1529, whence the name of the mineral, from Latin *fluere*, to flow. When gently warmed the mineral emits light; this is termed *fluorescence*, a word showing that the growth of a language may cause derivatives to assume a meaning entirely different from that suggested by their roots.

In Napoleonic times Derbyshire fluorspar was exported to France where it was termed the *bleu jaune* or blue-yellow stone; it was shaped into fancy articles which were subsequently re-imported into Britain as the anglicised Blue John.

It is usually stated that the corrosive action of hydrofluoric acid, which is readily obtained by the action of sulphuric acid upon the mineral in the warm, was first observed by Herr Swanhardt, an artist of Nuremberg, in 1670. Some accidentally fell on to his spectacles and etched the glass; from that time onwards Swanhardt etched glass with the vapours from fluorspar and sulphuric acid. But this pretty legend has been exploded by Partington‡ who

---

*Will the student notice that this is not "flour" spar. Judging from examination papers many students appear to confuse the two words.

†GEORGIUS AGRICOLA, 1490 (or 1494) to 1555, was a physician who took unusual interest in metallurgy and mining. His monumental work "*De re Metallica*" did not appear until 1556 but the MS was evidently finished several years before that as it bore a dedication dated 1550. He was author also of several other works, including "Bermannus".

‡PARTINGTON, *Chemistry and Industry*, 1941, p. 109. *Mem. Manchester Lit. Phil. Soc.*, 1922–3, **67**, 73.

finds that the first authenticated mention of the acid is in 1720; he further adds that the discovery of the acid was probably a British achievement.

In 1771 Scheele was the first to recognise in fluorspar the calcium salt of a new acid which latter he obtained later by distillation of fluorspar with sulphuric acid using a tin retort. He called the product fluoric acid and in 1807 Gay-Lussac and Thenard prepared the anhydrous acid. In accordance with Lavoisier's theory the acid was regarded as a compound of water with the oxide of an element "fluorium" and hence contained oxygen.

In 1810, however, Ampère suggested to Davy that the acid was probably a compound of hydrogen with an unknown element and contained no oxygen. In 1813 Davy in turn developed these views. Assuming fluorspar to be analogous to calcium chloride in that it contained an element analogous to chlorine, he suggested the new element be called *fluorine*.

Every effort to isolate fluorine was futile until Gore obtained a little momentarily in 1869 by electrolysis, but it immediately combined explosively with hydrogen. It was not until 1886 that Moissan succeeded in obtaining pure fluorine by electrolysing a solution of anhydrous potassium hydrogen fluoride in hydrofluoric acid, using electrodes of an alloy of platinum and iridium.

Despite its intense chemical activity which rendered its isolation so difficult, its first oxide, F_2O, was not discovered until 1927 by Lebeau and Damiens.

Fluorine, like iodine, in minute amount is essential to the human body; it enables the teeth to develop a hard enamel and resist decay. But this is a case in which it is easy to have too much of a good thing. In 1934 the children at Malden in Essex were found to be suffering from mottled teeth — a name that explains itself. This was traced to the presence of excess fluorine ions in the water to the extent of 4·5 to 5 ppm. Small quantities up to about 1 ppm appear to be beneficial.

Fluorine has a great affinity for carbon; considerably greater than that of hydrogen or the other halogens, so that the fluorides of carbon are extremely stable. This is evident from the bond strengths which are believed to be as follows; C—H, 80; C—Cl, 83; C—F, 120 Calories per gm.-atom. A relatively new thermoplastic, known technically as *fluon* has been made by polymerising tetrafluoethylene, $F_2C:CF_2$, yielding $(C_2F_4)_n$, variously known as polytetrafluo-ethylene or PTFE. It is of special interest to engineers on account of its inertness. There appears to be a wide field opening up for research on fluocarbons and their value in industry.

From the Periodic Table it seems that element 85 should be the highest member of the halogen group. In 1931 a claim was made* that the presence of the element had been detected and it was given the name *alabamine*. This story requires confirmation. For the element obtained synthetically through fission of uranium the name *astatine* has been suggested.

---

*ALLISON and CO-WORKERS, *Physical Review*, 1931, **37**, 1178; 1930, **35**, 285.

CHAPTER 5

CARBON

Carbon, in the forms of charcoal, graphite and diamond, has been known from very early times. Acquaintance with charcoal would be roughly synchronous with that of fire (p. 8). In later years the charcoal was used by man as a pigment in decorating the walls of his caves; later still it played a great part in his metallurgy.

Graphite would certainly be a much later discovery than charcoal; nevertheless it was known in early times and esteemed because of the greyish black streak left behind when it was rubbed against a roughened surface. The word is derived from the Greek *grapho*, I write; the names *plumbago* and *black lead* show that the mineral was regarded as a form of lead. The Greek word *molybdos* was apparently employed to denote lead and materials that resembled lead in physical appearance, and thus included galena, PbS, graphite and molybdenite, MoS_2, these two latter minerals being regarded as identical. Indeed pencils have been found containing molybdenite instead of graphite. Pliny (A.D.23 to 79) used the words molybdæna and galena synonymously. It was Scheele, in 1779, who first distinguished between graphite and molybdenite. Acting on them with nitric acid he obtained with the one merely gaseous carbon dioxide, whereas the other yielded a white solid which Scheele termed molybdic acid. From that time onwards the two minerals have been recognised as distinct, the term graphite being given to the one consisting of carbon only, and molybdenite to the other, namely molybdenum sulphide. In 1800 Mackenzie showed that graphite burns like charcoal, producing carbon dioxide.

The exceptional properties of graphite are due to its unique structure which is the most perfect example known of layer lattices. It consists of sheets of carbon atoms linked hexagonally like wire netting (fig. 4) each sheet representing a gigantic, two-dimensional molecule. Adjacent atoms are 1·421A apart* and statistically rather more than three valencies out of the four of each carbon atom are absorbed in the C—C bonds in each layer. The valency forces left over are absorbed in holding the various layers

---

*A = angstrom unit, that is 10^{-8} cm.

together, the bonding assuming the form similar to that in metals. The electrons are but loosely bound and, in consequence, graphite possesses metallic conduction in the direction of the planes.

These planes, too, are 3·354A apart and, as interatomic forces are inversely proportional to about the eighth power of the distance between the centres of the atoms, the layers can easily slide over each other like the leaves of a book. Thus graphite functions as a lubricator. Normally the different layers are out of step as shown in Fig. 4.

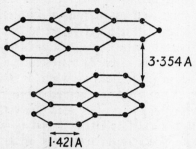

Fig. 4 — The structure of graphite

All forms of carbon seem to possess a graphite structure with the exception of the diamond (p. 59). So-called "amorphous" carbon consists of small sheets of hexagonal structure and the smaller the sheets the more widely do they tend to lie apart. A variation in the properties of carbon with its fineness of division is thus to be expected.

Some 12 per cent of the world's graphite is used in the pencil trade. The finest graphite in the world was found at Borrowdale in Cumberland, but the supplies are now largely worked out. The Keswick pencils were world-famous. In early days the mineral was cut to shape and inserted in grooves in cedar wood to form the pencil; but the result was poor as only short lengths of graphite were possible, and even these contained the natural grit of the mineral. Now the graphite, whether natural or artificial, is pulverised, mixed with a little clay and gum solution to a paste, and squeezed through a die.

Foundries consume considerable quantities of graphite; the pattern is buried in moulding sand, the surface of which, after removal of the pattern, is coated with graphite often mixed with talc to provide a smooth surface and prevent the casting from sticking.

Graphite is also used for making crucibles for melting steel and brass; as a lubricant, sometimes alone and sometimes mixed with grease or water; as a constituent of paint, stove polishes; for coating blasting powders to protect from damp; for electrodes and electrodeposition of metals on non-conducting surfaces, such as wax, etc. Graphite is used in the construction of atomic piles; but for this an extremely pure product is essential and this is manufactured in the electric furnace at such a high temperature that virtually every trace of impurity volatilises. Indian ink is finely pulverised graphite baked with a glutinous paste.

Diamond

The word "diamond", derived from the Greek *adamas*, invincible, bears witness to its extreme hardness, and the term was used in reference to this stone in A.D.16. Pliny speaks of the diamond as the most valuable of gems. The brilliant lustre and play of colours of the "cut" stone are due to its high refractive index and dispersive power. Sometimes diamonds are also doubly refracting, in consequence of internal strain; such specimens have been known to crack and even burst spontaneously.

Although mentioned by name several times in the Old Testament it is considered unlikely that the early Hebrews were acquainted with the diamond. The "diamond" of *Exod.* xxviii. 18, and xxxix. 11, was an engraved stone, and could therefore hardly have been the gem we know under that name. It was probably quartz. The so-called Bristol, Cornish, and Derbyshire "diamonds" are merely quartz (p. 61). The later references in *Jer.* xvii. 1, and *Ezek.* xxviii. 13, may possibly be genuine.

Diamonds were first discovered in the sands of India; they were not known in Europe until Alexander the Great returned from India 327 B.C. The Romans introduced them into Western Europe and used them for graving tools, producing cameos and intaglios in hard stone. They do not appear to have used diamonds as jewels. The Indian industry was centred round Golconda, near Hyderabad; it was a fortress and market for the gems, but is now merely a ruined city.

In his "Voyages and Travels" Marco Polo*, the famous Venetian traveller (1254 to 1324), known as the Columbus of the

---

*"The Voyages and Travels of Marco Polo". Cassell's National Library, 1886. Chap. xxviii. Marco was probably the first European ever to visit the diamond territory of India.

East Indies, states that he visited a district in India known as the Kingdom of Murfili, now generally identified with Golconda. Here were rocky mountains and steep precipitous valleys into which men were afraid to venture partly because of the large number of venomous serpents. He was informed that after the rainy season these valleys were rich in diamonds which lay on the surface having been washed down from the mountain sides. To obtain them the men were wont to throw chunks of raw flesh into the valleys; perceiving which the local white eagles would swoop down and pick up the flesh in their talons, with the soil and diamonds clinging to it, and carry it to their nests. When the eagles left their nests again the men raided them for diamonds.

Marco gives a very human touch to his story when he adds that "the kings and great men in this country keep the fairest and finest stones to themselves and suffer the merchants to sell the rest." Nevertheless the reader may be pardoned if he queries the accuracy of the story as it stands. Probably it took its rise from some sacrificial custom in connection with the worship of the goddess of riches, Ammarwaru. The flesh cut from a slaughtered cow or buffalo was probably thrown on the ground as an offering and would naturally be picked up and carried off by the birds*.

In 1725 diamonds were found in Brazil; miners searching for gold had found some curious pebbles and, unaware of their value, used them as counters and gave them to children to play with. An officer who had spent several years in the East Indies was struck by the appearance of the pebbles and sent some to a friend in Lisbon to be examined. They proved to be diamonds, equal to those of Golconda. But popular prejudice against Brazilian diamonds was strong; to be fashionable the diamonds must come from India; many therefore were shipped from Brazil to India and re-exported from thence to Europe as "Indian" diamonds, when they were readily marketed. The soil at Diamantino in Brazil appears to have been singularly rich in small diamonds; a negro is reported to have found one of 9 carats among the roots of some vegetables from his own garden; diamonds have also been found in the crops of chickens. John Mawe†, in an account of his travels in Brazil mentions that a negro wrote to the then Prince Regent announcing the discovery of an enormous diamond which he begged to have the honour of showing to his majesty in person. A carriage and

---

*V. BALL, Nature, 1881, 23, 490.
†JOHN MAWE, "Travels in the Interior of Brazil" (London, 1812).

escort were accordingly sent and the negro was brought to the royal presence when he handed over the precious stone weighing nearly 1 lb. It was sent to the royal treasury and deposited in the hall of gems, its value being estimated as at least a million sterling. One or two persons at court, however, appear to have entertained some doubt as to the genuineness of the stone and when Mawe was in Rio de Janeiro he was requested, as a known authority, to examine it. At a glance he saw that it was merely quartz and confirmed his opinion by scratching it with a diamond. The negro who had been brought to Rio in such pomp had to find his way back home as best he could.

In 1867 even more important deposits were found in S. Africa. An intelligent pedlar noticed that a Boer child on a farm near Hopetown on the Orange River was playing with some peculiar pebbles and submitted one to a mineralogist who identified it as diamond; it was shown in the Paris Exhibition in the same year. There was in consequence a rush to S. Africa and extensive river diggings were undertaken which extended to the R. Vaal. By 1869 dry diggings had begun in several shallow depressions or "pans" and this led to the founding of Kimberley. In 1888 Cecil Rhodes effected the amalgamation of the Kimberley mines into the De Beers Consolidated Mines.

Sir Isaac Newton as early as 1704 suspected that the diamond might be combustible, and it was shown by Lavoisier in 1772 that such was the case provided air was present, carbon dioxide being produced. Tennant, in 1797, showed that when equal weights of diamond and graphite are separately burned, equal quantities of carbon dioxide result. It was still necessary to prove that there were no other products. The matter was clinched by Sir Humphry Davy who had a wealthy wife; he burned with the sun's heat a diamond in oxygen in Florence, during March 1814, using the great lens then recently acquired by the Cabinet of Natural History in that city. He used the precious lens with characteristic agility which made the savants tremble lest he should break their newest acquisition. But Davy did not; instead he showed that there was no change in volume of the gas when the diamond had disappeared and that the sole product was carbon dioxide. The diamond and charcoal were thus chemically identical. Up to that time it was generally believed that bodies could not have the same chemical composition if their physical properties were different. Davy's experiments showed this to be untrue and paved the way for the later conceptions of allotropy and polymorphism. It was Berzelius who, in 1840, described the different varieties of an element as allotropes (Greek *allos*, other; *tropos*, manner).

The weight of a diamond is expressed in *carats**, the carat being originally the average weight of the seed of the locust, Kuara, or carob tree — a native of Africa. The word is said to be derived from the Greek *keration*, which refers to the horn-like shape of the pods. The seeds are remarkably uniform in the pod, those at the ends being as large as the middle ones; they have been used from time immemorial for weighing gold, and were transported to India in early times and there used for weighing diamonds. In 1888 the Board of Trade fixed the *English carat* at 3·1683 grains, equivalent to 205·310 milligrams. The *metric carat*, now universally adopted, was legally fixed at 200·000 mgm. The metric carat became compulsory in Britain in 1914.

Many attempts have been made to produce the diamond artificially. In 1880 Hannay obtained diamonds of microscopic size by heating to dull redness for many hours a mixture of paraffin and bone oils with metallic lithium in a closed wrought-iron tube. On opening the tube minute isotropic crystals were extracted from the black residue; they were sufficiently hard to scratch all other crystals. For many years doubt was expressed as to the identity of these crystals with diamond, but X-ray examination has justified Hannay's claim†.

Moissan, the French chemist, who was the first to isolate fluorine, also claimed‡ to have synthesised the diamond by causing it to crystallise out from molten iron under great pressure. The minute crystals conformed to all known tests for the diamond, but unfortunately the X-ray method, which could have placed the matter beyond all doubt, was not then known.

Not all diamonds are of gem quality; some 60 per cent of the raw stones are unsuitable for gems; industry absorbs about 80 per cent of the diamonds by weight, the remaining 20 per cent being used for jewellery, etc. Black diamonds known as *carbonado*§ have no gem value; they are peculiar to Bahia in Brazil and contain up to 2 per cent of impurity. They are nevertheless as hard as the

---

*A historical account of the carat is given by DR. SPENCER in the *Mineralogical Magazine*, 1910, **15**, 318.

†BANNISTER and LONSDALE, *ibid.*, 1943, **26**, 315.

‡See "The Electric Furnace" by MOISSAN, English Edition, 1904.

§The largest carbonado was found in Bahia in 1895 and weighed 631·9 grams.

pure stone and tougher; they show no cleavage tendency. They do not soften when heated and are in great demand for drills. The Simplon tunnel opened in 1906 was the first major operation with diamond drills. Irregular aggregates of bad colour and flawed are known as *bort* (Old French *bort*, bastard); they are obtained mostly from the African fields and are extensively used as an abrasive dust, for dies, for "cutting" and faceting precious stones* and for drillings.

The first diamond ever cut in Birmingham occupies a place of honour in the Lord Mayor's chain. It lies at the centre of a Maltese cross in the badge suspended from the central link of the chain. Beneath this is a wreath suggesting laurel and oak; it surrounds a shield on which appear the Birmingham Arms, in enamel. Above the shield, mounted on a plate of gold, is the motto "Forward" and on the back is engraved: "This diamond, the first cut in Birmingham, was manufactured, mounted in badge, and presented to the Corporation of his native town, by William Spencer, 1873 (during the mayoralty of Ambrose Biggs)."

Diamond tools are now made to obtain a high finish necessary for many engine components, particularly for aircraft. Diamond dies are made by rotating a needle fed by diamond dust and ore, and are sometimes of minute diameter; they are so hard that they will pass many miles of wire without change in diameter; this is important when uniformity is essential as in electrical work such as tungsten filaments (p. 246), resistances, etc. Diamonds are also used for cutting glass, for drilling glass and porcelain, for engraving metal work, etc.

The diamond possesses cleavage planes in four directions and despite its phenomenal hardness it may be easily shattered by a blow. An old method of testing stones reputed to be diamonds was to strike them on an anvil. If they broke they were not diamonds! Probably many a valuable stone was lost in that sad way.

The hardness of the diamond is due to its symmetrical structure. Each C atom has four others arranged tetrahedrally and perfectly symmetrically round it (Fig. 5). The diamond is thus one huge molecule with no weak spot. Carborundum, SiC, has a similar structure and is also extremely hard. It might be thought that close-packing would explain the hardness, but the diamond has a relatively open structure; if close packed it would be possible for

---

*The pioneer in this art was Louis de Berquem, of Bruges, who, in 1476, conceived the idea of using diamond dust for this purpose.

12 spheres to touch the central one, in which case the density of the diamond would be 7·653, instead of 3·01 to 3·56*.

The beauty of the diamond is due to its high refractive index coupled with great dispersive power. The crude diamond as found looks anything but attractive; the art of the lapidary consists in cutting the stone and polishing it to bring out its brilliancy.

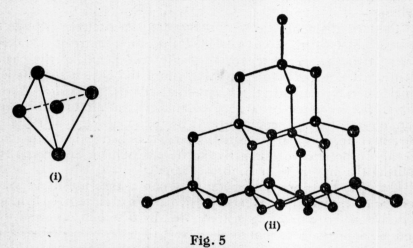

Fig. 5
(i) **Tetrahedral arrangement of carbon atoms**
(ii) **Arrangement of carbon atoms in the diamond**

The purest diamonds are crystal clear and colourless. Such stones are described as of the "first water" or as "blue-whites". Diamonds may be of any colour; when ruby red they are almost priceless. There was a small ruby red one among the Russian Court Jewels many years ago.

In 1926 a small red diamond was found in alluvial diggings near Kimberley and was expected to weigh 6 carats when cut and to be worth close upon £1000. A clear apple green stone of 41 carats is known as the Dresden Diamond, an Indian stone purchased in 1743 for the Crown of Saxony. Blue stones are almost as rare as the red, the most famous example being the Hope Diamond (p. 62); it is thought that the Brunswick Blue Diamond may have been cut from the same stone. Yellow is the most common colour, the most famous being the Austrian Yellow Diamond (p. 61), the

---

*The theoretical value for the perfectly pure diamond is 3·515.

Tiffany Yellow from Kimberley, 1878, the Tennant and Colenzo stones.

When strongly heated in air absence the diamond either sublimes or is converted to graphite; it never melts. The somewhat slippery feel is regarded as due to the assumption by the electronic orbits of surface atoms of a pseudo-graphitic structure.

In 1663 Boyle observed that diamonds become luminous if rubbed in the dark; they become luminous, too, after exposure to light or to cathode rays. When exposed to ultraviolet light some diamonds yield a blue glow. They are more transparent to X-rays than other gems and after prolonged exposure to radium a colourless diamond becomes green.

Many stones that are not genuine diamonds are popularly so called. Thus Brazil, Bristol*, Cornish*, Derbyshire, Alaskan, Arkansas, Marmora and German "diamonds" are quartz. Matura or Ceylon "diamonds" are white zircons. The Saxony "diamond" is white topaz; the Simili or Strass "diamond" is merely a paste (glass). Carbonado and coal are frequently termed black diamonds — and not without reason.

Some famous diamonds

The story of the diamond could hardly be complete without some reference to a few of the more important diamonds known to the civilised world. The diamond is the only gem stone that comprises one element only. It appeals to popular taste because of its rarity, unique hardness, which prevents it from being scratched, and exceptional optical properties.

The Austrian Yellow or Grand Duke of Tuscany Diamond, known also as the Florentine Diamond, is probably of Indian origin; it was cut as a briolette in 1476 for Charles the Bold. It is pale yellow in colour, and weighs 137·27 metric carats. Prior to World War II it was kept in Vienna. It was one of the heirlooms of the Royal House of Austria.

The Cullinan Diamond is a famous stone. In 1897 Thomas Cullinan purchased a farm near Pretoria in the Transvaal, which was believed to contain diamonds; and so it proved; in a few years the land was valued at £20 million. In 1903 a diamond mine was discovered there which came to be known as the Premier Mine, and in January 1905 a diamond was unearthed, the largest gem

*These are mentioned by C. MERRET, *Phil. Trans.*, 1866, **12**, No. 138, p. 949.

ever found in historic times*; nevertheless it was probably only a portion of a still larger stone as it had one large cleavage surface. It measured $4 \times 2\frac{1}{2} \times 2$ cubic inches and weighed 621·2 grams or 3016 metric carats, equivalent to 1·3695 lb. (avoir). It was named after (later Sir) Thomas Cullinan.

In 1907 the Transvaal Government, acting on the suggestion of General Botha, purchased the diamond for £150,000 and presented it to King Edward VII. The stone was remarkably pure, of the first water or bluish white; it was cut yielding two magnificent brilliants, 7 smaller stones and 96 still smaller ones. The total weight of the cut diamonds was 1063·65 carats, equivalent to a yield of about 34 per cent of the rough stone, the remainder being converted to dust. The two largest stones are set in the English Crown.

The De Beers Diamond found in 1888 in the De Beers mine at Kimberley was pale yellow and weighed 88 grams or 440 metric carats. When cut it yielded a magnificent brilliant of 234·5 carats.

The Excelsior Diamond was found in June 1893 in the Jägersfontein diamond mine in the Orange Free State of S. Africa. Next to the Cullinan it was the largest of known diamonds, weighing in the rough 199·04 grams or 995·2 metric carats†. A glass model is in the possession of the British Museum, and measures $2·3 \times 2·15 \times 1·08$ cubic inches, approximately. It was not cut until 1903 when it was converted into 21 brilliants ranging in weight from 69·68 metric carats downwards.

The Hope Diamond has been much to the fore in recent years. Dull, slaty blue in colour it is generally acknowledged to be the world's most perfect blue diamond. It weighs 45·5 carats. It has had a chequered history. Its existence was revealed by the Great Mogul for the first time to a European, the celebrated French traveller Jean Baptisté Tavernier‡, who was his guest in the middle of the seventeenth century. He said that, in a temple in the ancient town of Pagan, there was an idol named *Rama Sita*, adorned by a magnificent blue diamond. Tavernier was interested; he was a

---

*The Bahian carbonado (p. 58) was a little larger, but it was not a gem.

†SPENCER, *Mineralogical Magazine*, 1911, **16**, 140.

‡TAVERNIER (1605 to 1689) was the son of a German map engraver who had settled in Paris. He travelled widely, made much money by trading in jewels and was ennobled by Louis XIV, becoming Baron d'Aubonne. For a detailed account of his travels see "The Six Voyages of John Baptista Tavernier, Baron of Aubonne, through Turkey into Persia and the East Indies" (London, 1678).

connoisseur of gems having been supervisor of the treasures of Louis XIV. After leaving the Mogul, Tavernier went to Pagan to visit the temple; this was easy; he was the friend of the Great Mogul. With several accomplices he stole into the temple at the dead of night, bound and gagged the priests, extracted the diamond from the forehead of the idol and fled. The curse of the Indian god is reputed to fall on all who possess the stone. Certainly its career has been accompanied by misfortune. Tavernier sold it to Louis XIV and died soon after*. The stone remained a French Crown jewel until the Revolution. After receiving the stone Louis XIV lost several members of his family and himself became gravely ill. One of his mistresses, Mdlle de Montespan, wore the stone on several occasions and then fell from favour. Another, Mdme de Lavallière, wore it and became strangely depressed, so entered a convent. Marie Antoinette, wife of Louis XVI, wore it and was guillotined soon after her royal husband. The Assembly annexed the royal jewels but the diamond was stolen, reappearing later in Amsterdam, where it was cut by Fala, whose son stole it, sold it, squandered the money and then committed suicide. Eventually the stone came into the possession of Francois Beaulieu who cut it in two, sold the smaller part and took the larger to London where it was purchased by Henry Philip Hope, a wealthy Londoner, for £18,000; it was described in the catalogue of his collection in 1839, the year of his death, and thus came to be known as the Hope Diamond. Henry was a bachelor, but the diamond remained in the family passing in due course to Lord Francis Hope. The latter became involved in financial and domestic difficulties; his actress wife May Yohe, at her divorce proceedings in 1902, attributed all their ill-luck to the stone. The gem was sold and became the property of a Polish prince in 1908 who lent it to a Paris actress who was shot from a box whilst on the stage. The prince was himself stabbed to death a couple of days later.

The stone now came into the possession of Abdul, Sultan of Turkey, who shot his wife whilst wearing it and was himself later deposed. A Persian merchant who next had it was drowned. In 1911 Edward McLean, a Washington millionaire, purchased it, paying, it is said, some £60,000, and gave it to his wife Evelyn Walsh McLean. She very naturally scoffed at the idea of ill-luck;

---

*Some say he was killed by wild animals on his travels. Different accounts of the diamond vary considerably in the details of its early history. The Author has endeavoured to include only the most authentic data.

nevertheless to be on the safe side she arranged for it to be blessed by a priest. This apparently, didn't do much good, for Evelyn saw her eldest son run over by a car and killed; her husband became involved in financial difficulties and she divorced him in 1933. He died insane. Evelyn herself broke her leg and it never healed properly. In 1941 her 25-year-old daughter married and Evelyn wore the diamond at the wedding. In 1946 the daughter was found dead in her home in Washington as the result of sleeping tablets. Evelyn once asked the Bishop of Washington to hide the diamond in his cathedral, but this the reverend gentleman was unwilling to do. "I do not know" wrote Mrs McLean "if the bishop was afraid of the diamond's curse, but I do know that I could not persuade him to have anything to do with it." Mrs McLean died from pneumonia in 1947. In April 1949 it was announced that Mr Harry Winston, a New York jeweller, had purchased the diamond, the purchase price not being named. "It is childish", he said, "to suppose that diamonds themselves exert any influence for good or evil; it is not the diamonds themselves that cause misfortune, but the people who handle them." We will let it rest at that.

The Imperial Diamond, known also as the Victoria or Great White Diamond probably came from the Jägersfontein mine of the O.F.S. It appeared on the London market in 1884 and had been presumably stolen from the mine. Its original weight was given as 457 carats; it was cut into an oval brilliant of 180 carats and a smaller round brilliant of approximately 19·6 carats. The former was purchased by the Nizam of Hyderabad.

The Jonker Diamond is the fourth largest gem diamond known. The story of its discovery is a real romance. Jacobus Jonker, a South African farmer and prospector, had a claim at Elandsfontain, not far from the Premier Mine near Pretoria. For 18 years he toiled with unexampled perseverance but with little result. In due course his luck turned. After a heavy rain storm in January 1934 he put a native to work on gravel that had been washed up. He found a stone in size and shape like a hen's egg, about $2\frac{3}{4}$ inches long by $1\frac{1}{2}$ inches wide and deep, weighing 145·2 grams or 726 carats. That night the stone was hidden in a stocking tied round Mrs Jonker's neck and the hut was guarded by armed men. Next day it was taken to safety; in due course it was purchased by Sir Ernest Oppenheimer, Chairman of the Diamond Corporation, and *sent to London by ordinary registered post* — what a tribute to the

postal system of those days! It was seen by the King and Queen
but a suggestion that it should be added to the Crown jewels did
not materialise. It was kept in the vaults of the Corporation until
it was sold in 1935. Because of heavy insurance it cost about £10
per day to keep the diamond. The purchaser was Mr Harry
Winston of New York, who recently purchased the Hope Diamond
(p. 64); he paid £150,000. The next problem was to get it cut.
This was done by Lazare Kaplan who studied the stone for a whole
year in order to ensure that he had diagnosed its cleavage planes
correctly; an error in their determination might ruin the diamond
which even Lloyds were not prepared to insure against accident.
At long last, taking his courage in both his hands, Lazare began
his task which ended in complete success. The diamond yielded
12 gems weighing about 400 carats, the largest gem weighing
about 170 carats, some 300 carats being "lost" as dust. The cut
stones were then valued at £400,000.

The Kohinoor Diamond or Mountain of Light, is a magnificent
stone. Many centuries ago a beautiful diamond was found in one
of the Golconda mines; according to Hindoo tradition it belonged
to Kama, a King of Auga, 3000 years ago, but that is typical oriental
exaggeration. The stone was kept by the rulers of the kingdom of
Golconda until they were conquered in the seventeenth century by the
Moguls. During a visit to India in the second half of the seventeenth
century, the French traveller Tavernier (p.62) was shown a diamond,
known as the Great Mogul, by the Mogul ruler Aurungzebe,
whose guest Tavernier had the honour to be. In the rough it
weighed about 300 carats and was sometimes worn by the Mogul
himself or it adorned his famous peacock throne. In 1739 the
Mogul Empire was over-run by the Persians under Nadir Shah,
into whose keeping the Mogul treasures now passed. When Nadir
Shah was murdered by his own subjects, a large diamond, believed
to be the Great Mogul, was carried away by Ahmed Shah and remained in his family until 1800 when the then owner was over-
thrown by Shah Shuja, who, himself in 1813 was compelled to
hand over the stone to the Rajah of Lahore, who wore it as an
armlet and sometimes decked his horses with it.

On the annexation of the Punjab a diamond, known as the
Kohinoor, and believed to be the Great Mogul, was handed to the
East India Company and by them to H.M. Queen Victoria, being
brought to London in 1850. Up till then the stone had only been
rough cut; it was now re-cut to a brilliant of 108·9 carats and

F

exhibited at the famous 1851 Exhibition. It was unfortunately cut too broadly for its depth and does not in consequence show its full brilliance. It is a Crown jewel and the superstitious Indians regarded its loss as the downfall of their empire.

The Pitt or Regent Diamond, is a remarkably clear stone said to have been found in the Kistna River at Hyderabad in 1701, but may equally well have been stolen from some mine in the Golconda area. It was bought by Thomas Pitt, known thereafter as Diamond Pitt, Governor of Fort St. George, Madras, and grandfather of the great English statesman, the Earl of Chatham. He paid some £20,000 for the diamond in 1715. Two years later he sold it, still in the rough, to the Duke of Orleans, Regent of France, for £135,000, for presentation to Louis xv. The rough stone weighed 410 carats and was cut as an extra deep brilliant of 135 carats, an operation that took two years. When Louis xv was crowned the diamond was set in his crown; later it was worn in a brooch by his queen Marie Leczincka. During the Revolution it was stolen, but recovered and adorned the state sword of Napoleon. During the Franco-Prussian War it was placed for safety in the arsenal at Brest and later in the hold of a French warship. It is now exhibited in the Louvre, Paris.

The Sanci Diamond is believed to be the first to be cut and polished in Europe. It weighed about 53·75 carats. It belonged to Charles the Bold, Duke of Burgundy, who wore it at the Battle of Nancy in 1477, where he was defeated and killed. The diamond was found by a Swiss soldier on the field of battle; it was sold to a Frenchman named Sanci and kept in his family for nearly a century, when Henry iii desired to borrow it from one of the captains of his Swiss troops to whom it had descended. This young Sanci accordingly gave it to a trusted servant to take to the king, but both man and diamond mysteriously disappeared. Sanci had the greatest confidence in his servant and made a thorough search for him, learning later that he had been waylaid by robbers, murdered and buried in a forest. He proceeded to the spot indicated, had the body disinterred and cut open. In the man's stomach lay the diamond. The faithful minion had swallowed the stone sooner than allow it to fall into wrong hands.

The diamond later came into the possession of the English crown and was taken across to France by James ii when forced to leave England in 1688. Louis xv wore it at his coronation. In 1835 it was purchased by a Russian nobleman for £80,000. Presumably it now lies behind the "Iron Curtain".

In 1948 Tanganyika presented H.R.H. Princess Elizabeth, on the occasion of her wedding, a pink diamond, the largest and purest known, weighing, when cut, 23 carats.

CHAPTER 6

THE METALLOIDS BORON AND SILICON

THE term metalloid was introduced by Erman and Simon in 1802 to indicate such elements as possess metallic physical properties, but non-metallic chemical properties. These include boron, silicon, arsenic, antimony, selenium and tellurium. Sometimes iodine is added to the list. Unfortunately in 1811 Berzelius employed the term metalloid as synonymous with *non-metal* and at the present time the French still adhere to its use in that sense. In the present chapter we shall deal with boron and silicon only.

Boron

Borax has been known in commerce for many centuries, its name being derived from the Arabic *bauraq* probably from the Persian *burah*. The word occurs in early alchemical writing, but may not always have referred to the same substance since the Arabs applied the term also to nitre. Agricola (*circa* 1530) called it *chrysocolla* (Greek *krusos*, gold) because of its use in soldering gold, but that name is now reserved for another mineral, namely copper metasilicate, $CuSiO_3.2H_2O$. Borax was originally obtained from a salt lake in Tibet and sent to Europe in the crude state as *tincal*.

In 1702 Homberg prepared the free acid from borax and called it *sal sedativum*. In 1747 Baron discovered that borax is a compound of soda and *sal sedativum*; in other words, it is a salt and with the establishment of Lavoisier's system of nomenclature, introduced in conjunction with de Morveau, Berthollet, and Fourcroy in 1787, the incorrect appellation *sal sedativum* gave place to *boracic acid*, subsequently shortened to *boric acid*. Lavoisier regarded it as an oxide. The news reaching Paris early in 1808 that Davy had, in the previous October, isolated the alkali metals potassium and sodium stimulated chemists generally to attempt the isolation of other metals. Gay-Lussac and Thenard prepared potassium that year (1808) by a new process, namely heating potash with metallic iron, a method which Davy himself subsequently adopted as more convenient than his own electrolytic one. The potassium was now heated with boric anhydride in a copper tube and, after cooling, the residue was washed free from soluble matter, and christened *bore*. To complete their investigation they oxidised some of this bore, converting it to boric acid. About the same time Davy similarly prepared boron, and his paper announcing his success was read before the Royal Society in June 1808. As obtained in this way the boron was very impure. It was not until 1909 that a really pure sample was obtained by Weintraub.

Although compounds of boron are widely used in industry, the element itself is seldom if ever required. Ferro-boron, an alloy with iron, has been used to a limited extent in the manufacture of boron steels.

Silicon

Silicon, like boron, possesses too great an affinity for oxygen to be found free in nature. Next to oxygen it is the most abundant element in the earth's 10-mile crust, of which it constitutes some 26 per cent. Its oxide in one form or another has been utilised by man from primeval times, as witness the flint implements dating back even to eolithic ages. In more civilised times quartz, onyx, agates and opals came to be prized. The word silica is derived from the Latin *silex*, flint. The scientific history of silicon compounds dates back to the time of Becher (1635 to 1682) who stated that siliceous minerals are suitable for glass making and contain an "earth" which he called *terra vitrescibilis*. Tachenius showed in 1660 that this earth was acidic because it would combine with alkali. Davy thought that silica was undoubtedly the oxide of an unknown element and endeavoured to decompose it electrolytically in the same way as he had tackled the caustic alkalis, but without success. Gay-Lussac and Thenard were probably the first to obtain the element, albeit in a very impure form, by a method similar to that already adopted with success in the case of boron. In 1809 they passed silicon tetrafluoride, discovered by Scheele in 1771, over heated potassium and obtained a reddish-brown, combustible solid. Crystalline silicon was first obtained in 1854 by Deville. He was preparing aluminium by the electrolysis of fused sodium aluminium chloride which contained silica as impurity. The silicon crystallised from the aluminium on cooling and remained behind when the mass was treated with acid just as graphite is left when cast-iron is similarly treated.

Compounds of silicon are widely used in industry. The element is much less in demand. At one time it had a restricted use as a de-oxidiser in metallurgy. Silicon steels were invented by Hadfield in the early eighties of last century and may contain up to 20 per cent silicon. With 14 to 15 per cent the steels are very resistant to attack by chemicals and are useful for chemical plant. With 20 per cent they are even more resistant, but are brittle. *Stalloy* is an alloy with iron containing 3 to 4 per cent silicon whilst silicon bronze, a copper-tin alloy containing merely a trace of silicon, is used for telegraph wires. Cast-iron is really an alloy of silicon (up to about 3·5 per cent) and iron containing some 3 per cent of carbon with smaller amounts of manganese and other elements. Alloys with aluminium are now stepping into prominence and are mentioned in connection with this latter element.

With the extension of radio-communication to ultra-high frequencies the use of point-contact crystal rectifiers in telecommunication circuits has become an established practice. Both silicon and germanium (p. 174) crystal rectifiers are now in use.

CHAPTER 7

THE SULPHUR GROUP

THE sulphur group comprises sulphur, selenium, tellurium and polonium. Although *polonium* belongs chemically to this group it is convenient to discuss it later along with the radio-elements (p. 311)

Sulphur

Sulphur or brimstone occurs native in many parts of the world and could hardly fail to be observed in those districts at an early date. The word sulphur or sulfur is Latin. The term brimstone or burning stone refers to its combustibility. Its occurrence in the neighbourhood of volcanoes and the disagreeable smell produced when it burned caused it to be regarded as symbolic of the powers of evil. In ancient writings the term brimstone frequently refers to the idea of combustibility, and not to the material element as explained on p. 22. Thus, in the Old and New Testament alike, fire and brimstone are frequently associated in terms of punishment. On the other hand, the disinfecting properties of the pungent fumes appear to have been recognised in early times, for Homer, *circa* 880 B.C., represents Odysseus, after the slaughter of the suitors, as calling for fire to burn some sulphur for general cleansing. A millenium later Pliny mentioned the fumigation of houses with sulphur, and Ovid (43 B.C. to A.D. 17) referred to the use of eggs and sulphur for a similar purpose.

In later years the term sulphureous was synonymous with inflammable. The early alchemists represented fire by an equilateral triangle. Fire, or heat, was known to effect the decomposition of most substances; it was supposed to penetrate into them and split them up. An equilateral triangle has the most acute angles of any regular two dimensional figure. So it was chosen to represent fire. As the spiritual sulphur represented the essence of fire or inflammability it, too, was represented by an equilateral triangle, but with the sign of the cross beneath it, thus ⚴.

This double meaning, spiritual and material, for the term sulphur naturally led to much confusion. Material sulphur came to be recognised as an element only when Lavoisier explained the

71

process of combustion generally as due to union with the oxygen of the air, although Davy, as late as 1812, suspected sulphur to contain hydrogen on account of its inflammability.

The sulphur–mercury theory of metals has already been discussed (p. 15).

The *Codex Germanicus, circa* A.D. 1350, says that pure sulphur will crackle if held in the warm hand, and that this may be used as a test, because impure sulphur does not. This, of course, is generally true.

The invention of gunpowder, a mixture of charcoal and nitre with sulphur, is usually attributed to Roger Bacon about 1242, but tradition ascribes the discovery of its propellent force to a second monk, one Berthold Schwarz, a century later.

At one time the main uses of sulphur were in the manufacture of gunpowder and of sulphuric acid. Nowadays its use for these purposes is more restricted. Sulphur is used in the manufacture of carbon disulphide, ultramarine, vermilion and numerous other compounds. Vulcanisation of rubber may be effected with sulphur. Enormous quantities are converted to bisulphites for treating wood pulp in the manufacture of paper. Sulphur is employed as a preventive of the growth of fungus on vines, and mould on hops; it is burnt in the oast house to improve the flavour of the hops; it is used as a disinfectant, a familiar form being "sulphur candles".

Sulphur also finds application medicinally. Our thoughts at once revert to Mrs Squeers of Dotheboys Hall in Dickens's immortal "Nicholas Nickleby". That worthy, or perhaps better described as unworthy, dame was wont to give the young hopefuls under her care substantial doses of brimstone and treacle each morning 'partly because if they hadn't something or other in the way of 'medicine they'd be always ailing and giving a world of trouble, and partly because it spoils their appetites and comes cheaper than breakfast and dinner."

Pliny mentions the use of sulphur in combination with turpentine as a cure for skin diseases, the mixture being known as *harpax*, from the Greek meaning to carry away.

Selenium

The oldest copper mine in Sweden is at Fahlun, about 100 miles N.W. of Stockholm, once the home of Gahn and Sefström, the discoverers of manganese and vanadium, respectively. The copper occurs as pyrites and the sulphur obtained by distillation from these was used at Gripsholm for the manufacture of sulphuric acid by the chamber process. A red deposit was observed to collect on the floor of the chambers when the Fahlun sulphur was used, but not when sulphur from other sources was employed. Both Berzelius and Gahn held shares in the works at Gripsholm and became interested in the phenomenon. As the result of a preliminary investigation in 1817 they concluded that the deposit was tellurium, but by February 1818, Berzelius had satisfied himself that he was dealing with a new element. As it closely resembled the element then recently named tellurium by Klaproth, Berzelius suggested that his be called *selenium* from the Greek *sēlenē*, the moon. Sometimes, to emphasise its metalloidal nature, it is called *selenion*.

Selenium exists in several allotropic forms; the grey "metallic" allotrope sustains an enormous increase in its electrical conductivity when exposed to light and loses it again in the dark. Observed by W. Smith in 1873, this remarkable property is utilised commercially in various ways, as for example, in the optophone, photophone and in television. Thus, it is possible to transmit photographs by wire to illustrate newspapers; to synchronise sounds with moving pictures; to register the moment the runner reaches the tape and the racehorse passes the finishing post; to measure the density of smoke emitted by chimneys, stacks or apparatus designed to produce smoke screens. The feeble light of stars may be measured with the aid of selenium; explosives may be fired at a distance with a beam of light and a selenium cell; burglar alarms are based on the same principle.

The main use of selenium is in the glass and ceramic industries. Small amounts serve to decolorise glass which would otherwise show a green tint owing to the presence of iron, although manganese is now largely used as it imparts a pinkish tint. With larger selenium content ruby glass is obtained, the selenium being in colloidal form, just as gold is in the classical ruby glass. The selenium ruby glass is particularly useful for signals, tail lights on automobiles, etc, because it transmits virtually all the red rays, and eliminates almost all others. Red enamels and glazes are similarly produced. The total world consumption of selenium is of the order of 300 tons annually.

Tellurium

In 1782 Müller von Reichenstein, chief inspector of mines in Transylvania, extracted from a bluish white gold ore, now recognised as an auriferous native tellurium, but then known variously as *aurum problematicum, paradoxicum* or *album*, a substance thought to resemble antimony, but which he regarded as new to science. He despatched a fragment to Bergman, then recognised as one of the leading analysts in Europe, who satisfied himself that it was not antimony; but, with so small a piece at his disposal, he would not commit himself further. Seven years later, in 1789, a Hungarian chemist, Kitaibel, independently discovered the same element. Klaproth, a famous Berlin mineralogist, read a paper on the gold ores of Transylvania and called attention to Müller's discovery, which had been either forgotten or overlooked by chemists. Klaproth had confirmed the existence of the new element and suggested the name *tellurium*, from Latin *tellus*, the earth. He was the first to isolate the metalloid by igniting a paste of the oxide with oil in a glass retort. On cooling, globules of tellurium were found. Like beryllium, therefore, tellurium was not named by its discoverer — an unusual state of affairs. A systematic study of the element was first effected by Berzelius in 1835.

For a long time tellurium was a puzzle to chemists because its atomic weight exceeded that of iodine, which was contrary to what was to be expected from Mendeléeff's periodic table. Believing in the absolute truth of Mendeléeff's system, many chemists made a study of the atomic weight of tellurium and probably methods of purification of no element have ever been so carefully studied as those of tellurium. The classical research of Baker and Bennett* in 1907 appeared to confirm for all time that tellurium must be regarded as an exception to the Periodic Law. As a mean of 43 determinations obtained from various highly purified derivatives of the element a mean value of 127·605 (O = 16·000) was found — a value that is accepted to-day (1950) by the Committee on Atomic Weights of the International Union of Chemistry, in the form of 127·61.

In 1889 Brauner suggested that tellurium was a mixture of two elements which could not be separated by chemical means, and was severely attacked by Wyrouboff† in 1896 for his heretical views. "He has therefore submitted tellurium" wrote this cynic "to all the tortures which a substance can undergo. He has melted it, sublimed it, oxidised it, hydrogenised it, dissolved it, precipitated it and finally arrived at the result, which everybody had reached before him, that the atomic weight varies between the wide limits

---

*Baker and Bennett, *Trans. Chem. Soc.*, 1907, **91**, 1849.
†Wyrouboff, *Chem. News*, 1896, **74**, 30.

of 125 and 129. Hence he concludes that we have here a complex body composed of two elements of very different atomic weights. What are these weights and what are the distinctive properties of tellurium α and tellurium β he does not tell us for he has not been able to separate them."

There is invariably stern opposition and oft-times, as here, ridicule for those who suggest revolutionary ideas; yet how true Brauner was in his ideas. We now know that tellurium consists of not merely two but actually four forms, chemically indistinguishable. We call them isotopes, all having the same atomic number 52, and possessing atomic weights of 130, 128, 126 and 125 respectively in order of abundance. Had the element possessed a higher proportion of isotope 126 and/or 125, the anomaly would not have occurred. Iodine has no isotopes; there is only one form. It is sometimes incorrectly stated that iodine has one isotope; but this is a "terminological inexactitude". The word isotope (Greek *isos*, equal; *topos*, position) is intended to indicate that the varieties have the same atomic number and therefore occupy equal positions in the Ideal Periodic Table. If there is only one form its position is unique and not equal to that of another. The only child is not a twin.

Turning now to its properties and commercial applications, tellurium is not very poisonous but human beings are easily indisposed by small amounts. Workers are apt to acquire a very offensive "tellurium breath".

Tellurium is used as a colouring agent in glass and porcelain, yielding a blue to brown colour. Certain alloys possess high electrical resistance and have been used in electrical equipment. Addition of 0·05 to 0·085 per cent tellurium to lead greatly increases its strength and hardness; it is recommended (1933) for pipes carrying water. Tellurium is sometimes added to copper alloys to assist machining; it is used for staining silver in electroplating, the ware being dipped into a solution of tellurium chloride, when a dark "platinum" finish is acquired.

CHAPTER 8

THE PHOSPHORUS GROUP

THE phosphorus group comprises phosphorus, arsenic, antimony and bismuth.

Phosphorus

This term (Greek *phōs* light, *pherō* I bear) was applied in the seventeenth century to any substances that luminesced in the dark. Thus in 1602 a Bolognese shoemaker, Casciorolus by name, observed that the mineral now called barytes became phosphorescent when ignited with a combustible substance; such was the origin of *Bolognian phosphorus* or *lapis bononiensis*. In 1693 Homberg heated salammoniac and lime, a phosphorescent calcium chloride resulting, known as *Homberg's phosphorus*.

About this time there lived in Hamburg a merchant, Hennig Brand — not to be confused with the Swedish chemist, Georg Brandt (p. 292) who discovered cobalt. Brand is described as a charlatan and was ironically called Dr. Teutonicus. He became wealthy by marriage and spent his days in his laboratory, seeking to make yet more money, as many a worse man has since tried to do. He turned his attention to urine. Why? Probably because of the doctrine of signatures which was widely believed at the time. This doctrine is discussed more fully later in connexion with nickel; suffice it to say that natural objects of a golden colour were supposed to contain gold, this being Nature's way of assisting mankind to understand her mysteries. Though urine did not give Brand gold directly, it did so indirectly. It yielded him, in 1669, a waxy, easily melted, highly inflammable substance which luminesced in the dark. This was the "Führer" phosphorus; very phosphorus of very phosphorus, if one may venture to adapt an ancient quotation.

The process was kept secret. Probably the urine was evaporated to small bulk, allowed to ferment and then distilled with sand, the distillate being collected under water. Brand was patronised by dukes and urged to hide himself in the Hartz mountains lest his secret should leak out. Leak out it did.

The news of the discovery spread rapidly throughout Europe.

Kirchmaier gave a description of it in 1676 and Brand, who had shown the element to Kunckel, eventually sold the secret to Dr. Krafft, of Dresden, for 200 thalers. Krafft exhibited "das kalte Feuer" at various courts including that of our English King Charles II in 1677. The fact leaked out that the phosphorus was obtained from urine and Johann Kunckel or Kungelius, at one time Counsellor of Metals to Charles XI of Sweden, experimented with the liquid until he succeeded in 1678 in preparing phosphorus and casting it into sticks. He designated it *phosphorus mirabilis*. Robert Boyle saw the element at court and apparently independently worked out a method of extracting it from urine in 1680. He described the method in a sealed paper which was deposited with the Royal Society and published in 1693. Boyle's assistant, Hanckewitz and his son Ambrose Godfrey, prepared this *noctiluca* commercially and even exported it to the Continent. It was there known as *English Phosphorus* and *Boyle's Phosphorus*. Godfrey made fame and fortune from it. When continentals wrote to him they addressed their letters to "Mr Godfrey, Famous Chemist in London". That was sufficient.

For a century phosphorus remained an expensive chemical curiosity. In 1769 Gahn recognised it as a constituent of bones and Chéel, a pupil of Bergman, showed how phosphoric acid could be obtained from calcined bones by treatment with sulphuric acid. It was then only necessary to mix the acid with charcoal powder and distil off the phosphorus. The price accordingly fell instanter. The elementary nature of phosphorus was first recognised by Lavoisier in 1777.

The match industry

Large quantities of phosphorus are used in the match industry, the total annual consumption being estimated at 1000 tons. In England alone 125,000 million matches are consumed annually despite the extensive use of automatic lighters by cigarette smokers. The first *chemical matches* are generally supposed to have been made by Chancel of Paris in 1805 and were manufactured from 1812 on. They contained no phosphorus, however, but consisted of sticks of wood the ends of which had been dipped in molten brimstone and then coated with a mixture of sugar and potassium chlorate then newly discovered by Berthollet. To ignite, they were dipped into a bottle containing asbestos moistened with oil of vitriol. These "oxymuriate matches" continued to be sold down to

1845. In 1827 the first commercially successful friction matches, known as *friction lights*, were invented in England by John Walker, a chemist of Stockton on Tees — not to be confused with Johnnie Walker of 1820, still going strong! His sales book is still in existence and shows that he sold his first box of matches on 7th April 1827, to a local solicitor. They again contained no phosphorus, being tipped with a mixture of stibnite, potassium chlorate, and gum. Rubbing on sandpaper effected their ignition, and Walker sold the sandpaper in the shape of a cocked hat with his matches. His invention was not patented and his matches became superseded about 1834. These later matches were called *lucifers* the name being invented by Samuel Jones, a vendor in the Strand, London*. In 1833 matches were first prepared containing phosphorus and were known as Turin Candles. These were made simultaneously in several countries, but as they were found to be somewhat dangerous, the chlorate was later replaced by lead dioxide and pyrolusite.

In 1844 Arthur Albright of Birmingham suggested to his partner that phosphorus ought to be manufactured on a large scale and placed more cheaply on the market. He accordingly built a sulphuric acid plant in Birmingham, where Roebuck in 1746 had introduced his leaden chambers to replace the earlier and more costly glass globes. Calcium phosphate was obtained from South America, and production began.

In 1845 Albright went to Galatz on the Danube, to buy bones left from canning beef. Dodging the Turkish quarantine regulations he found Wagner's beef bones rather odorous to say the least; so he built a furnace to calcine them on the spot.

The same year (1845) Schrötter of Vienna showed that white and red phosphorus are chemically identical. As soon as Albright learned of this he decided to manufacture red phosphorus and obtained the necessary patent in 1851. He had been greatly impressed by the death through phosphorus poisoning of large numbers of young girls in the German match-making industry and he hoped it might be possible to avoid this by using the non-poisonous red phosphorus in place of the white. As is well known, white phosphorus is extremely poisonous; two grains may prove fatal. The workers engaged in the manufacture of lucifers were subject to *"jaw disease"*, *Phossy jaw* or *necrosis* of the lower jaw. In addition to this, even when finished, the ordinary match made

*See CLAYTON, *Chem. News*, 1911, **104**, 223. Also anon., *Nature*, 1898, **58**, 345.

with white phosphorus was a source of danger, being both liable to spontaneous ignition and poisonous. Children had frequently died as the result of using them as playthings; they moreover absorbed moisture and became useless by age.

By using red phosphorus Albright thought that the position would be greatly improved, and an end would be put to necrosis. Red phosphorus is much less chemically active than white. As it is insoluble in most ordinary solvents it will pass through the animal system if taken internally and duly excreted without doing much harm. It evolves no poisonous fumes, is not luminous in the dark, and is less likely to ignite spontaneously.

But here was a difficulty. When red phosphorus is brought into contact with potassium chlorate a slight touch is sufficient to induce an explosion. Many attempts to form a paste for the match head were made, but none with success; indeed in some cases fatal accidents occurred. Prizes were offered by manufacturers but still the problem remained unsolved. At last, however, someone hit upon the happy idea of splitting the process. Instead of attempting to use a paste containing both phosphorus and oxidiser, the two were kept separate until ignition was required, by putting the red phosphorus on the box and the oxidiser on the match head*. When wishing to obtain a light the consumer himself brings the two together as he "strikes a match". It is said that Böttger prepared the first safety matches in 1848. These were tipped with gum, sulphur, and chlorates. They could be ignited by rubbing on a surface containing red phosphorus, gum, and antimony sulphide.

In 1851 Albright moved his works to Oldbury, and the same year he exhibited a specimen of his new red phosphorus at the Great Exhibition. This eventually brought him a large order from a Swedish firm, the Lundstrom Brothers, who had large match factories in Sweden and wished to protect their workers from phosphorus poisoning by introducing the safety match. At first Albright refused to consider the order.

"Gentlemen," he wrote, "amorphous phosphorus in such quantities as stated in your letter can, to the best of my judgment, only be used for the purposes of war." But the Swedes convinced him that in matches it was to be used "for the enlightenment of mankind".

Phosphorus is now prepared on a very large scale, in England by Messrs Albright and Wilson at Oldbury, as the raw material

---

*TOMLINSON, *Nature*, 1876, **13**, 469.

for the manufacture of the various compounds of phosphorus used in industry. Calcium phosphate, in the form of apatite, $CaCl_2.3Ca_3(PO_4)_2$, or some other mineral, is heated in a furnace with sand and some form of carbon, the distillate being collected under water. Thus —

$$Ca_3(PO_4)_2 + 3SiO_2 = 3CaSiO_3 + P_2O_5$$
$$P_2O_5 + 5C = 5CO + 2P$$

In this way very pure products are obtainable; the standard grade of white phosphorus is over 99·9 per cent pure and contains only the merest traces of sulphur and arsenic. It is extremely reactive chemically and it is said that an excise officer once found this out very much to his cost. When prowling round Albright's factory he wrapped a piece of the curious "barley sugar" or "lemon rock" in paper, and put it in his pocket and — lived to regret it.

Red phosphorus is used as a deoxidising agent in the manufacture of non-ferrous alloys. It is common practice to prepare phosphor–copper, containing 10 to 12 per cent of phosphorus, and other alloys of high phosphorus content and to use these as deoxidisers. White phosphorus is used also in chemical laboratories, in rat poisons, fireworks, smoke bombs, etc. The standard grade of the red has not less than 97 per cent of phosphorus and is free from its white allotrope. Apart from its use in the match trade, already mentioned, it is used as a "getter" in electric lamp manufacture; it is also used in certain organic syntheses and to some extent in the manufacture of non-ferrous alloys for de-oxidising purposes, although white phosphorus is normally preferred owing to its lower cost. Heated with copper turnings for example, it yields copper phosphide used in the manufacture of phosphor bronzes (p. 106).

Much of the phosphorus is burned to the pentoxide from which phosphoric acid and the numerous phosphates of commerce are prepared. These include, for example, the ammonium phosphates used in fireproofing of timber, sodium metaphosphate or calgon (calcium gone) for water softening; calcium and sodium phosphates used in flour and various medical preparations; organic phosphates used in ever increasing amounts as plasticisers in the plastics industry. Some phosphorus is consumed in preparing metallic phosphides such as calcium phosphide in Holme's signals, etc; ferrophosphorus, a convenient reagent for introducing phosphorus into steel when needed; zinc phosphide, an effective poison for rats and mice.

Arsenic

Ancient prehistoric implements of arsenical bronze, containing up to 4 per cent of arsenic, have been found in Egypt. They were "natural" alloys produced by reduction of arsenical ores, and not with the intentional addition of arsenic. Arsenical compounds have been used from very early historic times. The native yellow sulphide, As_2S_3, now known as orpiment (Latin *auri* of gold, *pigmentum* pigment) was used at Tell el Amarna in the Eighteenth Egyptian Dynasty. Aristotle (384 to 322 B.C.) used the term *sandarakē* in his writings and is believed to refer to the ruby coloured sulphide, As_2S_2, often called realgar (Arabic *rahj al gāhr*, powder of the mine). The Greek herbalist Dioscorides (*circa* A.D. 50) uses the term *arsenikon*, presumably for realgar, and recommends as a cure for asthma that it be burned with resin and the fumes inhaled. Pliny similarly recommended its use and this may possibly account for the presence of the realgar discovered in the Roman stratum on the floor of Wookey Hole, near Wells, Somerset*; there is no indication of its use as a pigment for mural decoration there.

The word arsenic would thus appear to have reached us from the Greek; it meant masculine, or powerful, and evidently referred to the great activity of the substance as a medicine. Possibly the word is connected with the Persian *zarnick* or *zirnuk*, *zar* meaning gold, with reference perhaps to the yellow colour of orpiment. During the first century of our era the sandarach mines of Pompeiopolis, in Paphlagonia, were worked by slave labour, involving enormous losses of life†.

The sesquioxide, As_2O_3, known familiarly as *white arsenic*, must also have been known at an early date. In Shakespeare's day it was known as *ratsbane* because of its use in poisoning vermin. Thus in Henry VI, Act V, Scene IV, the old, broken-hearted shepherd says to his much-loved daughter, Joan la Pucelle, commonly called Joan of Arc,

> "I would the milk
> Thy Mother gave thee, when thou suckst her breast,
> Had been a little ratsbane for thy sake."

Then had she not been compelled to suffer at the stake or he to witness it.

---

*FRIEND, *Nature*, 1937, **139**, 72.
†STRABO, "Geographia" **12**, (3), 40.

G

Roger Bacon, the inventor of gunpowder (p. 72), in "Breve Breviarum de dono Dei" (thirteenth century) showed that *arsenicum album* resulted on heating orpiment with iron scale and the substance soon became familiar to medieval alchemists. Zosimus* in the fifth century A.D. is believed to have described the preparation of elementary arsenic; but Albertus Magnus† is usually credited with being the first to obtain it; he heated orpiment with twice its weight of soap. Paracelsus (p. 85) stated that arsenic metal could be obtained by ignition of "arsenic" with eggshells whilst Schroeder in 1649 mentioned that metallic arsenic resulted on reduction of white arsenic with charcoal or the sulphide with lime.

The alchemists viewed arsenic as a "bastard metal" or semi-metal‡. Some regarded it as akin to quicksilver, its red sulphide resembling cinnabar, and the volatility of its compounds that of mercury salts. To it they gave the symbol o—o often accompanied by a coiled snake. Brandt observed that white arsenic, As_2O_3, was the calx of the semi-metal.

Arsenic is sometimes used in the manufacture of its compounds, but more often in alloys. Small quantities, 0·1 to 0·2 per cent, are added to lead for the production of shot (p. 196). Arsenical lead anodes are used in the electrolytic production of zinc. Alloys with antimonial lead containing 1 to 2 per cent of arsenic and sometimes other elements are used for sheaths for electric cables, etc. Arsenical coppers and bronzes are used for high temperature work such as locomotive fireboxes, etc.

Antimony

Bronze age implements have been found in Hungary containing copper alloyed with antimony up to 4 to 5 per cent. Like the Egyptian arsenical copper already mentioned, this was purely a natural alloy. Undoubtedly metallic antimony was known in very early times. A vase, found by de Saizec at Tells in Chaldea, was analysed by Berthelot in 1887, who found it to consist of almost pure antimony, whilst a copper ewer and basin dating from the Fifth or Sixth Egyptian Dynasty have been shown to be coated with antimony (p. 93). Ancient beads of fairly pure antimony were found by Petrie in a tomb at Illahun dating back some 800 B.C.

---

*BERTHELOT, *Ann. Chim. Phys.*, 1888, (6), **13**, 430.
†ALBERTUS MAGNUS, "Theatricum Chemicum", 1613 Edition, **4**, 931. He lived 1193 to 1280.
‡BRANDT, *Arch. Akad. Upsala*, 1733, **3**, 39.

It is difficult, however, to trace the history of metallic antimony back through history because both terms *antimonium* and *stibium* are used to indicate sometimes the metal itself and sometimes its naturally occurring sulphide, stibnite. The last named, under the Arabic name of *kohl*, was used in the form of a fine powder in the toilet of oriental women. It was used to paint the eyebrows and to increase the apparent size of the eye, whence the term platy-ophthalmon ore (Greek *platus*, broad; *ophthalmos*, eye). Reference to this practice apparently occurs in Holy Writ for we are told (2 *Kings* ix. 30) that Jezebel, true to her feminine instincts, when she heard that Jehu had slain her son Jehoram (842 B.C.) and reached Jezreel, first painted her face and then looked out of an upper window on to the conqueror, hoping thereby to win favour in his eyes and preserve her life. But Jehu was not so easily beguiled. Ezekiel (xxiii. 40) refers in terms of reproach to the painting of the eyes, and Jeremiah (iv. 30), that embodiment of human cheerfulness, speaks in like manner. What these venerable prophets would have said had they seen the modern species with their bloodred finger nails can hardly be imagined. Dioscorides, the Greek physician who lived in or about the second century A.D. gathered much scientific information on science and medicine during his travels with the Roman army, which he accompanied on several expeditions as medical adviser. Later he wrote his monumental work "Peri Hules Iatrikes" which for many centuries remained one of the authentic medical treatises, the first Latin edition appearing in 1478. Dioscorides mentions that in order to roast the crude stibnite it must be heated in a current of air until it burns; if more strongly heated it ignites and melts like lead. From this it is concluded that Dioscorides was acquainted with metalloidal antimony.

For a long time antimony and bismuth were not distinguished from each other; even Andreas Libavius (1540 to 1616) confused the two.

The word kohl referred to above as denoting stibnite in a finely powdered state came gradually to mean any fine powder. Thus reduced iron was known as alcohol of Mars, and as late as 1812 Davy referred to flowers of sulphur as alcohol of sulphur. In the theatrical profession pigments used for darkening the eyes are still known as kohl. Francis Bacon in his "Sylva Sylvarum or a Naturall Historie", 1626, p. 739, says "The Turkes have a black powder made of a mineral called alcohole."

As powders obtained by sublimation were very fine, kohl came to mean a sublimate. It was not a great jump for it eventually to mean a distillate, for sublimation and distillation are closely analogous processes. Thus in 1773 Baumé, in his work entitled "Chymie Experimentale" defined an alcohol as either —

  (i) A powder of the finest tenuity, or

  (ii) Spirit of wine rectified to the utmost degree.

The distillation of alcohol had then been known for about 400 years and in course of time it was felt that this was the only distillate worth bothering about by the man in the street; it was therefore designated as *the kohl* or *alkohl*, which soon became our alcohol, the Arabic prefix *al* being merely the definite article.

Pliny referred to two varieties of antimony which he terms male and female. The latter was white and shiny and bore several names, such as *stibi* and *larbasis*. This is thought to be the native element. By the male form Pliny probably meant the less attractive stibnite.

The origin of the word *antimonium* is uncertain. A popular story credits its origin to the escapades of a mythical monk, Canon of the Priory of St. Peter at Erfurt, Basil Valentine, who is supposed to have lived in the fifteenth century, though some authorities have suggested earlier dates. The worthy monk, after experimenting with antimonial compounds, threw his residues out of his cell window. Some pigs ate them up greedily, were promptly sick and then began eating vigorously to make up for lost meals. This fattened them in a very gratifying manner for Christmas. Basil, a keen observer of nature, thought it would be good to treat his frugal colleagues in a similar manner, and invited them to partake of this antimonial refreshment. Their bodies, weakened by asceticism, could not stand the strain and several perished; whence the term antimony or *anti-monakhos*, that is, monk's bane. It is a mere bagatelle that the word antimonium was in use long before Basil was thought of!

In those days the semi-metals or metalloids were regarded as variations of true metals, probably much as we regard allotropic forms to-day, though of course their ideas were confused. Basil thus termed antimony *plumbum antimonii*, that is, the antimonial form of lead. He was familiar with the characteristic fern leaf and star appearance on the surface of the solidified metalloid which, he stated, the learned before his time had termed the *philosophical signet star*.

In his book* entitled "The Triumphal Chariot of Antimony" Basil gives instructions for the preparation of the *Fire-stone*, an inferior type of Philosopher's stone which would transmute silver into gold, but could not change iron or copper, whereas the true Philosopher's stone was all-powerful. After devoting several pages to the process he naïvely ends up by the words "I have told you enough; and if, after all that has been said, you do not discover the secret, it will not be my fault." To use an army term, Basil was an adept at "passing the buck".

Antimony compounds were largely employed in the Middle Ages in medicinal preparations. Paracelsus† used them; his pharmacy was a strange mixture of chemistry and superstition. His real name was Philipus Aureolus Theophrastus Bombast von Hohenheim, but he used Paracelsus for short. His arrogance and self assurance give the word bombast its present meaning. He made *butter of antimony*, as the trichloride $SbCl_3$ was first called, by distilling corrosive sublimate, that is mercuric chloride, with stibnite; it was at one time thought to be a compound of mercury, but Glauber disproved that in 1648. At the end of the sixteenth century the trichloride was introduced into medicinal preparations by the Veronese physician Algarotus, under the name *pulvis angelicus*. Probably this was a mixture of the trichloride and oxychloride, which latter became known as *powder of algaroth*.

Basil Valentine refers to the use of antimony in medicine in his characteristic bantering style. Thus —

"Antimony, you affirm, is a poison; therefore let everyone beware of using it!

But this conclusion is not logical, Sir Doctor, Magister or Baccalaureus; it is not logical, Sir Doctor, however much you may plume yourself on your red cap.

Theriac is prepared from the venom of the viper, the most deadly poison in the world. Does it therefore follow that Theriac ought not to be used as a medicine?

You know that it is so employed."

The word theriac as used by Valentine deserves explanation. It has long been believed that "like cures like". As the viper brews a

---

*This book, purported to have been written by Basil, is well worth reading for its humorous style. An English translation, in 1893, by WAITE, of the Latin version of 1685 is as entrancing as a Dickens novel.

†Paracelsus is variously stated to have been born in 1490, 1491 and 1493. Various dates are given for his death, ranging from 1535 to 1541.

deadly poison in its body, how comes it that it does not poison itself? It was supposed that the blood of the snake possessed its own antidote. If therefore a person were bitten all he had to do was to catch the viper, slit it open and bind it on the wound.

But one could not always be sure of catching the viper, it was better to have the remedy to hand in advance; the Greeks therefore compounded a medicine containing vipers' bodies. Now the Greek word *therion* referred to any savage animal and came to be applied specifically to the viper. The medicine prepared as above came to be known accordingly as *theriaka* from which our word "treacle", used as early as 1124 by Fourcher de Chartres, is derived. Thus Venice treacle comprised 12 adders soaked in white wine, and in France a charlatan or quack doctor was known as a *triacleur*; in course of time the word was used to denote any thick and viscous medicine. It was used in that sense in the so-called "Treacle Bible", published in 1568, in which the well-known words of *Jer.* viii. 22 "Is there no balm in Gilead" are rendered as "Is there no treacle in Gilead" — a perfectly correct rendering, be it said, in those times. Eventually the word was used to indicate any viscous fluid until the time came that there was only one such fluid worth bothering about, namely that obtained from the crystallisation of sugar.

During the sixteenth and seventeenth centuries antimony cups were used by the monks, particularly in Germany. Wine kept in these became slightly impregnated with antimony, and monks who had partaken too freely of the good things of life were made to drink this wine which functioned emetically. The cup was known as *poculum emeticum*. This practice persisted to the time of Boyle.

Antimony pills were in use about this time, also known as "the everlasting pills". It is recorded that a lady swallowed one and was alarmed at its not passing through. The physician comforted her, however, saying that it had already passed through 100 patients without difficulty!

The alchemist sign for antimony was ♁ — an inverted copper sign — and a wolf. Boyle (1627 to 1691) was familiar with the starred appearance of the cast metal which he termed in 1772 "the starry regulus of Mars and antimony".

The great majority of liquids contract on solidification and with some organics this contraction is very considerable, amounting in the case of acetic acid to 16·7, and of naphthalene to 16·2 per cent. Ice, on the other hand is exceptional in that it expands on freezing, namely by 9·06 per cent. The majority of metals also contract upon solidification, gold by 4·92, silver by 4·76 and copper by 3·89 per cent. Were it otherwise, and our coinage metals expanded on solidification, our coins could be cast and the expensive process of stamping avoided. Antimony, bismuth and gallium are exceptional. Like water they expand on solidifying, antimony by about 0·96, bismuth by 3·43, and gallium by 1·84 per cent.

This expansion by molten antimony upon solidification renders it a valuable constituent of many alloys. A familiar example is *type metal*, an alloy of lead, tin and antimony (p. 197). *Babbitt's metal* (p. 212), *pewter* (p. 211) and *Britannia metal* (p. 212) also contain antimony.

Alloys of antimony and aluminium look very much like silver and have been used in the past in forging our coins. One such florin analysed by the author in 1911 contained aluminium 53·40, and antimony 46·38 per cent with traces of lead, arsenic and iron. With copper a violet alloy, probably a compound $SbCu_2$, is formed known as *regulus of Venus*. Small amounts of antimony are used in stiffening lead. Antimony oxide is used, associated with titanium oxide, as a white pigment, as for example in *titanox*.

Bismuth

Apparently the earliest reference to metallic bismuth is that of Agricola in "De re Metallica" in 1556. In recognising bismuth as a separate metal he was in advance of his time, for even as late as the eighteenth century the miners regarded it as a variety of lead, well on the way to being transmuted to silver. If they happened to strike the ore they would say "Alas, we have come too soon."

No doubt bismuth was known at a much earlier date, but its history is confused because it was called *marcasite*, a name that has been used for many other substances also and is now mainly used to denote a rhombic variety of iron pyrites FeS_2. Most of the later writers regarded it as a semi-metal. Barba, a South American priest, wrote in 1640 that bismuth had been discovered in Bohemia and that it was "a metal somewhat like a cross between tin and lead, without being either of the two". It was apparently used in the manufacture of pewter rendering it harder and more sonorous. Hellot, the French chemist noticed that Cornish smelters added it to their metal, and in 1737 he succeeded in preparing a button of bismuth from a cobalt ore. Geoffroy in 1753 showed conclusively that bismuth was not a variety of lead, but a distinct metallic species.

For a long time it was confused with antimony (p. 83). It is one of the few solids that contracts on fusion (p. 87).

The origin of the name is uncertain, but a possible derivation is from the miners' term *wis mat* (German *Weisse Masse*) white mass*.

The main industrial use of bismuth is in alloys, notably those of low melting point, called *fusible metals*. These are useful as fuses in electrical work and for a variety of automatic contrivances where undue rises in temperature will cause them to melt and function in one way or another. Wood's metal contains bismuth 50, lead 24, tin 14 and cadmium 12 or thereabouts, and melts at about 70° C. In bending thin-walled tubes of other metals this alloy can be used as a filling to prevent kinking and is readily removed after bending by steaming. An amalgam of bismuth and mercury has been used in dentistry. As alloys of bismuth with other metals expand on solidification they yield sharp castings.

---

*Smythe Palmer connects bismuth with the ancient Egyptian *Mesdemet*, eye-paint. "Some Curios from a Word Collector's Cabinet" (Routledge, p. 150).

CHAPTER 9

THE COINAGE METALS

THE coinage metals are copper, silver and gold.

Occurrence of native copper

Although not generally plentiful in Europe, native copper occurs in Cornwall in many of the mines near Redruth; one huge mass from Mullion weighed about three tons. The native metal occurs more plentifully in Australia and in various parts of the New World. The most famous locality is the Lake Superior copper region near Keweenaw Point in Northern Michigan. Here the copper is practically all in the native state and is found in an area over 200 miles in length. Dana* states that the yield of native copper from this region in 1887 was about 37,000 tons. In 1857 a huge mass of copper was found in the Minnesota mine weighing some 420 tons; it was 45 feet long, 22 feet at its greatest width and 8 feet at its thickest part. Silver was present in the copper, sometimes in visible grains or lumps; occasionally, when polished, the metal appeared sprinkled with large silver spots resembling a porphyry with felspar crystals.

Copper, like silver, sometimes occurs as fine threads. These, when intertwined or matted together, are known as *copper moss*.

Native copper was known to stone age man many thousands of years ago. He no doubt regarded it as a particularly useful kind of stone that could be hammered or cold-worked into various shapes for personal use or adornment. Within the environs of Lake Superior, where native copper is relatively abundant, numerous axe and lance heads and other primitive implements of native copper have been unearthed at various times, all shaped by hammering.

Primitive metallurgy of copper

When man first observed that copper or its alloys could be obtained by heating certain kinds of "stone" in an ordinary fire he made a

---

*DANA, "A System of Mineralogy" (Chapman and Hall, 1914) 6th Edition, p. 22.

real epoch-making discovery. He passed from the age of stone to
that of metals and thus opened up vast new realms to exploit and to
conquer. It has been suggested that the discovery of copper
originated in the ordinary domestic fire of neolithic man, the metal
being reduced from its ore which by chance formed part of the
ring of stones of his primitive hearth. "The camp fire" wrote
Gowland* "was in fact the first metallurgical furnace, and from it,
by successive modifications, the huge furnaces of the present day
have been evolved."

This sounds reasonable enough and its probability is supported
by the fact that the presence of metal has sometimes been made
evident within historic times in a similarly accidental manner.

The presence of silver at Pasco in Peru† was discovered in this
way three centuries ago by an Indian shepherd. Whilst watching
his flock he lit a fire on the side of a hill, for the weather was cold,
and lay down to rest for the night. Next morning he awoke to find
that the stone beneath the ashes of his now dead fire was overlaid
with silver. He told his master and a rich vein of silver ore was laid
bare; works were erected for the extraction of the precious
metal and the "Discovery Mine" as it was called, soon became
locally famous.

Beads of copper have been found on the sites of native camp
fires in the Belgian Congo. These resulted from reduction of
surface ores on which the fires had been laid. History repeats itself.

Gradually the camp fire of the primitive metallurgist was modified to increase the yield of metal. Furnaces came to be constructed
with shallow circular cavities in the ground, about 12 inches in
diameter, into which the molten metal trickled. Fortuitous wind
supplied the blast. When sufficient metal had collected, the fire
was raked away; as soon as it had solidified, the metal was dragged
out and broken to pieces for subsequent re-melting and casting.
At the copper mine of Kapsan in Korea this primitive procedure
was still being practised in 1884, when Gowland visited it.

As time progressed the cavity in the ground was made bigger
and its capacity increased also by surrounding with a wall of stones.
As obtained in this way the metal was dirty, soil and ashes
being included in its bulk. To obtain a cleaner product the hearth
cavity was subsequently lined with clay. Finally this clay lining was
made detachable; in other words it became a crucible which could

---

*GOWLAND, *J. Inst. Metals*, 1912, **7**, 24. *The Engineer*, 1912, p. 65
†W. JONES, "The Treasures of the Earth" (Warne) p. 40.

be lifted out of the furnace so that the metal could be teemed direct into moulds, thus obviating a second melting. The blast, too, was improved by building furnaces on the windward side of hills or a forced draught was initiated by the use of bellows, as depicted in Egyptian mural paintings dating back some 1500 B.C.

The composition of the crude metal thus produced would vary according to circumstances. In Hungary, where copper ores are associated with those of antimony, the early implements consisted of copper containing up to 4·5 per cent of antimony. Implements from Germany have been found with 2 to 4 per cent of nickel, those from Egypt with a like amount of arsenic—all for the same reason. In Cornwall, copper and tin ores are found together and the earliest metal implements are in consequence "natural" bronzes.

The *intentional* addition of tin to copper to increase its hardness was a later procedure and represented a more advanced knowledge of metallurgical technique. In Ireland the first metal implements were essentially copper as neither ores of tin nor those of copper containing tin were known there in early times. The Irish copper age lasted for about 700 years before the introduction of bronze, the knowledge of which probably spread from Britain.

Stone age man might thus pass direct into the bronze age, or stepwise through the copper or chalcolithic age to the bronze age, according to local circumstances. A curious reversal of this procedure appears to have taken place with the Sumerians who, after using bronze, reverted to copper. Possibly this was due to shortage of tin*.

In early Sumerian dynastic days copper was already being used extensively for religious purposes. Thus, at Al'Ubaid a flight of stone steps led up to a shrine built in the first dynasty, *circa* 3100 to 3000 B.C. At the stair head was a porch with wooden columns overlaid with copper or with a mosaic in mother of pearl, etc. The entrance to the shrine was flanked by life-size heads of lions worked in copper, with inlaid eyes and teeth. Above the door was the Imgig Relief† or Copper Imgig (Plate 1) which represents the lion-headed eagle of the Lagashite god *Ningirsu* grasping two stags by their tails; it measures 3½ feet in height and 7 feet 9½ inches

---

*"Copper through the Ages" (Copper Development Association, 1934) p. 12.

†*British Museum Quarterly*, 1927, **1**, (4), 85. FRIEND and THORNEYCROFT, *J. Inst. Metals*, 1929, **41**, 105. Plate 1 is reproduced through the kind permission of the late Dr H. R. Hall, when Keeper of the Department of Egyptian and Syrian Antiquities.

across and is one of the most important existing relics of the
nascent art of Mesopotamia of the period. Even the nails fastening
the relief to the wood back are of copper. The antlers were made of
hammered copper bar and had been fixed into the heads of the
stags with lead poured into the root-holes (p. 190). The walls of the
shrine, made of mud-brick, were adorned externally with copper
statues of bulls modelled in the round with a copper frieze in
relief*. The relief may be seen at the British Museum.

Copper and the Egyptians

The Egyptians were highly skilled in the art of working metals
at a very early date (p. 10); it is possible that copper was the first
metal known to them as it occurs in early predynastic graves,
whereas gold, silver and lead do not appear until middle predynastic times. Both casting and hammering or forging of the
metal were practised.

In the First Dynasty, *circa* 3500 B.C. copper wire was in use; it
was not made by drawing through dies, however, but by the
laborious process of cutting thin strips from sheets and hammering
them into round shape.

The *waste wax* or *cire perdue* method of making hollow castings
is believed to have originated in Egypt about this time†. A nucleus
of suitable material such as sand or clay was prepared and coated
with wax. The wax envelope was suitably shaped and the whole
covered with a layer of fine clay and then with loam. The wax was
now melted and allowed to flow away whilst molten metal was
poured into the hollow mould thus produced.

Who has not heard the legend of Daedalus who, with his son (or
nephew) Icarus, was gaoled by King Minos of Crete? Daedalus
fixed wings with wax to their shoulders and they escaped, flying
across the sea. Unfortunately Icarus flew too near to the sun, the
wax melted and his wings became detached; he fell into the sea
and was drowned; whence the name of the Icarian Sea. Daedalus,
however, reached Greece in safety. This is now regarded as the
legendary way of stating that Daedalus was the inventor of the
sails or wings of ships, and that, moreover, he introduced the
cire perdue or waste wax method of casting.

---

*WOOLLEY, "The Sumerians" (Oxford, 1928), pp. 41, 42.
†COOK, *The Metal Industry*, 1937, **50**, 534. Also "Copper through the Ages"
(Copper Development Association, 1934) p. 16.

PLATE 1 [*Facing p.* 92

The Imgig Relief

The Imdugud or Imgig Relief dates from early
Sumerian dynastic days (*circa* 3100 to 3000 B.C.) and
comes from above the door of a shrine at Al'Ubaid.
It is a representation in copper of the lion-headed
eagle of the Lagashite god Ningirsu grasping two
stags by their tails. One of the most important existing
relics of the nascent art of Mesopotamia of the period,
it measures $3\frac{1}{2}$ feet in height and 7 feet $9\frac{1}{2}$ inches across.
The Relief is in the possession, and the illustration is
reproduced by permission, of the British Museum
Authorities. (See page 91.)

Icarus has been chosen by Dr Baade, of the Mt. Palomar observatory, as the appropriate name for a new minor planet he discovered in June 1949*. It is a tiny body, probably less than a mile across, with an eccentric orbit which takes it from beyond the orbit of Mars to within the orbit of Mercury — nearer to the sun than any other known asteroid. It can approach to well within four million miles of the Earth. It is quite possible that Icarus will eventually enable the first really reliable estimate of the mass of the planet Mercury to be made; the present figure of 0·04 times the mass of the Earth is admittedly an uncertain one.

The Sinaitic Peninsular was one of the earliest and most important sources of Egypt's copper. As the ore is free from tin, the true bronze age in Egypt was late in development, reaching its zenith during the Saïte Period, which included the 25th to 27th Dynasties, 712 to 332 B.C. All the same, bronze was probably known in the First Dynasty. The existence of ancient mines, ruins of settlements, remains of furnaces, slags, crucibles, moulds and weapons all confirm the early working of copper ores in the Sinai area. Inscriptions tell the same tale. From the amount of slag left it has been estimated that some 10,000 tons of copper may have been obtained, enough to keep ancient Egypt going for a long time.

During the pyramid age copper water or drain pipes were made from hammered sheet; copper swords were in use and soldiers' helmets were constructed with copper and leather. A painting on the tomb of Rekh-my-Re, dating back to the middle of the 15th century B.C., depicts the casting of two copper doors for the temple at Karnak. Old cast bronzes are frequently found to contain from 6 to 12 per cent of lead, added presumably to increase the fusibility; later hammered bronzes sometimes contain 1 to 2 per cent of iron, which renders them hard. The iron probably came from the copper pyrites used. No tinned copper vessels have been found as yet in Egypt, but a copper basin and ewer belonging to the 5th or 6th dynasties, *circa* 2750 to 2475 B.C. were found coated with a hard adherent film of antimony. This may have been effected by boiling the metal in a bath of stibnite and sodium carbonate solution†, but

---

J.B.A.A., 1950, **60**, 96. *B.A.A. Circular*, 1950, No. 316. Icarus is one of a number of small bodies, moving in similar eccentric orbits, which have been discovered since 1932. In 1937 one of them, Hermes, came within one million kilometres of the Earth (less than three times the distance of the moon). Apart from size, there is probably no distinction between these objects, meteorites, and certain meteors (cf. HOFFMEISTER, *Observatory*, 1950, **70**, 70).

†FINK, *Industrial and Engineering Chemistry*, 1934, **26**, 236.

other methods are possible. Both vessels showed wear and were evidently not new when put into the grave; nevertheless the antimony bottoms had not been worn off during their life before being put into the tomb. This indicates how hard and closely adherent the film had been.

Copper in Holy Writ

Copper and "brass" are mentioned by name in Holy Writ; the "brass", mentioned 84 times, was usually our bronze. The "tin" of the Old Testament was not the metal we know by that name but an alloy of copper and tin, richer in the latter than bronze.

"Brass" is mentioned before the Deluge (*Gen.* iv. 22), Tubal Cain being named as the first worker in that metal as also in iron. Copper itself is named only once (*Ezra* viii. 27) when reference is made to "two vessels of fine copper, precious as gold". The book of Ezra was probably written about 300 B.C. The coppersmith is likewise referred to but once in the Bible, this time by St. Paul in his letter to Timothy (2 *Tim.* iv. 14) wherein he says "Alexander the coppersmith did me much evil; the Lord reward him according to his works" — a pious wish, very human, but not altogether consonant with his Master's injunction to offer the other cheek (*Matt.* v. 39) when smitten.

Palestine is described as "a land whose stones are iron, and out of whose hills thou mayest dig brass" (*Deut.* viii. 9). David prepared "brass in abundance" to be employed in building Solomon's Temple (1 *Chron.* xxiii. 3). Upon request, Huram, King of Tyre, sent to Solomon the son of a man "skilful to work in gold, and in silver, in brass, in iron, etc" (2 *Chron.* ii. 14). Job (xxviii. 2) says that "brass is molten (i.e. melted) out of the stone", which presumably means that it was obtained by the usual primitive method of setting fire to a mixture of fuel (wood) and ore. This would appear to the lay observer like melting the stone. No doubt the Hebrews acquired their knowledge from the Egyptians, but such large castings as were required for the temple pillars, etc, required more skill than the Hebrew workers possessed; hence the need of assistance from Tyre.

Copper and the Romans

The Romans had vast supplies of copper at their disposal for they were able to work the mines with slave labour in various parts of their far-flung empire. Pliny specially mentions Cyprus where, he says, copper was first discovered, Corduba in Spain, and other localities which are less easy to identify. The Romans mined copper extensively in our Islands, notably in Cumberland and North Wales, including Anglesey. Roman cakes of copper have been found in North Wales; one found near an old mine at Llandudno was stamped with the words *Socio Roma* that is, "to my partner at Rome", indicating that the metal was intended for export*.

Copper and its alloys were used extensively by the Romans for statues, temple ornaments and later for domestic furniture such as banqueting-couches, and the like. Pliny† states that the first bronze image cast in Rome was that of Ceres, the goddess of corn, after whom our element *cerium* was named many centuries later (p. 182). In later years statues were erected in honour of prominent citizens, and were sometimes gilded. An amusing story is told by Pliny of the sale of a bronze lamp-stand, the condition of sale being that the purchaser must also take, as part of the lot, a hunch-backed slave of hideous aspect. The purchase was made by a member of an ancient noble family at Rome, a lady named Gegania. At an entertainment to her friends she exhibited her purchases and, for the further amusement of her guests, made the deformed slave attend the assembly entirely unclothed. Gradually, however, she became infatuated with the hunch-back, recalling to our minds Shakespeare's Titania who fell in love with the clown with the ass's head, and eventually left him all her estate.

The earliest Roman bronzes that have come down to us date from the fifth century B.C. and contain tin about 7 per cent, and lead from 19 to 25 per cent. This was the alloy used for casting the large coin (8 to 11 oz) of the Republic, known as the "As". These ternary alloys were continued in use as coinage until 20 B.C. but from that date until two centuries later lead is seldom found in Roman coins except as an accidental impurity. The lead was no doubt added partly to increase the fusibility of the alloy and also because of its cheapness as compared with copper and tin. Roman bronze statues often contain 6 to 12 per cent of lead. Gowland states that the Japanese were accustomed to add lead to bronze, not merely for cheapness and increased fluidity but also to enable the development, under suitable treatment, of a rich brown patina‡. Pliny gives a tip to the house-wife. When bronzes are cleaned,

---

*GOWLAND, *J. Inst. Metals*, 1912, **7**, 40.
†PLINY, *Opus. cit.*, Book 34, Chaps. 6, 9, 21 and 22.
‡GOWLAND, *J. Inst. Metals*, 1912, **7**, 41.

he says, they oxidise more quickly than when left alone unless rubbed over with oil.

The Romans knew how to use copper for joining pieces of iron together — a process that may be regarded as the fore-runner of modern brazing (p. 273).

Copper in Britain

Although the conquest of Britain by the Romans undoubtedly led to a great increase in the mining of copper, the metal and certain of its alloys were already well known in the British Isles. Prehistoric relics have been found in Ireland, such as flat celts, made of almost pure copper, many specimens containing no more than 0·1 per cent of tin and cannot therefore be classed as bronze. They may date back as far as 2500 B.C.

In England bronze objects have been found in burial mounds of the late Neolithic period, some 2000 B.C. As the objects are small it may well be that they indicate merely the beginning of the bronze age; as the years rolled on, metal objects increased in range and dimensions. Riveted bronze cauldrons and buckets have been found from time to time; a cauldron recovered from the Thames near Battersea, 16 inches high and $22\frac{1}{2}$ inches in diameter is shown in the British Museum and possibly dates from about 700 B.C.

In 1914 a hoard of bronze vessels was found at Wotton in Surrey; it comprised amongst other things several perforated bowls or water-clocks and a curious vessel very much like a frying-pan. It appears that the bowls, perforated at the base were placed empty in larger bowls containing water and as the water slowly entered the perforation the bowl gradually sank until it reached the bottom of the larger containing vessel. R. A. Smith* considers that the vessels of frying-pan shape were gongs which were suspended, perhaps to a wall, and every time the bowl sank the gong was struck by an attendant whose duty it was to keep a check on the time. Similar methods of measuring the time have been used in India. This type of water clock, however, was not known to the Hindoos till after A.D. 350; it appears, therefore, to have been a British invention.

For several centuries after the Romans had left these islands very little copper was produced, practically all the metals required were imported from Europe.

---

*R. A. SMITH, *Proc. Soc. Antiquaries*, 1907, **21**, 319; 1915, **27**, 76. FRIEND, "Iron in Antiquity" (Griffin and Co., 1926) pp. 59 *et seq.*

The English are supposed to have used brass or bronze cannon for the first time during the reign of Edward III (1327 to 1377), possibly at the siege of Cambrai in 1339 or a few years later at Crecy in 1346. These were perhaps imported from abroad, but cannon are believed to have been made in Britain not long after; the experience that had been gained in the bell foundries (p. 107) no doubt proved invaluable.

Brass guns are said to have been made for the Sheriff of Northumberland in 1385; but guns of this alloy soon proved too weak and were superseded by wrought-iron and cast-iron cannon (pp. 274, 277).

It was not wise, however, for Britain to be dependent on the good-will of her neighbours for her copper. A war might cut off the supplies and leave her stranded. An effort was therefore made in the sixteenth century by Henry VIII (1509 to 1547) to develop the home-mining of both copper and zinc, and skilled workers were invited over from the Continent to assist. In 1566 a rich deposit of copper ore was discovered at Newlands near Keswick in Cumberland, whilst calamine (zinc carbonate) was found at Worle near Weston super Mare in Somerset.

At this period the woollen industry was of supreme importance to Britain; copper and brass wires were required in quantity for "wool cards" used for working short fibres into a fluffy mass prior to spinning. These were wooden instruments with wire teeth on one side set in leather.

The wires had been mostly imported, but in 1582, during the reign of Elizabeth (1558 to 1603), a brass factory was opened at Isleworth near London to meet the need. Hitherto such wire as had been made in England had been done by very primitive processes involving either hammering or drawing. In the latter case the method was extremely crude. Two men sat facing each other on swings. Each man had a waist belt to which one end of the same strip of brass was attached. Moving the swings with their feet they were able to swing apart thus stretching the brass strip into a crude form of wire.

By the close of the century, the continental method of drawing wire through a die had been introduced; it is believed to have first been used in Nuremberg in the fourteenth century and operated by hand labour; but machinery driven by water or other power was subsequently employed.

About this time, also, hammers worked by water-power were

H

introduced from Germany for the production of sheet metal, ingots being beaten into plates by a variety of hammers, some weighing as much as 500 lb. The difficulty of course lay in obtaining a uniform thickness, but this was remedied later by the introduction of the more efficient rolling-mill late in the seventeenth century, with the result that battery works gradually faded from the picture.

By the accession of James I (1603 to 1625) the manufacture of brass pins had become an important industry and at the close of the century about a ton of wire was produced weekly at Esher in Surrey, alone, most of which was used in making pins. The wire, after drawing, was pickled in waste acid liquors, rubbed with the pulp of rotten oranges to give it a clean finish, drawn again and made into pins. It is said that the best workers could produce some 24,000 pins a day.

At first wood and charcoal were used in smelting copper ores, but in 1632 Edward Jorden patented the use of coal, peat and turf, whilst four years later Sir Phillibert Vernatt patented the use of coal alone as fuel. These inventions stimulated the production of copper, especially in South Wales where coal was abundant. By the close of the eighteenth century Britain was the largest producer of copper in the world. This could not last for long. In 1830 the enormous Chilean deposits began to be developed; the resources of Australia and North America rapidly followed suit; the tables were now turned in earnest, the procedure of Henry VIII reversed, and expert smelters from Britain now travelled to all parts of the world to show others how best to carry on.

Copper and the alchemists

Copper was regarded by the alchemists as under the patronage of the planet Venus, and, as we have seen (p. 13), was designated by the symbol ♀, known as Venus's looking-glass.

Every schoolboy knows the trick of initialling the blade of his penknife with copper. The blade is dipped in molten wax; on cooling, the initials are scratched out with a pin and the blade dipped into a solution of copper sulphate. Where the naked metal makes contact with the solution, iron dissolves and an equivalent amount of copper is deposited. The alchemists used to try the same experiment in front of a credulous laity, claiming to have transmuted iron to copper.

Round 1735 a company was floated in Paris for the transmutation of iron into copper. The fraud was exposed by Claude

Geoffroy, and the manager disappeared with the cash leaving a quantity of copper sulphate and some old iron.

The copper springs in the County of Wicklow, Ireland, owed their discovery to a chance experiment of this kind. About the middle of the eighteenth century a workman left an iron shovel in a part of the Crone-Bawn mines, through which a stream was passing. Some weeks later on fetching the shovel he found it to be thickly encrusted with copper, due to copper salts in the stream reacting with the iron. This suggested the laying of iron bars in the water; and 500 tons were accordingly spread out in the pits; the copper was precipitated out as a fine mud, each ton of iron yielding $1\frac{1}{2}$ tons or more of dried mud, each ton of which in turn produced 16 cwt. of commercially pure copper.

In order to ascertain whether or not copper is present in an ore miners will drop a little nitric acid on the mass and, after a while, dip a feather into the acid and draw it over the polished blade of a knife. The presence or absence of copper is immediately indicated. Many modern "wet processes" for the recovery or extraction of copper from waste products or ores are based on this principle.

Brass

Brass was known long before metallic zinc. Although beads of zinc blende, ZnS, have been found in Predynastic Egyptian graves there is no evidence that the early Egyptians were familiar with brass. The alloy termed brass by early translators of the classics was usually bronze. Thus, in Holy Writ, Tubal Cain is named as the first worker in "brass" as in iron, but true brass was generally unknown in Old Testament times (p. 94) although it was occasionally made by accident by reduction of a copper ore containing zinc, a "natural" brass resulting. Macalister states that brass containing 23·4 per cent of zinc has been found in Palestine dating back to a period between 1400 and 1000 B.C. This alloy was probably used for cymbals and bells. Zinc is present in some Grecian alloys up to 2 per cent, but merely as impurity. It is also found in early Roman coins in like capacity; but in the reign of Augustus, 20 to 14 B.C., zinc ore was added intentionally to that of copper, thus producing, on reduction, a true, synthetic brass. An early coin dating back to 20 B.C. was found to contain 17·31 per cent of zinc.

The Romans were thus the first intentional makers of brass, and coins were made of it even down to the time of Diocletian

99

(286 to 305), during whose reign 6 parts of brass were equivalent to 8 of copper. The proportion of zinc was very variable ranging from about 11 to 28 per cent. The alloys containing 15 to 20 per cent of zinc, possessing a maximum ductibility, were used for scale armour and ornamental purposes. Several rosettes and studs, which had formed the mounts of a casket, unearthed in 1900 in the Roman city of Tilchester, possessed a rich golden colour. These were analysed by Gowland* and found to contain 17 or 18 per cent of zinc. This alloy is virtually identical with the imitation gold known as Tournay's alloy (82·5 copper, 17·5 zinc) which is used in the manufacture of French jewellery.

The Roman method of making brass consisted in mixing ground calamine with charcoal granules and small fragments of copper, and heating in a crucible to a temperature suitable for reducing the calamine to metal, but not sufficiently high to melt the copper. The zinc vapour penetrated the copper, converting it to brass. The temperature was then raised to melt the brass which was then poured into moulds.

The Indian alchemists were familiar with this method of making brass at quite an early date. The Tantra *Rasaratnakara* (p. 114), written during the seventh or eighth century A.D. purports to give the wisdom of Nagarjuna, *circa* A.D. 150, and contains an obvious reference to brass. Amongst its recipes we read that "calamine . . . roasted thrice with copper converts the latter into gold."

The Roman method was so efficient and easy to manipulate that it remained the standard European procedure for many centuries, the product being known as Roman or Calamine brass.

It appears that by the eleventh century considerable pains were being taken to purify copper used in making brass for ornamental purposes. Brass containing lead was difficult to gild, so the removal of this element was important. Rugerus Theophilus†, a monk who lived in the earlier years of the eleventh century, described in detail a method for doing this. The copper was heated in a clay-lined iron dish under charcoal until it melted; the liquid was then stirred with a dry stick to which the lead scum adhered.

In 1781 John Emerson patented the method now universally used for making brass, namely addition of metallic zinc to copper. This gradually superseded the Roman method, although this

---

*Gowland, *J. Inst. Metals*, 1912, **7**, 44.

†Theophilus, "An Essay upon Various Arts", translated by Hendrie. (Murray, 1847), p. 313.

latter was still employed at Pemberton's works in Birmingham until shortly before 1861.

Brasses are easily machined, spun, stamped and polished. They resist corrosion well and are used in the form of sheet, strip, rod, wire, tubing and castings. Cartridge brass with copper 70, and zinc 30, is particularly tough and strong.

Uses of copper

The ease with which copper conducts the electric current has enabled it to play a vital part in most phases of electrical development. It had been noticed as early as 1678 that contraction of the muscle occurred when a silver wire in contact with the nerve touched a copper wire on which the muscle rested. It cannot be said that science moved rapidly in those days, for it was not until 1786 that similar observations were made by Galvani, professor of anatomy at Bologna. The story goes that Madame Galvani was ill; some luscious edible frogs, intended to make soup for her, were lying on a table in a laboratory in which stood a machine for generating frictional electricity. It was observed that every time a spark was emitted from the machine, the frogs would twitch, although they had been dead for hours.

Galvani's attention having been drawn to the matter he decided to investigate it more fully. During a thunderstorm he connected the leg of a dead frog with a lightning conductor, and found that the limb kicked every time the lightning flashed. Next he attached several dead frogs by means of copper or brass hooks to an iron trellis in his garden in anticipation of another storm. As it happened the weather proved fine and sunny, with no suspicion of thunder in the air, yet each time he pressed a metal hook against the trellis the leg fixed to it twitched, and the twitching was continued as long as the contact was maintained.

Galvani concluded that the electric "fluid" was already present in the frog's legs and that the metals merely served to release it, just as pipes can draw off water from tanks or reservoirs.

This conclusion, though incorrect, is quite understandable because at that time the attention of scientists had been directed to the peculiar electric shocks given by certain eels. In 1793, however, Volta, professor of natural philosophy at Pavia, dissented from this view in a paper presented to the Royal Society and suggested that the observed agitation was caused by an electric discharge due to contact of the two dissimilar metals, copper and iron. In 1799 Volta described his "pile" and "battery", with which it became possible for the first time to produce at will a continuous electric current. The pile consisted of discs of zinc resting on silver, each pair being separated from the others by moist pasteboard. On connecting the uppermost zinc with the lowest disc of silver an electric current would flow. The voltaic battery was similar, strips of zinc and silver or copper being dipped into cups containing dilute acid which took the place of the pasteboard in the pile.

Before long a large battery was installed for research purposes in the Royal Institution under the direction of Humphry Davy. It had 2000 pairs of plates — copper and zinc — with a total surface of 890 square feet. With its aid in 1807 Davy was able to isolate for the first time the alkali metals sodium and potassium (p. 144). It was soon realised that, of all the base metals, copper was the finest conductor of electricity. It was rapidly put into use in the construction of lightning conductors for chimneys, etc, and by 1811 it was similarly employed for the protection of ships' masts. If it was not an unqualified success in this capacity, it was not altogether the fault of the copper. Examination of one Man-of-War showed that a conductor had actually been laid through the powder magazine!*

A few years later it was realised that messages might be sent by electricity for long distances with extreme rapidity through copper wires with the aid of a pre-arranged code. The railway authorities felt that this might be a valuable method of communicating the movement of trains and in 1837, a month after the first train had steamed into Euston station a telegraphic system was installed on a section of the L.M.S. railway between Euston and Chalk Farm. This was the first to be put into commercial use. It was an enterprising innovation, however, for Euston only boasted six trains a day, three in and three out. But what was lost in magnitude was gained by drama. The guard wore resplendent scarlet, and gaily tootled a hunting horn. In 1843 a similar service was installed on the G.W. line between Paddington and Slough; but these were, in a sense, specialised applications and did not interest the public in general. In 1845, however, an event happened that thrilled the man in the street, and opened his eyes to the enormous possibilities of the invention†. A woman was brutally murdered not far from

---

*"Copper through the Ages" (Copper Development Association, 1934) p. 41.
†C. A. MITCHELL, "Science and the Criminal" (Pitman, 1911), p. 24.

Slough. A neighbour, hearing her screams, ran to the spot just in time to see a man in Quaker garb hurrying away. The man succeeded in reaching Slough station unchallenged and boarded a train to London. The police, however, telegraphed through and the man was met by detectives and later arrested. In due course he was tried at the Aylesbury Assizes, convicted and executed.

The next important move was to connect England with France by telegraph. In 1850 a copper wire, insulated with gutta-percha but otherwise unprotected, was laid across the Channel. It worked all right until it broke — after one day's operation. But the principle had been established and a year later an armoured copper cable was laid and this proved successful.

A more ambitious scheme was now embarked upon, namely the connecting of this country with America by cable. To bridge the "herring pond" some 2,500 miles of cable were required. The first attempt in 1857 was unsuccessful; a second attempt with 3000 miles of cable was successful for the moment but failed after but a few weeks of service. The third attempt was permanently successful, the cable being put into commercial operation in 1866. More than 365 tons of copper were used in the construction of this cable.

These were but small beginnings; to-day tens of thousands of tons of copper are in use in various ways in electrical plant and in the distribution of electricity. A single building may have many miles of copper wire laid on so that its rooms may be illuminated, warmed, and provided with an adequate telephone service. The electrical industry absorbs nearly 60 per cent of the world's production of copper.

Because of its elasticity, copper wire is favoured by rope dancers.

The resistance of copper to corrosion renders copper particularly valuable for water tanks and pipes, cooking utensils, sheathing of ships, etc. It possesses many advantages over lead for the covering of domes and other outdoor structures. It was used in a temple frieze at Al 'Ubaid (Plate 1), near the ancient city of Ur of the Chaldees, Abraham's reputed city, some 3000 to 4000 B.C., worked up from sheet copper, and has been used by numerous peoples for like purposes ever since. The dome of the Library of the British Museum, London, dating back to 1857, is the largest copper-covered dome in the world. St Paul's Cathedral is lead-covered; Wren would have preferred copper, but his workmen appear to have been unequal to the task (p. 195). Copper possesses four main advantages over lead —

(i)   It is less dense and can be used in thinner sheets so that its weight is much less.

(ii)   Copper has a higher melting point, 1083° C, than lead, 327° C. In case of fire, therefore, there is much less danger of its melting and injuring firemen and others.

(iii)   Copper does not "creep" like lead.

(iv)   Copper ultimately develops a decorative and protective green patina that is pleasing to the eye, whilst lead is always dull and "leaden". It should be mentioned that the green patina is *not* verdigris, as is popularly supposed. In the neighbourhood of cities it is, in the limit, largely basic copper sulphate, $CuSO_4.3Cu(OH)_2$, of similar composition to the mineral brochantite, admixed with more or less basic copper chloride, $CuCl_2.3Cu(OH)_2$, similar to atacamite, in proximity to the sea*.

All of these compounds are bactericidal and the ancients knew that they helped to prevent wounds from festering. Accordingly, Achilles has been represented in ancient pictures as scraping the "rust" or oxidation products from his bronze sword or spear into the wound of Telephus†. These oxidation products are frequently but incorrectly called *verdigris*, which latter is really a basic acetate of copper, and is not produced by ordinary atmospheric corrosion of the metal or its alloys.

In this connection it is interesting to note that Pliny was aware of the curative properties of copper for he mentions that nowhere do ulcers heal more rapidly than in the neighbourhood of copper mines.

Annealed copper is soft and easy to work. It admits also of being easily jointed by soldering, brazing or welding. This is an important advantage, particularly valuable in connecting electrical conductors, water pipes, etc, and in the manufacture of many domestic and other articles now on the market. Copper can be hardened and its tensile strength more than doubled by what is known as "cold working", that is by such treatment as hammering, rolling or drawing the metal at more or less ordinary temperatures. A still harder and stronger metal is obtained by the addition of small quantities of other metals. Thus, the addition of even less than one per cent of cadmium increases the tensile strength with-

---

*VERNON and WHITBY, *J. Institute of Metals*, 1929, **42**, 181; 1930, **44**, 389; 1932, **49**, 153; 1933, **52**, 93.

†PLINY, "Natural History". Translated by Bostock and Riley (Bohn, 1857). Book 25. Chap. 19.

out seriously affecting its electrical conductivity. Addition of some five per cent of tin will suffice to double the strength of copper whilst a little beryllium may render it as strong and hard as a mild steel. As these beryllium alloys are not easily "fatigued" they are particularly useful for the manufacture of springs.

Bronzes are alloys of copper and tin. The word "bronze" is not very ancient. It appears to have been introduced in the fifteenth or sixteenth centuries. In his *Pirotechnia*, published in 1550, Vannuccio Biringuiccio, an Italian, stated that alloys of copper and tin were termed *bronzo*. This is thought to be a contraction of the Latin *aes Brundusinum*, the brass of Brindisi. Some ancient bronzes contained up to 50 per cent of tin as in the case of ancient Chinese mirrors of the Chou period 1249 to 1122 B.C. But usually in ancient bronzes the tin content was very much lower. In Mesopotamia, for example, about 2000 B.C. an alloy containing 10 per cent of tin was made; it was almost what one might call a standard bronze, being suitable for most purposes. Bronze was known, however, in Mesopotamia at a much earlier date, probably before 3000 B.C. and in Egypt it has been found in a tomb dating back to the First Dynasty, *circa* 3300 B.C. The life-size statue of Pepi I of the VIIth Dynasty, now in Cairo Museum, is catalogued as bronze. By the XVIIIth Dynasty, *circa* 1580 B.C. bronze was in considerable use and reached its highest development under Psammetik I about the time of the fall of the Assyrian empire, coincident with the capture of Nineveh in 612 B.C.

Bronzes are to-day used for various architectural and ornamental purposes. The magnificent bronze gates of Henry VII's Chapel in Westminster Abbey, built 1503 to 1519, are the pride of that historic building. They are adorned with heraldic devices referring to the King's ancestry and his claims to the throne; the crown on the bush recalls the coronation on Bosworth Field in 1485; the Roses are those of Lancaster and York united by his marriage; the Lions are those of England, the Fleurs de Lis of France. Bronze lends itself admirably to decoration such as this.

Bronzes are used for statues, propellers, fire-boxes, etc.

Bronze coins have been circulated among the nations for several thousand years. Some unearthed at Snettisham in Norfolk in 1948 are of Celtic origin and date back to 85 to 75 B.C. They are perhaps the earliest minted in Britain.

Copper is used in all our coins including gold, silver and base metal. Our "nickel" threepenny bit contains 79 of Cu, 20 of Zn and 1 of Ni. Until 1942 our pennies contained 3 per cent of tin together with a little zinc but, in order to conserve our tin supplies, the tin content was reduced in that year to half a per cent and would no doubt have been abolished entirely had not the coinage acts required the presence of some of the metal. A ton of bronze will make pennies to the value of approximately £448, but farthings or half-pennies, being relatively heavier, amount to only £373. In 1943 the output of half-pennies, all of the "Ship" variety, reached the 76,200,000 mark, almost the greatest on record. Since this design was first struck in 1937, something like 400 million had been issued by 1944. There are still plenty of "bun" pennies, as they are called, in circulation estimated at some 90 millions, on which Queen Victoria is depicted as a young woman with her hair done neatly in a "bun" at the back. These coins were issued until 1894, by which time the young girl had become an elderly lady; they were then superseded by a more appropriate figure.

Much modern bronze contains 10 of tin, 2 of zinc, the remainder being copper. An alloy consisting of Cu:Sn:Zn as 16:2·5:1 was used in the construction of the Imperial Standard Yard in 1845 (p. 308).

Miscellaneous alloys

Our silver coins since 1928 have contained 40 per cent of copper, but in 1945 it was decided to replace them by a copper–nickel alloy, and that is gradually being done (p. 296).

After the invention of gunpowder, supposedly by Roger Bacon (1214 to 1294), a bronze containing 8 to 11 per cent of tin was found to combine great strength and resistance to shock and was thus valuable for making guns. It came to be known as *gunmetal*. The modern alloy usually contains also a little zinc up to about 3 per cent.

Mention should be made also of phosphor-bronze (p. 80) containing 5 to 15 per cent of tin and from a trace up to 1·75 per cent of phosphorus which imparts great hardness, elasticity, toughness and resistance to corrosion to the alloy. It finds application in pump plungers, valves and bushes of bearings, etc. Phosphor-bronze wire is used in stay ropes exposed to corrosive atmospheres; armature binding wires, overhead transmission cables, springs in electrical switches, and in wire cloth used in paper-making machines.

Manganese and silicon bronzes are also in vogue, the term

bronze being retained though the tin may be entirely absent. Bronze bearing-metal, employed for the bearings of locomotives, is an alloy of copper containing tin 8 and lead 15 per cent. The lead reduces local heating and diminishes loss by wear. The function of the tin is to facilitate the mixing of the lead and copper. Other alloys are bell metal (below), white bronze (p. 213), Muntz metal, brass (p. 99), the nickel silvers (p. 297), silver solders (p. 120) and duralumin (p. 163).

Small additions of copper to steel render it more resistant to atmospheric corrosion.

Bell metal

Once bronze came into use for cooking utensils it would soon be noticed that, upon being struck, the latter emitted a musical sound. The earliest "bells" would thus be cooking vessels used as gongs (p. 96). From these were evolved the bells and gongs known to the ancients. It was ultimately found that the best sounds could be obtained from alloys containing from 15 to 25 per cent of tin, the remainder being copper.

Although fairly large bells may have been made in China and used in the temples at an early date, church bells are supposed to have been used in Europe only since about A.D. 400. At first they were small; by the eleventh century a bell weighing 2600 lb. was given to the church at Orleans, France. In A.D. 1400 a bell weighing some 15,000 lb. was cast in Paris, and from this time onwards bells increased very much in size and weight. In 1497 a bell weighing 30,250 lb. was cast at Erfurt, Germany, the supposed home of that elusive monk, Basil Valentine (p. 84).

Bronze bells had been cast in England as early as the eleventh century and by the twelfth century the industry had attained national importance; in later years numerous bell foundries opened up in various parts of the country. The bell founder was known as a "bellyeter", and Billiter Street, off Leadenhall Street, London, E.C. derives its name from this as it was once a centre of the industry.

The largest bell in England is *Great Paul* of St Paul's Cathedral, London. It was cast at Loughborough in 1882 and weighs 39,200 lb; it is rung daily for 5 minutes at 1 p.m. Even bigger is that at St Peter's in Rome; 42,000 lb. That at Notre Dame in Paris is somewhat less, namely 35,600 lb. But all of these are dwarfed by the *Great Bell* or *Monarch of Moscow* cast in 1735 and weighing approximately 200 tons. It is, however, inarticulate. This gigantic casting, 24 inches thick at its thickest place and 6 inches at its thinnest, cracked in several places on cooling, one portion weighing 10 tons falling away. The crippled bell lay in its casting pit until 1836 when it was lifted out and placed on a granite foundation for all to see. Its inscribed date is 1732 but this refers not to the date of casting but to that of making the mould.

The carillon of Bruges Belfry is considered to be the finest in Europe and dates from 1745 to 1748. There are 48 bells, the largest weighing 11,589 lb. and the smallest 12 lb. The total weight of all 48 bells is 55,166 lb. The Bourdon or largest bell in the clock weighs 19,000 lb.

Silver

Silver, the "Queen of the Metals" does not often occur free in Nature and for this reason did not come into such early use as gold. It did not play an important part in primitive culture.

The earliest sources of the metal for economic use were most probably argentiferous lead ore or plumbiferous silver ores. In most cases the ore would belong to the former class and would usually be galena, that is lead sulphide, PbS, which usually contains some silver. Thus, for example, British galenas contain on the average some 4 to 5 oz. of silver per ton whilst some Devonshire ores contain up to 170 oz. (p. 189).

Galena has a brilliant, silvery lustre which could not fail to intrigue primitive man; but the brittleness of the ore made it impossible for him to use it direct to good purpose. But if by chance or intention a piece of galena were to fall into a blazing wood fire* it could easily be reduced to metal, that is, to lead with a certain amount of silver dissolved in it; if this alloy remained in the fire for some time, the lead would be oxidised leaving a small lump of silver. Thus would originate the economic discovery of silver, and the camp fire would thus constitute the first smelting furnace.

Some famous silver mines

The *Gogerddan mines* near Aberystwyth two or three centuries ago were very productive of silver; the ore was galena. It is said that they yielded to Sir Hugh Myddleton a profit of some £25,000 a year which enabled him to pursue and complete in 1613, with

---

*PERCY, "The Metallurgy of Lead" (Murray, 1870) p. 213.

the help of James I, his great scheme of bringing water to London from near Ware in Hertfordshire by the "New River" — a distance of some 40 miles.

The expense was so great that, although an act had been passed in 1607 empowering the City Corporation to construct the river, no attempt was made by the Corporation to implement it. The story goes that, after completion of the scheme, the King himself once fell into the river when riding — an unfortunate reward for his efforts but no doubt a joy to those who had opposed the scheme on the ground that the "ditch" would prove dangerous to hunters.

The *Salcedo Mine* in Peru had an interesting history. It was very rich in silver and was given as dowry in the middle of the seventeenth century to Salcedo, a poor Spaniard married to an Indian girl, by the girl's mother who had herself discovered it. Salcedo worked the mine most successfully and became sufficiently wealthy to excite the envy of the Spanish Governor of Peru. This worthy endeavoured to obtain possession of the mine and suggested to the Spanish Government that Salcedo was using his wealth in an endeavour to raise an insurrection amongst the Indians and throw off the Spanish yoke. Although there was not a vestige of truth in this, Salcedo was arrested, subjected to a mock trial and sentenced to death. It was dangerous in those days to be successful and Salcedo was duly hanged. Whilst in prison he had begged permission to send to Madrid and appeal to the Crown for mercy; he had promised to give the Governor a daily bribe of a silver bar for every day that the vessel took to sail from Callao to Spain and back again; but in vain. The vessel would take 12 months or more, and the mine must be marvellously productive, mused the Governor, if Salcedo can promise that. But the Governor over-reached himself. As soon as Salcedo was hanged, his mother-in-law caused the mine to be flooded and the works destroyed; the entrance was closed and camouflaged so effectively that no one could find it. When, afterwards, some who had known the mine were caught and questioned, both promises and torture failed to reveal the position of the mine, which is unknown even to-day.

The *San José Mine* in Huancavalica, Peru, is another very rich one. The owner was desirous that the Governor should be god-father to his first born and this was agreed to; but as important affairs of state prevented the Governor from attending the christening he sent his wife instead. To show his appreciation of the honour done to him and his family, the owner caused a triple row of silver bars to be laid the whole distance from his residence to the church where the ceremony was to be performed. Over this silver pavement the party passed to and from the christening. When the Governor's wife departed the owner presented her with the whole of the silver road.

These anecdotes give some idea of the enormous wealth of Peru.

Silver and the Egyptians

There were no silver mines in Egypt and, even as late as the rule of the Hyksos or Shepherd Kings *circa* 1780 to 1580 B.C. silver was twice the value of gold. But during the 18th Dynasty, which lasted from 1580 to 1350 B.C. the position was reversed, for silver became more abundant, 3 parts of gold being worth 5 of silver*. The reason for the greater abundance of silver was undoubtedly because of Egyptian marauding expeditions into Palestine and the North. Thothmes III, the Napoleon of Egypt *circa* 1500 B.C. captured huge quantities of silver in Asiatic cities which he repeatedly visited; he used gold and silver rings for trading purposes; some of these rings were very heavy, weighing as much as 12 lb. The Egyptian ladies of the period were wont to adorn themselves with silver chains of varying length up to five feet.

Even in the seventeenth century silver and gold were of equal value in Japan. To be born "with a silver spoon" in one's mouth is an old expression based on the once high cost of silver tableware.

Silver, being a soft metal, was sometimes used, like gold and lead, in the form of plates or tablets for keeping permanent records of important treaties or documents of state. During the reign of Rameses II, the King who was once regarded as the Pharaoh of the Oppression, the Kheta or Hittites were a source of considerable trouble to the Egyptians. In 1333 B.C. a treaty was drawn up between Rameses and Kheta-sar, which was inscribed on a tablet of silver and deposited in the palace fortress in the Nile Delta†.

In later days the Egyptians both knew of and practised the separation of silver from gold by the chloride method, but we cannot fix the date of its innovation.

Silver in Holy Writ

There are many references to silver in the Old Testament, but

---

*PARTINGTON, "Origins and Development of Applied Chemistry" (Longmans, 1935) p. 43.

†BUDGE, "A History of Egypt" (Kegan Paul, 1902), vol. v, pp. 48 *et seq.*

although both iron and "brass" are referred to by name before the Deluge, some 4000 B.C., there is no mention of silver. By the time of Abraham, who lived possibly 2160 to 1985 B.C., silver was common. Abraham is described as rich in both silver and gold; it is recorded that he paid 400 shekels of silver for a burial place for Sarah, his wife (*Gen.* xxiii. 15). The site chosen was the cave at Macpelah. The money was not in the form of coin but was weighed out in the presence of witnesses (*Gen.* xxiii. 15–16), just as it is weighed out even to-day in China because the silver coins are frequently cracked or in pieces in consequence of repeated stamping on changing hands.

The Jewish *shekel* was a unit of weight, equivalent to some 16 grams or slightly more than 0·5 oz. avoir. The word is derived from the Hebrew *Shakal*, to weigh: 50 shekels made one *mina* and 60 minas one *talent*. A talent was thus equivalent to approximately 106 lb. avoir., 128 lb. Troy or nearly 1 cwt.

It was not until many centuries later that the Jews had silver coins of their own, the word shekel then referring to a coin of approximately the same weight as the earlier bars. Two large hoards of silver coins, one found in Jerusalem and one in Jericho, are described by Reinach*. Some of the coins, the heavy shekel, weighed 14 grams, others, the light or half shekel, weighed just half this amount. They date back to the time of Simon Maccabæus *circa* 138 B.C. Judæa was then a free state and had been authorised to strike silver money of its own; it founded a mint and issued an entirely new coinage in which it endeavoured to portray its own peculiar national character. On the obverse was a chalice; on the reverse a branch of lily with three flowers; these were described by earlier numismatists as a "pot of manna" and "Aaron's rod budding".

The Hebrews were expressly forbidden (*Exod.* xx. 23) to make gods of silver just as they were censured for making a golden calf; no doubt they had ample silver to make them with; on leaving the Nile Delta they "borrowed" jewels of silver from the Egyptians, presumably on as generous a scale as they borrowed the gold (p. 127) for we read that "they spoiled the Egyptians" (*Exod.* xii. 36).

In Old Testament times silver was used in large quantity in domestic and ceremonial vessels. It was his own silver cup used

*REINACH. "Jewish Coins", translated by Mary Hill (Lawrence and Bullen, Ltd, 1903), p. 4.

for divining (*Gen.* xliv. 15) that Joseph caused to be placed in Benjamin's sack of corn as the Brethren left Egypt after their second visit in search of food.

Silver was used on a lavish scale in constructing the Ark of the Covenant (*Exod.* xxvi.) and in *Num.* vii. we are given a detailed account of the offerings brought to Moses. These included silver chargers or flat dishes weighing 130 shekels (4 lb.) and silver bowls weighing 70 shekels — massive vessels these. Tarshish, the modern Andalusia of Spain, is mentioned as the trading centre in silver as well as the base metals iron, lead and "tin" (*Ezek.* xxvii. 12).

In later years, when the Hebrews had become firmly established in Palestine, silver became very plentiful. Solomon, some 950 B.C., "made silver to be in Jerusalem as stones" (1 *Kings* x. 27).

The later Hebrews are said in *Num.* xxxi. 23, to have practised the refining of silver by fire. It is probable that cupellation is referred to for Ezekiel (xxii. 18) mentions "the dross of silver" which suggests litharge of cupellation, otherwise it is less easy to understand the analogy, given in verses 21 and 22, "I will gather you and *blow upon you* in the fire of my wrath . . . as silver is melted in the midst of the furnace."

The fining pot for silver is mentioned twice in the *Book of Proverbs* (xvii. 3; xxvii. 21) in connection with the furnace for gold and may be a reference to the chloride process used in removing silver from gold as practised by the Egyptians (p. 133). The "silver cord" mentioned in *Eccles.* xii. 6 is thought to refer to the spinal cord because of its bright appearance even in a dead body. Silver is but seldom mentioned in the New Testament. In *Acts* xix. 24, we read that Demetrius made silver shrines for Diana. This was evidently one of the trades in Ephesus.

Silver and the Romans

Pliny, after a lengthy dissertation on gold (p. 120), devotes a chapter to silver*, "the next folly of mankind", and mentions Spain as the best source. In the time of Strabo (p. 133) the silver mines were private property; they did not belong to the state like the gold mines. Enormous quantities of silver found their way into Rome as the result of her conquests. Cornelius Lentulus, for example, when *circa* 200 B.C. he was proconsul of Spain, brought 43,000 lb. of

---

*PLINY, "Natural History", translated by Bostock and Riley (Bohn, 1857), Book XXXIII, Chapters 31, 50 and 52.

silver to the city on the occasion of his entry in ovation. The Romans appear to have been very fond of silver plate and silver ornaments, many individuals possessing large supplies. One cannot help smiling at the Carthaginian ambassadors' sarcasm with reference to the Roman use of silver plate. No people, they declared, lived on more amicable terms among themselves than the Romans, for that wherever they had dined they (the ambassadors) had always met with the same silver plate. This, of course, was intended to indicate that the silver was lent from house to house for the occasion and that the Romans were not as wealthy as they pretended. "And yet, by Hercules!" says Pliny, evidently annoyed at the sneer, "to my own knowledge, Pompeius Paulinus .. had . . . a service of silver plate that weighed 12,000 lb." Bravo Pliny!

Sometimes the dishes were very heavy. Pliny mentions a silver charger weighing 500 lb., for the manufacture of which a workshop had been specially built. This charger was part of a set comprising eight other dishes, each weighing 250 lb. Pliny naively asks — Who were to be the guests served therefrom? Dean Swift would no doubt have supplied them from Brobdingnag.

An analysis of Roman silver objects in the British Museum showed them to contain from 92·5 to 92·6 per cent of silver. Couches on which ladies reclined, and banqueting couches were often covered with silver, as were ladies' baths. Vessels of silver were used "for the most unseemly purposes" — whatever that may mean.

The ease with which silver tarnishes has always been regarded as a disadvantage. Pliny knew that silver is readily blackened with the yolk of an egg and gives a useful tip to the housewife by saying that the tarnish is removed by rubbing with vinegar and chalk.

Galena invariably contains some silver (p. 189) and the Romans knew how to extract it by cupellation. The furnace or hearth was a shallow cavity lined with bone-ash, that is, calcined bones ground to powder. A charcoal fire was made and the lead placed on it to melt. When sufficient had collected in the hollow, the fire was raked to the sides and a blast of air introduced, which oxidised the lead but not the silver. The scum of lead oxide was absorbed into the bone-ash leaving a cake of silver, containing, however, any gold that was originally present.

Incidentally it may be mentioned that at about this time the Indian alchemists were also familiar with cupellation; an early

MS. containing the wisdom of Nagarjuna (p. 100) who lived about the second century A.D. states that "silver alloyed with lead and fused with ashes becomes purified". A later MS. dating back probably to the eleventh century and known as the Tantra Rasahridaya of Bhikshu Govinda speaks of a cupel made of ashes from the bones of a goat.

Silver and the alchemists

Silver has a beautiful appearance unequalled by any other ordinary white metal. The word silver is Anglo-Saxon; the Latin name *argentum*, from which the chemical symbol Ag is taken, is allied to the Greek *arguros*, silver, from *argos*, shining. The Hebrew name *késseph* is derived from a root meaning "to be pale". Owing to its ready tarnish and solubility in acids, silver was not regarded by the alchemists as so perfect a metal as gold. They therefore gave it only half a circle as its symbol, suggesting merely partial mathematical perfection; at the same time indicating a supposed connection with the crescent moon (p. 13).

The metal was known to the alchemists as *luna*, and its salts as lunar salts. Thus silver nitrate was termed *lunar caustic* and was prescribed during the Middle Ages for brain disorders, it being held that the moon controlled the mental faculties.

The alchemists were fond of producing the "silver tree" or *arbor Dianæ* by suspending some suitable metal in a solution of a soluble silver salt such as lunar caustic (silver nitrate) in much the same way as the better known "lead tree" is grown (p. 194). It is very beautiful to watch under the microscope the growth of silver on a piece of metallic copper*.

Uses of silver

The attractive appearance of silver has caused it to be in great demand for ornamental purposes. As has been mentioned, its main disadvantage lies in the ease with which it tarnishes, particularly in our centres of industry because of the presence of sulphur compounds in the atmosphere which induce the formation of a black, dull superficial layer of silver sulphide.

To counter this, plating with rhodium has been successfully applied to jewellery (1936); the process is known as rhodanising, but the details are kept secret. It may be applied equally well to old silver as to new (p. 305). Rhodium is a white metal like silver

---

*J. H. GLADSTONE, *Nature*, 1872, **6**, 66.

and is exceptionally resistant to tarnish. Unfortunately it is also extremely expensive; further, any scratching or mechanical abrasion of the thin rhodium coating cannot easily be repaired except by stripping and re-plating.

The most hopeful line of attack in preventing the tarnishing of silver appears to lie in the addition of some metal or metals which will form an adherent and protective oxide skin on the surface which will renew itself if and when damaged. Such skins are termed "self-healing".

If a really untarnishable silver could be produced it would no doubt have a ready sale; the chief difficulty lies in the insistence of the public that the metal shall be hall-marked, that is, it must be certified as containing at least 92·5 per cent fine silver. This allows only 7·5 per cent as a maximum for alloying elements, and hitherto that has proved insufficient. Although several non-tarnishing alloys have from time to time been placed on the market, none has so far given satisfaction.

Silver has long been popular for "challenge" cups, shields and other trophies. Some years ago it was used more frequently than now for vases and "the table", silver teapots, cream-jugs and the like being highly esteemed as lending brightness to the meal.

During the early years of the nineteenth century there was an old tavern in Peck Lane, Birmingham, known as the Minerva and kept by one Joe Lyndon. At this tavern the "cups" or tankards were of solid silver and the property of regular patrons. None of inferior metal was permitted. Uniform in size and shape the name of the owner was legibly engraved across the bottom of the "cup" in such a way that when hung in front of a top shelf in the bar it could be distinctly read.

There were 37 such cups. In addition there was another silver cup that held three pints; it was known as the "Fine Slapper" because if anyone committed a breach of good manners he was liable to a fine of "a slapper of ale" that is, three pints*. He was thus little likely to attempt to cover up lack of intelligence by rudeness.

Chance visitors to the tavern, who had no "cups" had to put up with jugs of the plainest brown earthenware! Unfortunately the tavern was demolished when the site was required for the New Street Railway Station, and there are no slappers now for the modern boor.

*R. K. Dent, "Old and New Birmingham", 1880, p. 316.

Sheffield plate*

Much silver was at one time consumed in the "Sheffield plate" industry, the invention of Thomas Bolsover, a cutler of Sheffield in 1742. Whilst making a knife in which both silver and copper were used, Bolsover noticed that the two metals could be made to adhere very firmly by merely beating and rolling together. A silver plating or veneer could thus be worked on to a copper base. It took a little while for the idea to be adopted, but gradually small articles came to be made, including snuff boxes, buttons and the like. The plating proved so excellent, however, that gradually a big demand arose and increasingly larger articles were produced. The industry flourished for about a century but production declined when the commercial electrodeposition of silver was invented in 1840. The plating was applied not merely to copper, but to brass and other base metals.

When fully established the Sheffield plate industry was concerned mainly with the production of fairly large articles; these were frequently copies of genuine silver wares under the name of "holloware".

About 1750 John Taylor introduced the process into Birmingham where the material was used for making small articles, such as buttons, buckles and trinkets of all kinds that comprised the toy trade of the city, the latter being described by Edmund Burke (1730 to 1797) as "the toy-shop of Europe".

Electrodeposition of silver is widely adopted both for purely ornamental purposes and also for table ware. In 1825 Justus von Liebig, professor of chemistry at Giessen, observed that when acetaldehyde is warmed with a slightly ammoniacal solution of silver nitrate in a glass vessel, metallic silver is deposited on the walls of the vessel appearing as a brilliant mirror when viewed from outside. The process is most widely used in making household and other types of mirrors; it also finds application in the manufacture of Dewar and Thermos flasks, silvered electric light bulbs and small glittering objects such as adorn the Christmas tree at the festive season. The thickness of a film may vary from $1 \cdot 2 \times 10^{-6}$ inch (30×10^{-6} mm.) to six times that amount. The process has been extended to include deposits on plastic materials, cast phenolics and vinyl resin giving good results.

The method widely used for silvering the mirrors of astronomical reflecting telescopes and other optical parts is a modification

*See E. A. SMITH, *J. Inst. Metals*, 1930, **44**, 175.

of Liebig's process due to John Brashear* of Philadelphia. Its great advantage lies in the fact that it can be effected at temperatures little removed from atmospheric. In 1877 Brashear, wishing to observe the favourable opposition of Mars in that year, set himself to grind and polish the mirror for a 12-inch telescope. Being then a rolling-mill foreman, with little time to himself, it was several months before the delicate task was completed and the mirror had the desired excellence of figure. Then tragedy ensued. During the silvering process a current of cold air struck the mirror as it was lifted from the hot solution and the brittle glass snapped in two. Not to be daunted, Brashear, within two months, had ground and polished a 12-inch disc superior even to the first. Meanwhile he had experimented with silvering odd pieces of glass and had found the method now known by his name. Forty years later, we are told —

Brashear stood beside the 100-inch mirror at Mt. Wilson, with Professor George W. Ritchey, the man who had ground and figured it, and remarked at the brilliance of the silver coating on that magnificent glass.

Said Ritchey — "It ought to be a good coat — it's silvered by Brashear's process"†.

Considerable attention is now being given to vaporisation methods of producing silver films, the advantage being that a more rigid control is possible. One method consists in placing small pieces of silver on the loops of a tungsten or molybdenum coil filament suspended in a chamber containing the articles to be silvered. The whole is evacuated; on passing the electric current the temperature of the filament rapidly rises, the silver melts, but does not fall away because it "wets" the filament. The molten silver evaporates and the vapour condenses on the cooler objects round it. In this way beautiful deposits may be obtained not merely on glass but on certain plastic materials, metals and enamels. Cellophane and paper have also been silvered in this way.

Silver coins

One of the most important uses of silver has hitherto been for coins. Silver pennies were used by our Saxon ancestors. "Standard

---

*BRASHEAR, J., *English Mechanic*, 1893. Accounts of the process will also be found in most books on telescope making or optical workshop practice; e.g. TWYMAN, F., "Prism and Lens Making" (2nd edition, in the press, Hilger & Watts Ltd, London).

†PENDRAY, G. E., "Men, Mirrors and Stars" (1935, New York).

silver" was established for British currency during the reign of Henry II (1154 to 1189) who brought coiners from Eastern Germany, where the coinage was famous for its purity, to improve the quality of British currency which at that time was debased. It was ordained that standard silver should contain 92·5 of pure or "fine" silver with 7·5 of base metal, usually copper. It remained at this figure until 1920 except for a brief lapse of some 20 years during the sixteenth century, when debasement was permitted. The inhabitants of Eastern Germany were known as Easterlings and our word *sterling* as applied to currency appears to be derived from this. John Stow* writing in 1603 says "the Easterling pence took their name of the Easterlings, which did first make this money in England in the reign of Henry II."

It is customary to express the silver content of coins in parts per 1000. Thus, sterling silver was described as "925 fine" meaning that it contained 92·5 per cent of silver. Very similar alloys were in use in Saxon and Norman times; a coin of William the Conqueror (1066 to 1087) was found to assay 922·8 of silver — not very different from the alloy used by the Romans (p. 113). This standard silver has been and still is largely used for "silver plate", but another legal standard for silver wares was introduced in 1696 containing 958·3 per thousand; this is softer and less resistant to wear and tear; it is known as "Britannia silver" because it is stamped with the figure of a woman commonly called Britannia instead of the lion passant, used by Government offices in hall-marking silver.

In 1920 the market price of silver had risen to 8s. per oz. so that illegally melting it down offered considerable profit. The government therefore reduced the silver content to 50 but did not state what the other constituent(s) should be. At first an alloy of equal amounts of silver and copper was tried. It had been used in England before in 1544 but discarded as unsatisfactory. An analogous alloy had also been tried in Russia, but it discoloured on circulation. Our coins soon resembled gorgonzola cheese, so a new alloy was tried containing silver, 50; copper, 40; and nickel, 10. For this, cupro-nickel coverings of bullets were used, relieving the Disposals Board of much lumber. The new coins were bright but too hard to work; they damaged the dies and many were imperfectly struck. In 1927 an alloy containing silver, 50; copper, 40; nickel, 5; and zinc, 5 was decided upon. It proved very

---

*JOHN STOW, "A Survey of London", 1603, p. 52.

satisfactory; it was pickled prior to issue to give it a good appearance. The richer silver coins were gradually withdrawn from circulation. It took the banks some 18 years to collect the pre-war coins.

Wars have curious effects on the circulation of coins. Simple people often bury their money hoping to return and dig it up. During World War II the florin enjoyed unusual popularity, next to the cupro-nickel threepenny bit it was the baby of our monetary family.

When the first silver florin was issued in 1849, the familiar letters DG, standing for *Dei Gratia*, by the will of God, were omitted from Queen Victoria's titles. This caused an outcry and the issue, which became known as the Godless florin, was stopped. Since 1937 no five shilling pieces have been struck. Two distinct patterns of our English shilling have been struck since 1937; one bears the King's English crest on the "tail", the other his Scottish crest — a graceful tribute to his Scottish Queen.

In 1945 it was estimated that 2000 million silver coins were in circulation corresponding to some 1400 tons of silver; it was decided to replace them gradually by an alloy of nickel and copper. All silver coins struck before 1947 are being withdrawn, and the reclaimed silver is to be sent to the U.S.A. in part payment of silver sent to this country under Lend-Lease. The recoinage will take at least 20 years.

It has been suggested that in time of war we could save metal by calling in our pennies and replacing them by a smaller coin of the same or some other metal. But even if the Mint dropped all other duties it would take some 10 years full-time work to replace the pence, so that the proposed saving in metal would take a long time to mature, and would have little effect on the general position during a merely temporary shortage.

Silver is resistant towards organic acids, and large silver components, sometimes weighing 3 or 4 cwt, are used in acetic acid manufacturing plants. Silver vats are employed in the vinegar, brewing, cider and milk industries because of their resistance to attack. Chemical plant need not, however, be composed solely of silver. A plant of copper is frequently rendered resistant to corrosion by coating with silver either by electrodeposition or by lining after the fashion of Sheffield plate. Thin coatings obtained by the former process are liable to be porous, whilst thick ones may peel on service, leading to expensive repair. The lining process is therefore favoured, a thin silver sheet, some 0·03 inch in thickness, is sweated or hammered on to the copper thus yielding a non-porous coat.

Modern silver solders are copper-silver alloys to which small additions of phosphorus or zinc have been made. They function as de-oxidants. The melting points of these alloys are much below that of copper; the joint is strong and resistant to corrosion; so silver soldering is useful where welding would be difficult or inadvisable. Until recently the main use of silver solders was for jewellery and other fine work. Now, however, they are being used in engineering, partly because of the strength and neatness of the joint, as in refrigerators and aircraft.

Silver is so ductile that 1 gram of the pure metal can be drawn out into a wire more than a mile in length; its malleability enables it to be beaten into leaf 0·00025 inch in thickness. Both wire and foil are used for ornamental purposes.

Silver is used in the "quartation" of gold. Pharmacists coat pills with silver not merely to enhance their appearance but also to act as preservative, largely against moisture.

Owing to its excellent electric conductivity properties — it is the best known metallic conductor — silver is employed in many electrical instruments.

Silver conducts heat more readily than any other metal. It is often convenient to take its thermal conductivity as a standard, namely 100, and express all others relatively thereto. On this basis the conductivity of copper is 92, gold 70 whilst that of nickel silver is only about 8. It is thus easy to understand why silver teaspoons rapidly become hot when dipped into a cup of tea whereas the common or garden variety of spoon does not.

Gold

Gold has been prized from the earliest times partly because of its colour and lustre, but also because of its resistance to tarnish and general incorrodibility. Pliny* lays particular stress on this latter feature. "Those persons" he writes "are manifestly in error who think that it is the resemblance of its colour to the stars that is so prized in gold." He then proceeds to eulogise the resistance of gold towards fire and other disintegrating forces. "Gold is subject to no rust, no verdigris, no emanation whatever from it, either to alter its quality or to lessen its weight. In addition to this, gold steadily resists the corrosive action of salt and vinegar, things which obtain the mastery over all other substances." To this

*PLINY, "Natural History", translated by Bostock and Riley (Bohn, 1857) Book 33, chap. 19.

catalogue of virtues the modern chemist would add one more, namely that there is only one single acid that by itself can dissolve gold, namely selenic acid.

The element is believed to owe its name to its brilliant appearance, the word "gold" being derived from the Sanskrit *Jval*, to shine, a word cognate with "yellow". The Hebrew word for gold is *Zâhâv* also meaning to shine. The modern slang term for a golden sovereign, namely *shiner*, would appear to be quite appropriate.

Some gold mines of interest

The *Clogan mine* has a romantic history. It stands above the great expanse of Barmouth estuary, fronting the lonely precipices of Cader Idris, which rise some miles away across the estuary. It has been worked at intervals from very early times, possibly by the Romans, who had a camp and a settlement near.

Early last century copper was mined there on a considerable scale, and about 1845 the miners found a lode in which small lumps of peculiar yellow metal were imbedded. When it was tested this proved to be gold, but attempts to work the mine further for gold failed owing to the very patchy character of the deposits.

The old refuse of the copper mine, however, yielded rich treasure. Gold was recovered from it in considerable quantities, one ton of refuse alone yielding gold valued at £6000.

In 1919 another vein of gold was struck in this mine, but was soon exhausted. In 1930 the Secretary of Mines instituted an inquiry into the gold position in Wales generally with a view to possible development of gold production. But the results were not encouraging; experts held out no hope of anything more than mere sporadic finds. The wedding rings of several members of the Royal Family, including the Queen Mother and Princess Mary, have been made of Welsh gold. In October 1934 it was announced that the wedding ring of Princess Marina was to be made of gold from North Wales mines and from the Pumpsaint mine in Carmarthenshire; so presumably this was done.

Gold has been found also in Ireland; tradition ascribes its discovery in County Wicklow to a poor schoolmaster who found a small nugget whilst fishing in one of the streams descending from the Croghan Mts*. Further search revealed more and the cautious

---

*W. JONES, "The Treasures of the Earth" (Warne), p. 25.

pedagogue enriched himself gradually by disposing of the spoil to a goldsmith in Dublin. He preserved the secret for many years but marrying a young wife he imprudently made her his Delilah "and told her all his heart" (*Judg.* xvi. 17). She, of course, couldn't keep the secret, she must perforce tell her people, with the result that in 1795 the existence of gold became popular knowledge and thousands of adventurers of every age hurried to the spot in one mad search for the precious metal.

The gold was so pure that the Dublin goldsmiths were wont to put gold coin in the opposite scale to it when purchasing and thus give weight for weight. In a couple of months the Government stepped in and took control until 1798 when all the machinery was destroyed in an insurrection. The gold was found in nuggets of all sizes up to one extraordinary mass weighing 22 oz. irregular in shape, measuring 4 inches long, 3 inches in greatest width and nearly one inch in thickness. A gilt cast of it could, and probably can still, be seen in Trinity College, Dublin.

The first discovery of gold in California was the result of accident. In 1847 Captain Suter erected a saw-mill in a pine forest; the water to work it washed down mud and gravel from the upper reaches of the stream. This mud was found to contain glittering particles which proved to be of gold. Public attention was soon drawn to the neighbourhood, for so remarkable an observation could not long be kept secret, and San Francisco became a centre of attraction to gold-seekers from all parts of the world. For some years gold was won exclusively from alluvial washings but by 1852 quartz mining had become the order of the day, some of the quartz veins being of very considerable size.

Great as was the Californian output of gold, it was soon eclipsed by that from Australia. In 1851 news reached this country that gold had been found in quantity in N.S. Wales, near Bathurst. An educated aboriginal returning home from tending sheep stated that he had seen a large mass of glittering metal among some quartz; his employer, Dr Kerr of Wallowa, went to investigate and three blocks of quartz containing about 1 cwt. of gold were discovered. As soon as it was bruited abroad, the discovery caused the greatest excitement and persons of all trades and pursuits set off in quest of gold.

Gold was found about this time also in Victoria* where mining operations began in 1851 and in a few years this area was producing

*See *The Engineer*, 1890, **49**, 15.

far more of the precious metal than any other in Australia. There was a fruitful field at Sandhurst distant about 100 miles from Melbourne; the old name of the town was Bendigo and any Bendigonian who had lived there prior to 1855 was known as an "old identy". Early in 1851 Bendigo Creek and the surrounding areas were known only to shepherds, the gullies and flats being covered with green grass and box trees. But before the middle of the year all this was changed, for it had become noised abroad that here gold was to be had for the digging. Men began to arrive from all parts of Australia, and not from Australia only. A motley group, they came in twos and threes, and then in tens and twenties. Some were shepherds, others included those who had "done time", run-away naval men, men who sought the solitude of the bush to escape from the consequences, and possibly the memories also, of a seamy life; it was hardly safe to inquire into a man's antecedents. As the weeks rolled by, town-dwellers were drawn to the spot; clerks, labourers, bankers, publicans and tradesmen. They came on horseback, in spring carts, by coach, by bullock dray, whilst not a few trudged on shanks' pony. Many of these had not known till then what entire liberty meant; few if any knew the meaning of unlimited money; each man was a law unto himself; no one was without some means of protection from assault. The majority resembled mobile arsenals, carrying pistols and knives in their belts; some had tents, others lay at night under the vast vault of the heavens. Jack was as good as his master; perhaps better; each had a pair of hands and arms; education, knowledge, culture — these counted as nothing. By 1853 some 60,000 men had assembled on the field, with only about 100 women. Each digger was allowed 8 feet square of ground for which he had to pay the Government a rental of 30 shillings monthly. The miners would dig square holes in their plots and, after taking off the surface loam, at a depth of some 7 or 8 feet they came to the "wash dirt" which contained the gold; this dirt being the last few inches overlaying the bed rock. The lumps of gold were now picked out or "nuggeted" with a knife, like taking the plums out of a cake; the residue was taken to the creek where the soil was washed away, leaving a residue of gold. The reward of a morning's work for four men would often amount to some 20 lb. weight of gold; in that case the men felt they had earned an afternoon's rest and in the evening the metal was dried and cleaned.

So long as the gold lasted, life continued much the same. The gold was squandered; men would throw nuggets to their favourite actresses instead of bouquets of flowers. But the time came when this rich ground was becoming exhausted and the miners found the rent of 30s. oppressive. They approached the Commissioner and asked for a reduction. The Commissioner said he had no power to grant this but would forward their wishes to the Government at Melbourne and advised the miners who had collected into a body of 20,000, to go quietly back to their tents.

The Government panicked on hearsay, printed notices on calico announcing the reduction of the licence to 10s. and sent soldiers with them to tack them on to trees that all might read — and this, before the Commissioner's report had reached them! At first the miners were surprised; then they realised their power; union was strength; together they could defy the Government. One man named Brown, determined to make capital out of this. He organised a band of ruffians who levied blackmail on storekeepers and had a guardroom with sentries and a system of passwords. A warrant was issued for his arrest, but the police hesitated to put it into execution with the result that Brown became increasingly troublesome.

One night a young cadet, Brooke Smith by name, quietly left his officer quarters and, dressed in diggers' clothes, went off to interview "Captain" Brown at his HQ. Arriving there he inquired if the captain was in. Yes, he was, but could the visitor give the password? No, said the cadet, but as his business was of exceptional importance, would the captain see him. On being informed that a young digger was waiting outside with an important message, the unsuspecting captain came out and, lured by the cadet's air of simplicity, he walked with him to the centre of the main street; the cadet now drew close to him and pushing a revolver into his ribs said "Captain Brown, I am a Government officer and arrest you". Brown, of course, started and began to tell the cadet that by merely raising his hand he could call a thousand men to his assistance. But the cadet calmly told him that if he attempted anything of the sort he would be shot at once.

Discretion was the better part of valour and with the revolver at his ribs, Brown was marched off to the guardroom, where he was handcuffed, placed in a cart and galloped off to Melbourne with an escort on horseback. They went at such a rate over the rough ground that Brown was almost killed by the jolting, but they reached their destination safely and Brown was duly sentenced.

The ignominy of the capture made the whole thing so ridiculous that the captain's sentries disappeared and his gang was broken up for ever.

New gold areas continued to be found for many years in Australia but it was not until 1892 that William Ford and a chance acquaintance discovered gold in Coolgardie in Western Australia. Ford died in Sydney as recently as October 1932.

The discovery of gold in Australia is regarded by the credulous as having been predicted several centuries earlier by that somewhat nebulous person known as Mother Shipton. This curious "witch" is supposed to have been born at Knaresboro' about 1486 and to have died at what was then considered to be a very advanced age in 1561. It is claimed that she was buried at York. Remarkable predictions attributed to her were published in 1641 and again in 1873. One runs as follows —

> Gold shall be found, and found
> In a land that's not yet known.

The discovery of Australia certainly took place during the period in which she is supposed to have lived.

The exact date is unknown; the existence of Australia was not made generally known in Europe earlier than 1511 or later than 1542. We put it that way because both the Dutch and the Portuguese appear to have known of its existence some years earlier, keeping it secret for commercial reasons, just as the Phœnicians kept the secret of the Cassiterides or Tin Islands to themselves (p. 200). It is fair to say that Mother Shipton could never have heard of Australia, and certainly gold was not discovered there until many centuries later (1851). There are other lands, however, that might claim the same distinction; two of these are Tasmania and New Zealand, discovered by Tasman around 1642. Whilst so large a part of the world remained undiscovered, Mother Shipton's prediction stood a very good chance of verification. But what are we to make of the addendum to her prophecies —

> The world will then be near the end
> And Germany will have to bend.

Is this a kind of world destruction by the atomic or hydrogen bomb? One wonders.

Canada has yielded gold for many years, official records going back to 1858 in which year some 34,000 oz. were won. Of course gold was worked there many years before that, but on a small scale. The first outstanding event in Canadian gold-mining was the *Klondike rush* of 1897 which focused the attention of the world on this bleak and dreary region. In September 1896 it had been reported to the Canadian Government that rich discoveries of gold had been made on Bonanza Creek, a tributary of the Klondike, which flows into the Yukon. The news spread rapidly and miners travelled in sleds over the snow from many places in the area until by January 1897 some 2000 men had assembled with scanty supplies and little protection against the frosts which brought the thermometer down to some 50° below zero Fahrenheit, that is 82 degrees of frost*.

In July the first miners from Klondike reached San Francisco, accompanied by about £400,000 in gold. The excitement reached fever heat and thousands started for the Yukon without sufficient supplies. Great sufferings were endured; nevertheless miners continued to flock to Klondike. Throughout 1898 and succeeding years gold was worked feverishly, reaching its maximum of 870,750 oz. in 1901. Since then the output has fallen.

Although the Portuguese brought gold-dust from South Africa to Europe in 1445, it was not until the nineteenth century that serious attention was directed to gold winning in this area. The first South African gold-mining company was the *Limpopo*, floated in London in 1868. This was the year also during which diamonds were discovered on the banks of the Vaal and it was generally believed that these would prove a more lucrative investment than gold-mining, so the latter was continued in but a half-hearted manner. In 1873 the *Lydenburg* gold-field in the Transvaal was opened up, and by 1884 it had been discovered that the Banket Reef was auriferous. T. B. Robinson was greatly impressed by the appearance of the ore and purchased the Langlaate Farm for some £20,000. This he subsequently floated as a public company for close upon half a million sterling.

The City of Johannesburg was founded on one of these farms, and sterile, unsaleable property of 1886 now became a much coveted land of promise; poor men became immensely wealthy almost "over night". The story reads almost like a novel.

Gold has from time immemorial formed one of the principal exports from Tibet. The principal gold-fields are found in the Chang-Tang, or Northern Desert, and also in the territory east of

---

*T. K. Rose, *Nature*, 1897, **56**, 615.

Lhasa, between that city and the Chinese frontier. The Tibetan gold-miner, however, only collects gold-dust, believing that should he remove any nuggets the supply of gold-dust will cease, as the nuggets are supposed to be alive and to produce the dust by breeding (p. 19).

It is stated that some years ago the Tibetan Government sent one of their most promising young men to this country to be trained as a mining engineer and metallurgist, and on his return instructed him to search for gold.

In a short time he discovered gold in large quantity and proceeded to extract it. Numbers of nuggets were also found. Just as the work was getting into full swing the local lamas arrived on the scene and not only forbade further operations but directed that all gold already taken out should be put back. The young engineer appealed to the Tibetan Government to sanction his carrying on work as the find was of great value and would give very considerable revenue. The lamas retorted that unless their instructions were carried out to the letter ill-fortune would surely come to the country, and especially to the State religion.

In the face of this attitude of the priests the Government was powerless and, in consequence, one of the richest gold-fields in Tibet, and possibly in Asia, must lie undisturbed for an indefinite period.

Gold in Holy Writ

There are 267 references to gold in Holy Writ. The first occurs in *Genesis* ii. 11, where Havilah, a land washed by a branch of the river flowing out of Eden, is said to yield the metal.

The statement (verse 12) that "the gold of that land is good" seems to imply a power to discriminate between different grades of the native metal.

There are frequent references to rings and chains of gold. When Joseph had interpreted the dreams of Pharaoh, the latter in his gratitude "took off his ring from his hand and put it upon Joseph's hand, and arrayed him in vestures of fine linen and put a gold chain about his neck" (*Gen.* xli. 42). When, many years later, the Hebrews escaped from Egyptian domination under the leadership of Moses they "borrowed" jewels of gold (*Exod.* xii. 35) from their late oppressors. This "borrowing" must have been effected on a fairly extensive scale because, after the departure from Egypt, the ear-rings alone, worn by the Hebrew men and women, sufficed to enable Aaron to fashion a golden calf to be worshipped as an idol.

The worker in gold was an important member of the community; he is mentioned in *Nehemiah* iii. 8 by name, along with the apothecary and, indeed, given pride of place before him. Gold was worked in various ways; it was refined in furnaces (*Prov.* xvii. 3), cast (*Exod.* xxxii. 4) and beaten into plates — the goldbeater being referred to as the carpenter in the Authorised Version.

Many references to gold in the Old Testament suggest the presence of enormous quantities of the metal. Very possibly the amounts are exaggerated. The Hebrews led by Moses are stated to have taken jewellery from the Midianites to the extent of 16,750 shekels (*Num.* xxxi. 52) or roughly 0·25 ton. Gold was used lavishly in the construction of the Ark of the Covenant and its furniture (*Exod.* xxv). Moses was instructed to overlay the wood of the Ark with *pure* gold and put four rings of gold at the four corners thereof.

Centuries later, when the Hebrews were established in the Promised Land, King David accumulated enormous quantities of gold and silver, spoil from his defeated enemies, and consecrated them to the Lord (2 *Sam.* viii). His son, Solomon, used enormous quantities of gold in adorning his Temple, erected *circa* 967 to 957 B.C.

Josephus* states that in his day (37 to 100) the Temple had ten gates, nine of which "were on every side covered with gold and silver, as were the jambs of their doors and their lintels; but there was one gate . . . which was of *Corinthian brass* and greatly excelled those that were only covered over with silver and gold."

This Corinthian "brass" was an alloy of gold, silver and copper which, according to an old legend, was accidentally produced when Corinth was burnt at the time of its capture, 146 B.C. It was highly esteemed in Roman days and was often used by the wealthy for domestic utensils†.

Sacred vessels used in Solomon's Temple were of gold as they had been in the Ark before it; they comprised basins, spoons, candlesticks, lamps, snuffers and even flowers. It is not difficult to believe that the description is substantially true for the building was closely paralleled, more than two millenia later by the Sun Temple of the Peruvian Incas (p. 135).

---

* JOSEPHUS, "Wars of the Jews", translated by Whiston, Book 5, Chap. 5, §3.
† PLINY, *Opus cit.*, Book 34, Chap. 3.

Solomon was not less lavish in the use of gold in his own royal household; all his drinking vessels were of gold, it being specifically stated that "none were of silver" (2 *Chron.* ix. 20).

Gold was used in Biblical times, as now, in making crowns for royalty. When David fought the Ammonites, Joab besieged Rabbah and destroyed it "and David took the crown of their king from off his head and found it to weigh a talent of gold, and there were precious stones in it; and it was set upon David's head" (1 *Chron.* xx. 2).

It would appear from the above quotation that kings wore their crowns in battle, and we are reminded of our own king, Richard III who, at the Battle of Bosworth Field in 1485, realising that defeat was inevitable, rushed into the thick of the fight, with the crown on his head, and met a soldier's death.

The crown of the Ammonite king is stated above to have weighed a talent, that is about 106 lb. (p. 111) or nearly one cwt—a load that no king would voluntarily carry into battle on his head. Probably this is a mistranslation, the original Hebrew scribe intending to convey the meaning that the beautifully wrought and decorated crown was "valued at" one talent of gold. This would be reasonable.

The desire to possess gold has at all times led some men to crime. Biblical times were not exempt from the curse of cupidity any more than we are. On the fall of Jericho, about 1400 B.C. it was ordained that the gold and silver together with the vessels of "brass" and iron were to be deposited in the treasury of the Lord. One man, Achan, could not resist the temptation to steal and kept back a little of the spoil for himself and his family. As he later confessed to Joshua — "When I saw among the spoils a goodly Babylonish garment and 200 shekels of silver and a wedge (or tongue) of gold of 50 shekels' weight, then I coveted them and took them" (*Joshua* vi and vii).

During excavations at Gezer in Palestine, a tongue of gold was found measuring $10\frac{1}{8}$ inches long, $\frac{3}{8}$ inch thick, $1\frac{1}{8}$ inch broad at one end and $\frac{7}{8}$ inch at the other. It was rather narrower in the middle and slightly curved. It weighed 27·6 oz. approximately equivalent to 50 Babylonian heavy gold shekels*. If this is not a mere coincidence, it indicates that these tongues or ingots were made into definite sizes for trade purposes and could thus be used as currency for large amounts.

---

*MACALISTER "The Excavation of Gezer" (Murray, 1912) Volume II, p. 259.

K

Man's cupidity

The first use of gold was undoubtedly for ornaments, but it was an easy step to employ it for barter and hence in later years to utilise it for coinage. The desire to possess this precious metal has led to many marauding expeditions, the classical example being perpetuated in the Legend of the Golden Fleece*. The cupidity of man is also well illustrated by the familiar story of Midas, King of Phrygia, who prayed of Bacchus that everything he touched might be turned to gold.

> "Gold, gold, money untold!"
> Cried Midas to Bacchus, beseeching.
> Said the god "I'm afraid,
> By the prayer you have made,
> You are vastly too over-reaching."

Nevertheless the prayer was granted. But Midas soon had cause to repent his greed as the very food he attempted to eat was transformed into indigestible metal, so that starvation stared the multi-millionaire in the face. His touch was as inconvenient as that of Autolycus, the classical thief of whom Hesiod wrote that "whatever he touched became invisible".

In despair Midas was compelled to ask the god to take back his dangerous gift. He was ordered to bathe in the river Pactolus. As the Jordan washed away the leprous scales from Naaman so did the Pactolus wash the golden touch from Midas. Where the king trod as he entered the water the sands were turned to gold, in proof of which the sands of the river, even to this day, yield alluvial gold to him who works for it.

Another ancient story pointing to the same moral is Chaucer's well known "Pardoner's Tale".

On the other hand the pursuit of gold has been an important factor in building up modern civilisation, though the cynic may urge that that is nothing to boast about. The pursuit of gold has led adventurous spirits into unknown lands, and our geographical knowledge has been greatly increased; the sciences of geology, metallurgy and mining have likewise been richly endowed.

---

*An excellent interpretation of this legend is given by ROBERT GRAVES in "The Golden Fleece" (Cassell, 1944).

Gold in Egypt

Gold was known to the Egyptians in predynastic* times and the goldsmith's art had already reached a high state of proficiency before the First Dynasty, about 3500 B.C. Examples have been found of solid gold hieroglyphs neatly let into ebony strips forming part of articles of furniture†. Among later pictorial rock-carvings in Upper Egypt there occur illustrations of the processes used in extracting gold from rocks. The latter were broken with stone hammers, ground in querns, and the matrix washed away with flowing water, the gold by virtue of its high density being left behind. Inscriptions depicting this process occur on monuments as early as the Fourth Dynasty, that is some 3000 B.C.

The washing of alluvial deposits in the Sudan was a flourishing industry at the time of Amenemhat II, 2200 B.C.

Until quite recent times the Japanese were following the ancient practice of grinding gold ores in querns before washing. The fine mud thus obtained was washed on inclined tables on which sheets of cotton were spread. The particles of gold were caught on the rough surface of the cloth whilst the earthy material was carried away by the water‡.

There were no silver mines in ancient Egypt, and during the reign of the Shepherd Kings, *circa* 1780 to 1580 B.C., gold was less expensive than silver (p. 110).

The position was reversed, however, by the 18th Dynasty, 1580 B.C., silver being more plentiful and proportionately less precious. Large quantities of gold were taken as tribute and spoils of war from Palestine and neighbouring lands after conquests by warlike kings and carried back to Egypt. Amongst the spoil taken by Thothmes III, *circa* 1530 B.C., on capturing Megiddo, were two chariots plated with gold, together with gold and silver rings weighing 966 lb.§ His son, Amenhetep II, after one of his foraging expeditions, took back to Egypt some three-quarters of a ton of gold. Year after year expeditions of this kind were undertaken by various monarchs whilst Egypt was at the zenith of her power and

---

*GARLAND and BANNISTER, "Ancient Egyptian Metallurgy" (Griffin & Co., 1927), p. 6.

†"The Art of Egypt through the Ages", edited by SIR E. D. Ross (Studio Ltd, 1931).

‡GOWLAND, "Huxley Memorial Lecture for 1912". Royal Anthropological Institute of Gt. Britain and Ireland.

§BUDGE, "A History of Egypt" (Kegan Paul, 1902) Volume 4, p. 36.

the sum total of gold, silver and other precious booty must have been prodigious.

Special interest centres around the tomb of Tutankhamen*. This youthful sovereign ruled over Egypt for a bare six years, about 1360 to 1354 B.C.; his tomb in the Valley of the Kings was discovered in 1922 by Lord Carnarvon and Howard Carter. The mummy was enclosed in three coffins, the two outer ones of oak overlaid with sheet gold, the innermost being solid gold elaborately chased and embellished with superimposed cloisonné work. The King's death mask was of beaten gold and represented the king at the age of his death — about 18 years. Mention should also be made of a statuette of Tut representing him as the youthful warrior Horus, throwing a javelin. It was carved in hardwood and overlaid with thin sheet gold.

One of the great difficulties facing the amateur collector in Egypt is the number of skilfully executed forgeries which so closely resemble genuine relics that even the expert may be non-plussed. In this connection Wakeling† tells an excellent story which we must not spoil by too close inquiry. At the time that predynastic graves were discovered in Nubia, there was a rush on the part of museums from all over the world to acquire specimens. The bodies were found in the graves lying upon one side with their legs drawn up and one hand placed before the face. They had not been embalmed; that was unnecessary owing to the dryness of the climate; the skin had the appearance of light-coloured leather. Around the body were placed jars and rough vessels, perhaps those that had been used by the occupant of the grave when alive.

As the demand for graves increased, the prices rapidly rose and the Arabs vied with a Coptic dealer in finding and selling graves, which were then taken whole to the museums. In course of time demand exceeded supply and the Arabs were hard put to it to supply their customers. But, as usual, where money was concerned, their native adaptability rose to the occasion. With sublime unconcern they killed their Coptic rival Aboutig, and buried his body in the approved position; the body rapidly dried before decomposition had a chance to set in and poor old Aboutig soon resembled a genuine predynastic mummy. Later on when a special request came from an important museum that could afford to pay

---

*HOWARD CARTER, "The Tomb of Tutankhamen" (Cassell, 1927).
†WAKELING, "Forged Egyptian Antiquities" (Black, 1912), pp. 117–118

well for the grave, the Arabs "found" this one, duly replete with jars, and sold it for a good round sum.

The Arabs could not keep their mouths closed and soon were openly heard to boast in the village that they had sold old Aboutig for £450!

We owe to Egypt the first mining map in the world*. It represents a mining district in the time of Seti I or of his immediate successor Rameses II, some 1320 B.C., the actual site of which has not been determined. It is crudely drawn on a papyrus, now in the Turin Collection, and depicts two parallel valleys among gold-bearing mountains, with houses for storage and tracks for transport.

Of course the gold contained varying amounts of silver, but the early Egyptians were unaware of this. By the second century B.C. however, the chloride method of removing silver from gold appears to have been practised in Nubia, for Agatharchides mentions that salt and bran were added to the native gold before melting. The salt would convert the silver to chloride and thus effect its elimination as dross or scum. As late as 1872 Gowland found that the Japanese were using this self-same method.

Gold and the Romans

Vast quantities of gold were accumulated by the Romans who obtained it partly as spoil from their conquered foes and partly by working the mines in various countries within their empire. As an example of the former, Livy† records that in 200 B.C. Cornelius Lentulus, proconsul of Spain, on the occasion of his entry "in ovation"‡ into Rome, brought 2450 lb. of gold with 43,000 lb. of silver.

The mines of Spain were perhaps the most important sources of the precious metal, particularly those of Andalusia, probably the Tarshish of *Ezekiel* xxvii. 12, the Turdetania of Strabo and part of the Iberia of Diodorus. Strabo§ waxes eloquent on the mineral wealth of Turdetania and states that the gold mines were the property of the State whilst the silver mines were privately owned

---

*GOWLAND, *loc. cit.*, p. 255.

†LIVY (59 to 18 B.C.), "History of Rome", translated by Sage (Heinemann, 1935), Book 31, Chapter 20.

‡As merely a proconsul he was not entitled to enter "in triumph". The ovation was a less important honour.

§Strabo was born in Amasia, Pontus, 64 or 63 B.C. The quotation is from the translation by H. L. Jones of STRABO's "Geography" (Heinemann, 1917 +). Book 3, Chapter 2. §§ 8 to 10.

(p. 112). "Up to the present moment" he writes "neither gold nor silver has been found anywhere in the world in a natural state, either in such quantity or of such good quality."

Diodorus*, writing over the period 56 to 36 B.C. gives a lengthy account of mining in his "Bibliotheca Historica" and mentions the use of the "Egyptian screw, which was invented by Archimedes of Syracuse at the time of his visit to Egypt", about 220 B.C., for pumping out the subterranean waters from the mines. He speaks of the screw as a masterpiece of mechanical invention. Several of them have been found in modern times in Southern Spain. This kind of pump is still used by the fellahin of the Nile Delta in raising water from the Nile for irrigation. The modern engineer would not share the enthusiasm of Diodorus for the efficiency of these screws. Twenty of them, each worked by a slave, would be needed to raise water 100 ft.

The Romans were, and could afford to be, lavish in the use of gold for religious, ornamental and utility purposes. Pliny† quotes a current belief that the first massive statue of gold, solid throughout — known as a *holosphyrata*, *i.e.* solid hammerwork as opposed to cast and hollow within — was one erected in a temple to the goddess Anaïtis. This was stolen during the Parthian War. On one occasion Emperor Augustus was dining with a Roman veteran and during the course of conversation reference was made to this statue. Augustus then asked his host if he was aware that the soldier who had desecrated the statue by taking it away from the temple had been smitten with blindness, paralysis, and finally with an early death — a warning to those who anger divinities. The soldier laughed and replied that it was he himself who had committed the sacrilege and, *horribile dictu*, the golden plate, from which his august Majesty was even then partaking, was shaped from one of the legs of the goddess.

Gold being so abundant when Rome was at the height of her power, one can almost forgive the arrogance of Poppæa, wife of Nero, who had her favourite mules shod with it.

Pliny‡ was aware that native gold usually contains silver ranging from small amounts up to about 12 per cent. Electrum was an alloy

---

*Diodorus was born at Argyrium in Sicily. The quotation is from "Diodorus of Sicily" by OLDFATHER (Heinemann, 1933 +), Book 5, Chapters 36 to 38. RICKARD, *Journal of Roman Studies*, 1928, **18**, 129.

†PLINY, *Opus cit.*, Book 33, Chapters 24, 17 and 49.

‡PLINY, *Opus cit.*, Book 33, Chapter 23; Book 34, Chapter 48.

containing 20 per cent of silver, and Pliny records an old belief
that it possessed the power of detecting poisons for, in such case,
"semi circles, resembling the rainbow in appearance, will form
upon the surface of the goblet and emit a crackling noise, like that
of flame, thus giving a twofold indication of the presence of poison."
Pliny also states that base metal articles were sometimes gilded
by dipping into molten gold in the same way as copper was tinned.

The gold of the Incas

South America is rich in gold. When the Spaniards conquered the
Incas of Peru early in the sixteenth century they were amazed at the
lavish profusion of gold in the temples and royal palaces. The
Sun-Temple* of the ancient city of Cuzco was outstanding for its
magnificence and for the treasures contained therein. The walls of
the main hall were covered from top to bottom with gold; at the
eastern extremity was a representation of the sun with solid gold
rays encircled with a frame of costly gems, whilst along the side
walls were ranged the golden thrones on which sat the mummified
bodies of former kings. The Temple doors were overlaid with gold
or silver and a strip of gold as thick as a man's finger, twice as
broad as his hand and surmounted by a golden cornice encircled
the entire building. In one of the Temple Courts was the "Golden
Garden", with "golden sacred columns, golden figures of animals,
silver bushes and trees whose delicate branches trembled in the
breeze, heads of maize with silver leaves and stalks bearing golden
grain, bearded with the most delicate silver filaments; on the
branches golden birds; cockchafers and butterflies with wings of
sparkling gems seemed to fly in the air, whilst lizards, serpents,
snails and little mammals, all made in gold or silver with eyes of
precious stones, crept along the ground. Wonderful fantastic
flowers adorned the beds and amidst all this artificial magnificence
rose the natural beauty of real shrubs kept moist by the water
flowing in golden pipes to basins of the same precious metal."

Gold was esteemed for its beauty and incorrodibility alone; it
did not excite cupidity amongst the Incas who had no money and
knew nothing of finance.

In spite of the almost incredible amount of golden treasures,
scarcely any of the Inca works of art remain. The Spaniards

---

*HANSTEIN, "The World of the Incas", translated by Barwell (Allen and
Unwin Ltd, 1924) pp. 65 *et seq.*

melted down everything they could into ingots for convenience in transport to their wretched capital.

Gold and the alchemists

The attitude of the alchemists towards gold and the possibility of transmuting base metals into the more precious one have already been discussed. The symbol for gold was a circle, the hall-mark of mathematical perfection (p. 12).

Although the quest of the alchemists ended in disappointment, the mass of chemical and metallurgical data* they accumulated proved of great value in laying the foundations of the modern sciences of chemistry and metallurgy.

Uses of gold

One of the most important uses of gold and its alloys is for jewellery. The craftsman has endeavoured throughout the ages to retain the attractive colour of the pure metal in alloys containing large admixtures of other metals. It is usual to express the quantity of gold present, not as a percentage, as is usual in most other alloys, but in *carats*. Here again, the carat is not the unit of weight as applied to diamonds (p. 58). The gold carat is a fractional part of 24; thus 24 carat is pure or 100 per cent gold; 18 carat is $\frac{18}{24}$ths pure gold, equivalent to 75 per cent and so on. The recognised carats in Britain since 1932 are 22, 18, 14 and 9. Wedding rings by tradition were invariably 22 carat and thus contained 2200 ÷ 24 or 91·7 per cent of gold: 7 carat gold is used for cheap ornaments and is not hall-marked.

Gold is very ductile and can be fashioned into wire or threads which may be spun or woven like wool. Pliny† quotes the statement that "Tarquinius Priscus celebrated a triumph, clad in a tunic of gold; and I myself have seen Agrippina, the wife of the Emperor Claudius, on the occasion of a naval combat . . . attired in a military scarf made entirely of woven gold without any other material."

Being soft and malleable, gold tablets were long used inscribed with treaties, laws, orders, etc, for which permanency was required. Pliny refers to the same practice with lead plates in his day (p. 189) and Rameses II in 1333 B.C. used silver for the same purpose (p. 110). When Marco Polo, the Venetian (p. 55) was, in 1290, about to set out on an expedition at the request of Cublai Khan, he

---

*Will the student try to remember that *data* is plural; *datum* is the singular.
†PLINY, *Opus cit.*, Book 33, Chapter 19.

was given a golden tablet, duly inscribed and signed with the Khan's name, which served as a passport throughout the Khan's empire. It called on the governors of provinces and cities to afford Marco every facility in the course of his duties and to defray his expenses.

Gold coins

The commerce of the nations has been built up on what is called the "gold standard". Gold has been used in coinage in the Western World since about 700 B.C. The parting of gold and silver was then practised and ancient Greek coins containing some 99·7 to 99·8 per cent of gold have been unearthed.

The famous "golden penny", first struck in Britain in 1257 during the reign of Henry III, consisted of pure gold and weighed 44 grains. But although it was our first golden penny, it was not our first penny. Silver pennies were used by our Saxon ancestors; in the eighth century a pound of silver yielded 240 pennies, and this is perpetuated in our Troy weight measure, namely 20 penny-weights make one ounce, and 12 ounces one pound. Henry III's golden penny was valued at 12 such silver pennies.

But pure gold is a soft metal and for most purposes it is now hardened with small quantities of silver, copper or other suitable metal. British gold coinage contains 916·6 parts of gold and 83·4 parts of copper; this is 22 carat gold (p. 136). The copper not only hardens the metal, thus increasing its resistance to wear and tear, but also lowers the melting point from 1062·6° to 949° C. which is an advantage metallurgically. The molten metal contracts on solidifying and this is the reason why our coins must be struck, a more expensive process than casting.

Pliny* speaks of an alloy called *electrum* which could be produced by melting silver with gold; he was also aware of the presence of silver in native gold and that its amount varied with the locality. If the native metal contained 20 per cent of silver it was called electrum just the same as the synthetic alloy.

Homer, writing about 880 B.C. refers to *elektron*, and from the fact that this is mentioned in connection with gold ornaments it is possible that the word was used to denote some sort of shining alloy. The word was later used by the Greeks to denote either the alloy or amber. The modern alloy called *electron* contains no

---

*PLINY, *Opus cit.*, Book 33, Chapter 23.

gold, but about 95 per cent of magnesium, with some 4·5 of zinc and a little copper (p. 152).

The so-called *white gold* alloys were introduced to resemble platinum when that metal was prohibitive in price, and their use in jewellery has been very successful. The earliest white gold contained gold, nickel and zinc. Gold-palladium alloys are easier to work and with 20 per cent of the latter element are completely white, but the high price of palladium militates against their use except in the most expensive jewellery. Green, blue and purple alloys are also easily made by addition of cadmium, iron and aluminium respectively.

Gold leaf

The malleability of gold has been noted from the earliest times. In the Old Testament we read of beaten gold on many occasions, as for example 1 *Kings* x. 16; *Numbers* viii. 4, etc. The gold beaters' craft is one of the most ancient that survives to-day. Pliny* mentions that gold was beaten out into thin leaves and used for gilding. The modern method is the same as that used in bygone centuries, save that machinery in the form of highly polished steel rolls is employed to reduce the cast alloy — usually containing from 95 to 96 per cent of gold, the remainder being silver and copper — to sheet or ribbon about 0·001 inch in thickness. Subsequent reduction to 0·000,004 inch is effected entirely by hand.

At the beginning of this century there were some 1500 gold beaters in Britain, but to-day only about one tenth of this number is employed, a considerable proportion in Birmingham. The machined rolled metal is cut into inch squares each being placed between the leaves of a *cutch* of 200 sheets of vellum 4 inches square and beaten until the metal has spread out to the size of the cutch. The leaves are then removed, quartered and placed between the skins of a *shoder*, containing 800 coarse skins, $4\frac{1}{2}$ inches square. Beating is continued with a 12 lb. hammer until the gold leaves have spread out to the size of the shoder. Again they are quartered and placed in a *mould* of gold beater's skin, $5\frac{1}{4}$ inches square and hammered once more. This is the most highly skilled part of the operations† and when the leaves have spread sufficiently they are trimmed and put into thin paper books ready for sale.

---

*PLINY, *Opus cit.*, Book 33, Chapter 19.

†See DOWNS, *Chemistry and Industry*, 1942, **61**, 156.

Gold leaf is used by book-binders for gold lettering, book-edges, etc. Carvers, gilders, picture-frame makers and sign writers use it, and many other trades. The intrinsic value of the gold itself is small, for 1 oz. Troy can yield 250 sq. feet of leaf; taking gold at its present price of 248s. per oz., 1 sq. inch of 23 carat metal is worth only about $\frac{1}{12}$ penny.

A considerable quantity of gold is used in the electroplating industry, the article to be plated being made the cathode in a bath of potassium auro-cyanide. The deposit aimed at is usually of the order of 0·0005 inch, but depends partly on the nature of the base metal to be coated and the use to which it is to be put. Plated surfaces take a high polish and are not liable to tarnish.

Cathode sputtering or dispersion is a recent development in processes for covering surfaces with a film of gold. The object is placed in a chamber fitted with an aluminium anode and gold cathode. On evacuation and passage of a high voltaged current the cathode disperses covering the object with a thin film of gold, less than one-millionth of an inch in thickness.

A vaporisation process is sometimes used, the gold being electrically heated to its melting point in a high vacuum, the vapour condensing in a molecular film on any article placed within the chamber. Spectacles lenses are sometimes treated in this way for people suffering from *iritis*; they exclude ultra-violet light and allow rays of a greenish, restful colour to pass.

In making gilt wire, a bar of silver, alloyed with copper, approximately 2 inches in diameter is plated with gold and drawn down to wire in the usual way. It is then used for weaving into gold braid and embroideries such as one sees on uniforms, clerical and masonic vestments, etc.

Rolled gold is manufactured by soldering or welding a plate of gold or alloy on to a base metal or silver and rolling to the required thickness. The gold film produced is hard and impervious, so that it resists wear and tear more effectively than ordinary electroplated films. Rolled gold consequently finds application in watch cases, pencils, spectacle frames, cuff links and cheap forms of jewellery. Very thin coverings of gold, about 0·000,005 inch are used for toys and trinkets and of course quickly wear off. In better class rolled gold objects the gold film may reach a maximum of 0·01 inch in thickness.

Prior to the introduction of rolled gold, imitation jewellery was made chiefly of copper or brass gilded with pure gold; the soft gilt surface, however, soon wore off. Towards the close of the eighteenth century, at the time when the manufacture of "Sheffield plate" had reached its zenith, the rolled gold industry was born in Birmingham*. The two processes are virtually identical, save that in Sheffield plate a base metal is veneered with silver whereas in rolled gold, silver is replaced by gold (p. 116).

Gold used for pottery is practically pure; it is usually applied as "liquid gold" with a brush before firing. The liquid consists of some organic gold derivative in oil, with some suitable adhesive.

Gold is used in producing some types of ruby glass; originally the gold was used in the form of purple of Cassius, a mixture of colloidal gold and colloidal tin oxide. This was the method employed by Kunckel (1630-1703). Later it was found that gold chloride would do equally well. By transmitted light gold is green; in glass the ruby colour is not that of gold but it is the colour of the light scattered by the gold particles of colloidal size within the glass. A similar effect is produced by selenium (p. 73).

Gold is used for chemical plant and laboratory ware on account of its resistance to acids and alkalies. The only single acid that will attack gold is selenic acid, H_2SeO_4. In the laboratory, dishes and crucibles made of a high melting palladium-gold alloy, melting at 1370° C. have been used when the cost of platinum has been prohibitive. In chemical plant gold-lined base metals are sometimes used and for the distillation of essential oils a solid gold still and condenser have been used; the thermal efficiency is high and corrosion does not occur.

Alloys of gold and the platinum metals are used in the manufacture of artificial silk. The viscous liquid used to produce the silk is extruded through fine holes in a spinneret. As these holes may be only 0·003 inch in diameter they must be perfectly smooth, and gold-platinum metals alloys serve the purpose admirably.

Gold has long been used in dentistry both for fillings and dentures; the latter are now usually made by pressure casting of a hardened alloy containing some 30 to 40 per cent platinum. Vulcanite plates may be strengthened by gold gauze or perforated gold sheet. The employment of gold in dental operations dates back to very early times. In the Corneto museum on the coast of Italy there were, and probably still are, two specimens of artificial teeth found in Etruscan tombs probably dating from four or five

---

*E. A. SMITH, *J. Inst. Metals*, 1930, **44**, 175.

centuries B.C. The graves contained the bodies of two girls; on the jaw of one, two incisors were attached to their neighbours by small gold rings*. In the other grave the rings remained but the artificial teeth had fallen out. These latter had evidently been taken from the mouth of some large animal. Cicero (106 to 43 B.C.) quoted a law forbidding the incineration or burial of costly golden articles but allowing an exception in the case of "teeth fastened with gold"†.

Amongst the numerous miscellaneous uses of gold may be mentioned its application as target in X-ray work, as a rival of tungsten; in certain thermocouples, such as the pallador thermocouple, for measuring high temperatures; as heat fuses; for hair springs for chronometers; for electrical equipment for measuring the speeds of aircraft engines; in radium therapy for the containers of the disintegration products of radon.

The annual world output of gold is about 1000 tons, the value of which in pounds sterling is placed at approximately 260 millions. From 90 to 95 per cent of this is absorbed in bars of statutory 400 oz. Troy weight for monetary purposes, international trade and exchange. The world's stock in hand of gold is believed to be worth some 4000 to 5000 million pounds sterling.

---

*Nature, 1885, 31, 564.
†Ibid., 1885, 31, 578.

CHAPTER 10

THE ALKALI METALS

THE alkali metals include lithium, sodium, potassium, rubidium and caesium.

The name *alkali* is derived from the Arabic *al-qaliy*, calcined ashes, and refers to the carbonates of sodium and potassium which were obtained by lixiviation of plant ashes. *Natron*, an impure sodium carbonate, was known in Egypt in very early times. It has been found in vases in tombs dating back as early as the xviiith Dynasty; Lucas regards it as probable that natron was already used for embalming royalty in the ivth Dynasty. The Latin word used by Pliny was *natrum*, but the salt came to be called Egyptian *nitre*, perhaps by confusion with the Greek word *nitron*. A reference to this salt occurs in Holy Writ—"As vinegar upon nitre so is he that singeth songs to an heavy heart" (*Prov.* xxv. 20). This was a puzzling statement, for vinegar does not visibly affect European nitre, *i.e.*, saltpetre, and the point of the proverb was lost until Boyle obtained a sample of Egyptian nitre in 1680 and found by direct experiment that it readily effervesced with acids. The meaning of the proverb then became clear. The ancient Hebrews prepared an impure carbonate of potash under the name *borith* by passing water through vegetable ashes, probably from the salt-wort. This is referred to as *soap* in *Jer.* ii. 22, and *Malachi* iii. 2. It was not until the eighteenth century that sodium carbonate or soda became well known in Western Europe. It was then prepared from the ashes of marine plants. Potash or pearl ash was similarly obtained, namely by extraction with water from the white ashes of burnt wood, whence the word pot-ash. These two carbonates were termed "fixed alkali" to distinguish them from the volatile ammonium carbonate.

That a difference existed between soda and potash was only gradually realised. In 1702 Stahl distinguished between "natural" and "artificial" alkalis, evidently referring to soda and potash, noting that salts of the former sometimes possessed a different crystalline form from the corresponding salts of the latter. In 1736 Duhamel de Monceau observed further differences between "mineral" alkali, that is soda, and "vegetable" alkali or potash, whilst in 1758 Marggraf noted the variation in the flame colorations. It was known to Geber in the eighth century that *mild* alkali, that is soda, could be converted into *caustic* alkali by the action of slaked lime, and soap was prepared at an early period by the action of this caustic alkali on fat. The causticity was attributed to lime dissolved in the alkali, but in 1756 Black proved that mild alkalis contained "fixed air" that is, carbon dioxide and no lime, whereas the caustic alkalis contained neither fixed air nor lime. They were regarded as elements by many chemists until the beginning of the nineteenth century. Indeed they conformed to Lavoisier's definition of an element, in that they had never been split up into anything simpler. Other chemists, however, doubted their elementary nature and the time for proving it was rapidly drawing near.

In 1799 the Italian physicist Volta, Professor of Physics in Pavia, described a method of producing an electric current using what are known as the "voltaic pile" and "battery" (p. 102). The first battery to be used in England was in the possession of Nicholson and Carlisle who, the following year, effected the decomposition of water with its aid into its two constituent gases. They used platinum wires. In 1803 Berzelius and Hisinger made the further observation that aqueous salt solutions could be decomposed in a similar manner, the acid of the salt collecting round the electrode at which the oxygen was liberated and base round the other electrode.

In 1801 Davy, on the invitation of Count Rumford, went to London to take charge of the laboratory at the Royal Institution*. This Count Rumford†, one of the Founders of the Royal Institution, was an interesting personality. His original name was not Rumford but Thompson; American by birth, he spent most of his life in England and on the Continent. In 1791 he was made a Count of the Holy Roman Empire and chose the name Rumford. In 1796, puzzled by the large amount of heat evolved in boring cannon, he began experiments from which in 1798 he concluded that heat was a form of energy — the first scientist to suggest this.

---

*See JOHN DAVY, "Memoirs of the Life of Sir Humphry Davy" (London, 1836). This authoritative and detailed work is somewhat marred by John Davy's almost spiteful recurrent criticisms of the "Life of Davy" written in a delightful popular style by his friend Dr. Paris in 1831. Probably Paris gave a truer picture of the man, Humphry Davy, than did John who appears to have suffered from hero worship.

†GEORGE E. ELLIS, "Memoir of Sir Benjamin Thompson, Count Rumford, with Notices of his Daughter" (Boston, 1873).

Up to that time heat had been regarded as a fluid. In 1801 he married Mdme Lavoisier, widow of the famous scientist executed in 1794.

In 1802 Davy was promoted to the Professorship and in 1805 to the Directorate of the Royal Institution.

Davy was keenly interested in the new applications of electricity to chemical problems, and prepared a powerful battery for his own use. Experimenting with solutions of caustic potash he found that hydrogen and oxygen alone were liberated; so then he tried the effect of the current on solid caustic potash, rendered sufficiently moist by brief exposure to air to conduct the current. The experiment was an immediate success and raised Davy instantaneously to the pinnacle of fame. At the electrode where, in previous experiments, hydrogen had appeared, globules like mercury, possessed of high metallic lustre and great chemical reactivity were seen. Some of them ignited explosively and burned with a bright flame, others remained and soon tarnished. His laboratory book, dated 19th October 1807, bears the comment — "A capital experiment". This new metal Davy named *potassium*. Shortly after Davy had isolated the metal, Dr. George Pearson called at the Royal Institution. Seeing the lustrous metal he said "Why, it is metallic to be sure", and then, balancing it on his finger, remarked "Bless me, how heavy it is!"* How easily we are misled by our preconceptions! To Dr. Pearson all metals were necessarily heavy. Actually, the density of potassium is well below that of water, and less than one-third that of aluminium.

Flushed with his success, Davy repeated his experiment a few days later, this time using caustic soda, and was rewarded by the liberation of his second new metal *sodium*. He also obtained this element by decomposing sodium chloride with metallic potassium.

Dr. Paris, in his very charming life of Davy published in 1831, states that Napoleon was extremely angry that the honour of discovering the alkali metals should have fallen to the English, the nation that stood between him and the conquest of Europe and who, though he knew it not then, were destined to rob him of the victor's laurels and consign him to eat his heart out in solitude at St. Helena. He called the French scientists together and demanded of them why they had not forestalled Davy. For want of a better answer they replied that they did not possess an electric battery

---

*PARIS, "Life of Sir Humphry Davy", 1831, vol. 1, p. 268.

sufficiently powerful. Napoleon commanded them to have one made at once and when it arrived he called at the Academy to see it. Before any one could stop him he placed the terminals in his mouth to try the strength of the current. The shock on his tongue must have been terrific; he left the Academy without a word!

Of the two metals it is only sodium that is used to any extent in its metallic state. It is required in manufacturing sodium peroxide, cyanide and sodamide. An alloy with potassium is liquid at the ordinary temperature and is used in thermometry. Sodium is a useful reagent in organic chemistry as in the manufacture of synthetic rubber; it was at one time used in manufacturing metallic aluminium and magnesium by replacement in the chlorides; but these metals are now obtained electrolytically. An alloy with lead finds application in the manufacture of "ethyl", that is, lead tetraethyl, for anti-knock motor spirit. Its property of emitting electrons when exposed to light enables it to be used in photoelectric cells.

Lithium

The next element of the alkali group to be discovered was *lithium* in 1818, by Arfvedson* who was working under Berzelius in his famous laboratory at Stockholm. Arfvedson was examining the mineral petalite, then recently discovered by d'Andrada in the iron mine at Uto, Sweden, and so named from the Greek *petalon*, leaf, because of its cleavage. The mineral was thought to be sodium aluminium silicate, but analysis on this assumption exceeded 100 per cent. Examination of the alkali portion of the mineral showed that it was not sodium but a new element which it was decided to call lithium from the Greek *lithos*, stone, in recognition of its being discovered in the mineral kingdom whereas the two previous alkali metals occurred in the vegetable world. Petalite is now regarded as lithium aluminium disilicate, $LiAl(Si_2O_5)_2$. The characteristic red colour imparted to the flame by lithium salts was observed by C. G. Gmelin in 1818, but neither he nor Arfvedson succeeded in isolating the metal, although they tried both to reduce the oxide with iron and carbon, and to electrolyse its salts; their voltaic pile was evidently insufficiently powerful. Both Brandes and Davy in 1820, however, succeeded in decomposing lithia

---

*ARFVEDSON, *Schweigger's J.*, 1817, **22**, 93; *Ann. Chim. Phys.*, 1819, (2), **10**, 82.

L

electrolytically, but only in small amount. It was Bunsen* and Matthiessen who, in 1855, obtained metallic lithium by electrolysis of the fused chloride in sufficient amount to enable them to make a careful study of its properties.

Lithium is used to a limited extent in industry in various alloys. It increases the tensile strength and resistance of magnesium alloys to corrosion; a calcium-lithium alloy is used in purifying copper for high conductivity work. Addition of about 0·1 per cent of lithium to aluminium-zinc alloys enhances their tensile strength.

Rubidium and caesium

The story of the discovery of rubidium and caesium introduces the spectroscope as an important adjunct to the chemist's equipment. In 1852 Bunsen succeeded Leopold Gmelin in the chair of chemistry at Heidelberg. He felt that chemists ought to collaborate as fully as possible with physicists, and when the chair of physics fell vacant in 1854 he strongly advocated the appointment of Kirchhoff who had been his colleague at Breslau. The two men then collaborated. Kirchhoff showed Bunsen that it was more efficient to examine the flames coloured with various salts through a prism than merely through coloured glass, and the two designed the Bunsen-Kirchhoff spectroscope, which proved invaluable both for chemical analysis and for the discovery of new elements. In 1859 Kirchhoff found the cause of the dark lines in the solar spectrum, first measured by the Munich optician Fraunhofer and now known as the Fraunhofer lines. As a result of extensive researches on the emission spectra of different elements, Bunsen and Kirchhoff in 1860 established the following fundamental principles —

(1) Every element when sufficiently excited in the gaseous state yields its own characteristic spectrum.

(2) The vapour of an element can be inferred with certainty when its spectral lines are present.

These conclusions were of unusual importance. To begin with they made it possible for the first time, apart from the examination of meteorites, to determine the chemical composition of celestial bodies such as the sun. We have already seen (p. 42) that in 1868 the presence of helium was detected in that luminary and since then some 40 more of our terrestrial elements have been detected there also.

Another direction in which these optical principles have proved

---

*BUNSEN, *Annalen*, 1855, **94**, 107.

valuable has been in detecting the presence of traces of substances in various materials. The eye is extraordinarily sensitive to light. If an ordinary pea is allowed to fall through an inch under the influence of gravity it yields a certain amount of potential energy, extremely minute, but none the less definite. If that minute amount of energy were converted into light, the average human eye could just detect it.

For many years the spectroscope afforded the only general method of detecting minute traces of elements and as it led to such far-reaching results much attention has since been paid to the detecting of traces by this and by other means, so that micro-chemistry has now become an extremely important branch of chemical science.

In 1860 Bunsen and Kirchhoff* announced the spectroscopic discovery of a new alkali metal in the mineral waters of Dürkheim. The waters had been concentrated and the spectrum examined with the result that two very characteristic new blue lines were observed, close together, indicating the presence of a new element. It was proposed to call the new metal *caesium* from the Latin *caesius*, sky blue. Some 50 grams of the hexachlorplatinate, Cs_2PtCl_6, were ultimately obtained by evaporation of 40 tons of the waters, more than a kilogram of lithium carbonate being obtained as by-product. A few months later, namely early in 1861, Bunsen and Kirchhoff announced the discovery of a second element, this time in lepidolite, which yielded, in addition to others, two magnificent dark red lines in its spectrum. The name *rubidium* was suggested, from the latin *rubidus*, dark red. Lepidolite or lithium mica, so called because of its bright scaly appearance (Greek *lepidos* scale, *lithos* stone) is essentially a fluo-silicate of lithium and aluminium.

Caesium is not only of interest as being the first metal to be discovered spectroscopically. As early as 1846 Plattner had examined polluxite, then believed to be merely potassium aluminium silicate, but the analysis, on this assumption, did not work out at 100 per cent. Some alkali appeared to be missing. After the discovery of caesium, Pisani†, in 1864, re-examined the mineral and showed it to contain this new element, and not potassium, whose salts its own so closely resemble. The higher atomic weight

---

*BUNSEN and KIRCHHOFF, *Pogg. Annalen*, 1861, **113**, 342; 1863, **119**, 1. *Annalen*, 1862, **122**, 347; 1863, **125**, 367.
†PISANI, *Compt. rend.*, 1864, **58**, 714. *Annalen*, 1864, **132**, 31.

of the caesium explained the missing percentage of alkali. Polluxite, usually given the formula $Cs_2O.Al_2O_3.5SiO_2.H_2O$, but more probably represented by $2Cs_2O.2Al_2O_3.9SiO_2.H_2O$, is the main source of caesium compounds to-day; clear, colourless crystals of polluxite from Oxford County, Maine, U.S.A. have been used as gem stones. Caesium beryl, $3BeO.Al_2O_3.6SiO_2$, contains up to 4.56 per cent of caesium, calculated as Cs_2O. It is usually pink and is known as *morganite* after James Pierpont Morgan.

Bunsen succeeded in isolating rubidium in 1863 by electrolysis of the fused chloride, but nearly twenty years elapsed before caesium was first isolated by Setterberg in 1882 by electrolysis of the cyanide in the presence of barium cyanide.

Rubidium has been, and caesium now is, used in photo-electric cells and thermionic valves.

Numerous attempts have been made to find *Eka*-caesium, the element of atomic number 87, that would normally occupy the position in the periodic table between radon and radium. In 1931 Papish, of Cornell University, claimed to have detected it in samarskite, a complex niobo-tantalate named after the Russian von Samarski; but the evidence is not substantiated. The name suggested was *virginium*. In 1933 Remy-Gennetè suggested that the helium content of certain minerals may have originated from the decomposition of *eka*-caesium, which has now almost if not entirely disappeared. In 1936 Professor Horia Hulubei, in Paris, believed he had detected the X-ray "L" spectrum of No. 87 in alkali metals obtained from polluxite and suggested the name *moldavium**. Element 87 was discovered in 1939 by Mlle Percy in Paris as a branch product of the actinium series and the name *francium* or *franconium* suggested.

---

*Hulubei, *Compt. rend.*, 1936, **202**, 1927; 1937, **205**, 854.

CHAPTER 11

MAGNESIUM AND THE ALKALINE EARTH METALS

THE group to be considered in this chapter includes magnesium, calcium, strontium and barium. Radium is discussed later (p. 313).

The modern conception of an earth is little different from that given by Nicholson in 1796 in his "First Principles of Chemistry". We now know their chemical compositions however. Briefly defined, they are refractory metallic oxides, incombustible, infusible, insoluble in water, and destitute of metallic splendour — to use Nicholson's words. They may be conveniently divided into four groups, namely —

(1)   Alkaline earths, such as lime and baryta.
(2)   Acid earths, including silica and tantala.
(3)   Rare earths, such as ceria and yttria.
(4)   Earths proper, e.g., ferric oxide and alumina.

We may now consider the first of these groups.

Owing to their prevalence among surface rocks, chalk, limestone, dolomite, magnesite, and other compounds of magnesium and the alkaline earths have been known to and used by man from very early times. But, of course, they were not distinguished the one from the other. The Romans referred to lime under the name of *calx* and both Dioscorides (*circa* A.D. 50) and Pliny (23 to 79) described lime-burning, which was probably even then an ancient process. Early mortars were made with equal quantities of sand and lime, but modern ones contain 2 of sand to 1 of lime as experiment shows this to give better results.

Mention has already been made (p. 76) of the fact that in 1602 a Bolognese shoemaker, Casciorolus, observed that "heavy spar", our barytes, became luminescent after ignition with a combustible substance and from that time *Bolognian phosphorus* became famous. Cronstedt called the mineral *marmor metallicum* and in 1750 Marggraf found it to contain sulphuric acid, but mistook the base for lime.

In 1774 Scheele gave a detailed account of his researches on pyrolusite, then known variously as manganese or magnesia. This mineral frequently contains barium compounds, and Scheele mentioned that in addition to lime it contained "a new species of earth which, so far as I know, is as yet unknown."

This earth was shown by Gahn the following year to be the same as that present in heavy spar, or barium sulphate, and in 1779 Scheele showed that the earth in heavy spar was quite distinct from lime.

Guyton de Morveau, who with Lavoisier, Fourcroy, and Berthollet, devised a more appropriate system of chemical nomenclature than then existed, suggested *barote* as a suitable name for this earth; Lavoisier preferred *baryta* (Greek *barus* heavy) and Kirwan, the Irish chemist, called it *barytes* — a name that has been retained for the mineral.

In 1782 Withering, the famous Birmingham doctor who introduced the foxglove into medicine, discovered barium carbonate in the Leadhills, Scotland. This was called *terra ponderosa aerata*, but later the cumbersome appellation was altered to *Witherite*.

Shortly after this a mineral found in lead mines at Strontian in Argyll was mistaken for witherite. In 1790 Crawford suggested that it contained a new earth which he called *strontia*. His views were confirmed by numerous other investigators. The mineral was named *strontianite*; it is the carbonate, $SrCO_3$. The sulphate was first found by Clayfield near Bristol, where it is still incorrectly called "strontia" in the trade. The beautiful blue colour of some specimens led to the name *celestine*; it is probably caused by traces of colloidal gold.

The medicinal value of Epsom spring water was discovered in the reign of Queen Elizabeth (1558 to 1603). According to local tradition it happened this wise. One very dry summer a farmer dug round a spring to make a pond for his cattle. But although dying of thirst the poor beasts would not touch the water. He marvelled at this, tasted the water, and marvelled no more. It was "bitter", but one thing it did do: it kept the flies off. The relaxing action of the water was soon noticed and by 1640 Epsom Spa had become famous; in 1695 Nehemiah Grew, a London physician, wrote an account of the medicinal salt from the spring. In 1700 George and Francis Moult established a factory for obtaining the salt from a spring at Shooters Hill near London. In England the salt was called *Epsom Salt*, but on the Continent it was referred to as *Sal Anglicum*. In such high esteem were the Epsom Salts held that at St. Bartholomew's Hospital alone, in the early years of the 19th century, no fewer than $2\frac{1}{2}$ tons were consumed annually. No wonder the springs became exhausted and Epsom lost its early prosperity as a spa.

About this time a white powder was sold in Rome as a medicine, and its source was kept secret — a procedure not unknown even in recent times with patent medicines. It was a basic carbonate of magnesium and was called *magnesia alba* in contrast with black oxide of manganese, which was often called simply magnesia or *magnesia nigra*. It was Black, who, in 1755, first distinguished between chalk, lime, and slaked lime and between these and magnesia. He pointed out that the latter gave a soluble salt with oil of vitriol, whereas lime gave an insoluble compound.

Although up to the close of the eighteenth century lime was generally regarded as an element, Lavoisier thought otherwise. He argued that if certain metals had a greater affinity for oxygen than carbon had, it might not be possible with the means then available to reduce their oxides. Hence many substances classed generally as earths might merely be refractory oxides. Davy was of a like opinion and his view was supported when he succeeded in isolating metallic sodium and potassium from their hydroxides. In November 1807, only a few days after his successful decomposition of the alkalis, Davy was taken seriously ill. His medical adviser, Dr. Babington, attributed it to overwork and excitement. It was not until March the following year (1808) that he was able to continue his researches. He then attempted to decompose the alkaline earths electrolytically. His efforts, however, were unavailing until he received a communication from Berzelius to the effect that Pontin and himself had succeeded in preparing amalgams of calcium and of barium by electrolysing an intimate mixture of mercury and lime (or baryta). Davy now tried again; he mixed moist lime with one-third of its weight of mercuric oxide and laid it on a platinum plate which was made anode. A small cavity in the centre of the mixture was filled with mercury and rendered cathodic with a platinum wire. Sufficient amalgam was obtained to enable Davy to distil off the mercury and obtain a little (impure) *calcium**. In a similar manner he obtained *barium*, *strontium*, and *magnesium*. The last-named metal he named *magnium*, lest it should be confused with manganese because, as mentioned above, pyrolusite was known

---

*Davy, *Phil. Trans.*, 1808, **98**, 341. Also "Alembic Club Reprint", No. 6, 1894. Berzelius and Pontin, *Gilbert's Annalen*, 1810, **36**, 255. Friend, *Nature*, 1950, **166**, 615.

variously as manganese, magnesia, and black magnesia; but the name magnesium has, by common consent, been retained. Magnesia was the name of a peninsular in East Thessaly where magnetic iron ore was found (p. 256), and the names of both manganese and magnesium appear to have been derived from this source.

Although barytes is dense the metal barium on isolation was found to be by no means dense (D = 3·78) and E. D. Clarke*, Professor of Mineralogy at Cambridge from 1808 to 1822, suggested that the name barium was in consequence a misnomer. He claimed to have obtained the metal by heating the monoxide to a high temperature in the oxyhydrogen flame and suggested that *plutonium* would be a more appropriate name. In Thomas Thomson's "System of Chemistry†" the metal is referred to by this name (p. 326).

Davy's specimens of the metals were both small in amount and impure. Magnesium was first prepared in coherent form by Bussy‡ in 1829. He ignited a mixture of magnesium chloride and metallic potassium. Upon extracting the potassium chloride with water, shining globules of magnesium were left.

Of the various metals of this group, magnesium is by far the most important in industry.

Magnesium is usually manufactured by electrolysis of the double chloride $KCl.MgCl_2$. It is used in pyrotechny, Bengal and flash lights. The metallurgist finds it useful in preparing brass free from blow-holes and in improving nickel castings. It was used during the war very extensively in making incendiary bombs which contained some 93 of Mg and 7 of Al. As ribbon and wire it is used in the degasification of radio valves; as rods, bars or plates to replace zinc in batteries as it gives a higher E.M.F. Magnesium enters in small or large amounts into several important alloys such as duralumin, magnalium, and electron, the last named consisting of approximately copper 0·5, zinc 4·5, and magnesium 95 per cent. The high per cent magnesium alloys are valuable when lightness combined with strength is required as in aircraft and automobile industries. Sheet and tubing are utilised in aeroplane fuselages,

---

*WEBB, *Nature*, 1947, **160**, 164. Reference is made to REV. W. OTTER, "Life and Remains of Edward Daniel Clarke" (London, 1825).

†THOMAS THOMSON, "System of Chemistry" (London, 1817) 5th Edition, Vol. 1, p. 342.

‡BUSSY, *J. Pharm. Chim.*, 1829, **15**, 30.

cabins and steering parts, electric fans and in some musical instruments.

The main use of metallic calcium is as a de-oxidiser in steel manufacture; as a hardening agent for lead when it rivals antimony or tellurium in quantities of less than 1 per cent; with lead it yields bearing metals when present in quantities exceeding 1 per cent; the *Bahn-metall* used by German railways contained calcium, sodium and lead. An alloy known as *ulco* comprised lead with less than 1 per cent of calcium and barium; it is harder than ordinary commercial lead alloys, expands on solidification and gives castings free from blow-holes. It has been used in shrapnel bullets. Calcium has also been used in the production of high vacuum, the separation of argon from nitrogen, as a reducing agent, and also for desiccation purposes in the laboratory.

Metallic strontium has no industrial application. Metallic barium finds a limited use in several alloys; e.g., with lead and calcium in bearing alloys; with aluminium, magnesium or nickel for radio-valves.

Although *radium* belongs chemically to this group of elements it is convenient to discuss it later in a section dealing with the *radio-elements* (p. 313).

CHAPTER 12

THE ZINC GROUP

THE zinc group comprises beryllium, zinc and cadmium.

Beryllium

The emerald has been prized from very early times and Cleopatra's Emerald Mines in Upper Egypt were worked in 1650 B.C. — many centuries before that famous queen saw the light. Stones with a bluish-green cast are known as aquamarines and H.M. Queen Elizabeth is said to have a collection of these, her favourite stones. The aquamarine is regarded as a lucky stone.

The famous French crystallographer, René Just Haüy, enunciator in 1784 of the Law of Rational Intercepts, believed that substances of identical crystal form must have the same chemical composition as well as the same constitution. This we now know to be absolutely true. This rule must not be confused with Mitscherlich's Law of Isomorphism which, of course, is not rigidly true — only approximately so.

Now Haüy observed that the beryl and the emerald were geometrically identical and he asked Vauquelin to compare their analyses. The beryl had hitherto been regarded as calcium aluminium silicate, but Vauquelin showed that not only were the beryl and emerald identical chemically but that they contained a new element, the oxide of which he called *terre du Béril*. This result was published in 1798 and the new earth was called *la glucine* at the suggestion of the editor of the *Annales de Chimie et de Physique* because Vauquelin stated that its salts were at first sweet to the taste. The Germans, however, adopted the term *Beryllerde* and the names glucinum and beryllium were subsequently adopted to denote the metal itself. In 1924 the Chemical Society decided to adopt the name beryllium instead of glucinum — a very sensible decision, though perhaps somewhat long overdue.

The metal itself was not isolated for many years. In 1828 Bussy* and Wöhler† independently obtained it by reduction of the

---

*BUSSY, *Dingler's Poly. J.*, 1828, **29**, 466.
†WÖHLER, *Ann. Chim. Phys.*, 1828, (2), **39**, 77.

chloride with metallic potassium. It is now usually prepared by electrolysis of the double fluoride, K_2BeF_4.

Owing to the resemblance of its compounds to those of aluminium it was at first thought that beryllium would be trivalent. This received support from specific heat determinations and the application of Dulong and Petit's rule. The combining weight of beryllium was found to be 4·7, and Berzelius regarded it as trivalent, so that its atomic weight was roughly 14. Its specific heat between 0° and 100° C. was 0·42 giving an atomic weight of approximately 6·4 ÷ 0·42 or 15·2. This supported Berzelius.

Mendeléeff had no room in his Periodic Table for an element with this atomic weight; he had, however, a vacancy for one of 9 and in his table dated 1869 (p. 170) he placed beryllium between lithium and boron, ascribing to it a valency of two. Confirmation was afforded when in 1884 Nilson and Pettersson* determined the vapour density of its chloride, showing its formula to be $BeCl_2$, and again when in 1887 Mallard† observed that crystallised beryllia is isomorphous with crystallised zinc oxide, ZnO, and must therefore have a similar structure, namely BeO.

Beryllium is too expensive to be widely used as a metal by itself or as the main constituent of alloys. It is claimed that 2·5 per cent of beryllium added to copper is useful for springs, giving a sixfold tensile strength and higher fatigue endurance limit especially under conditions of corrosion. One per cent added to silver is said to make it resistant to tarnish. The alloy is heated in hydrogen to 400° with a little water vapour whereby a thin protective film of oxide is produced.

Pure beryllium is now being used in the construction of the metal "windows" of X-ray tubes as it is more transparent to the rays than aluminium.

Zinc

Metallic zinc was not known to the ancients. The "brass" of the Old Testament was not usually our alloy of copper and zinc, but bronze, that is an alloy of copper and tin, although apparently brass was occasionally made by accident when copper ores containing zinc were reduced (p. 99). Certainly metallic zinc was not known,

---

*NILSON and PETTERSSON, *Compt. rend.*, 1884, **98**, 588; *Ann. Chim. Phys.*, 1886, (6), **9**, 554. COMBES (*Compt. rend.*, 1894, **119**, 1222) proved in a similar manner that Be is divalent in its acetylacetonate, $Be(C_5H_7O_2)_2$.

†MALLARD, *Zeitsch. Krysl. Min.*, 1888, **14**, 605; 1888, **15**, 650.

either, to the Egyptians as they had no word for it. Brass was well known to the Romans, but they made it by reducing calamine, or natural zinc carbonate, with charcoal in the presence of copper; brass was thus produced without the isolation of the zinc.

The Indians appear to have been the first to obtain the metal. In the *Rasarnava Tantra**, written about A.D.1200, a flood of light is thrown on the scientific knowledge of the Hindoos of the twelfth century. The tantra takes the form of a dialogue between the God Siva and his consort. We are told that "calamine mixed with wool, lac, ... and borax, and heated in a covered crucible yields an essence of the appearance of tin." Obviously this "essence" was zinc, although the Indian alchemists did not at first recognise it as a separate metal. But in the medical Lexicon ascribed to King Madanapala, written probably in 1374, zinc is clearly regarded as an individual metal under the name of *Jasada*. It would thus appear that the smelting of zinc was first carried out in India. From thence the art may have been carried to China or it may have been independently developed there. The Chinese were certainly acquainted with the metal in the sixteenth century; slabs of zinc of 98 per cent purity have been found in the Kuang Tung Province, dating back to 1588. A primitive method of extracting the metal from its ore is described in the Chinese book *Tien kong kai wu* of 1637.

The term *zinkum* was apparently first used by the arch-alchemist Paracelsus (1493 to 1541) and was applied, for long after, to both ore and metal. The word *spelter*, applied to commercial zinc, is regarded as allied to German *Spiauter* or *Spialter* pewter, and dates from the time of Boyle.

In 1546 Agricola (p. 50) mentioned a white metal *counterfei* found on the walls of furnaces smelting lead ore at Goslar in the Harz. This may have been zinc.

During the seventeenth century the nature of zinc was misunderstood; it was frequently confused with bismuth. In 1695 Homberg identified it as the metal in blende and about 1700 Johann Kunckel von Löwenstein recognised that calamine contains a metal that alloys with copper in the manufacture of brass. It may be recalled that both Homberg and Kunckel played an important rôle in the discovery of phosphorus (p. 76). Percy states that Henckel was the first person in Europe to make metallic zinc from

---

*P. C. RAY, "A History of Hindu Chemistry" (Williams and Norgate), 1902, Volume 1, pp. 39, 86.

calamine direct in 1721. In 1738 William Champion patented a method of obtaining the metal, likewise from calamine, and in 1743 erected a zinc factory at Bristol. The first Continental zinc works were established at Liége in 1807. The production of zinc in this country in the middle of the eighteenth century was small, the metal being imported from China and India as required. In 1731 it cost some £260 per ton. By 1820 the production had increased so much that the export of zinc from England about equalled the total imports, so that the country was in effect self-supporting as regards the metal.

Metallic zinc in one form or another finds a very wide application in commerce. Zinc dust, under the name of *zinc fume* or *blue powder* — which is really a mixture of zinc and its oxide — is used as a reducing agent, for example, in dye manufacture. Zinc shavings are precipitants for gold and silver. Zinc is sometimes used in coinage as sharp impressions are obtainable. In 1920, after World War I, Belgium was using zinc coins. They were very unpleasant to handle and left one's pockets in a messy state. In France zinc is used for statuettes, etc, these being usually coloured or bronzed afterwards. Some of the statuettes contain about 17 per cent copper as the alloy yields a sharp impression on casting. Important alloys such as brass, delta metal, nickel silver (p. 297) and our silver coinage (p. 117), have already been referred to or are dealt with later. Motor-car handles are made of an alloy containing 94 to 95 zinc, 4 Al, 1 to 2 Cu and 0·25 to 0·5 Mg.

An enormous amount of zinc is used in wet galvanising, a process that was patented by Crawfurd in 1837. It is still a more or less rule-of-thumb procedure and although only one quality of galvanised iron is recognised the amount of zinc actually present on the steel varies greatly. As a rule the resistance is roughly proportional to the amount of zinc present. In 1935 R. H. Vallance and the writer analysed several galvanised articles and were surprised at the variation in zinc content. A few of the results are as follow —

Sheet iron (i)	..	..	..	0·54 oz. per sq. ft.
„ (ii)	..	..	..	0·72 „ „
Soap rack	..	..	..	1·23 „ „
Bucket ..	..	..	..	1·36 „ „
Handbowl	..	..	..	1·94 „ „

The thickest Admiralty Specification is 1·25 oz.

Sherardising, a process which was introduced by Cowper Coles in 1900, and since 1923 firmly established as a trade in this country, as well as the direct spraying of zinc, afford further uses for the metal. Minor uses are in making the so-called zinc-copper couples, in granulated form in various chemical experiments in laboratories, as anodes in cells such as Lechanché and dry cells used extensively for bells in domestic service. Zinc "plating" of the inside of the nose was prescribed at one of the London Hospitals in 1937 as part of "defence measures" for hay fever victims.

Cadmium

The discovery of cadmium solved a puzzling pharmaceutical problem. Friedrich Stromeyer*, professor of medicine at Göttingen was also the Inspector General of the Hanoverian pharmacists. In 1817 he noticed that zinc carbonate was being used in a certain area instead of the prescribed zinc oxide in compounding a certain preparation. Upon inquiry he was informed that, on ignition to oxide, the zinc carbonate developed an orange-yellow colour, though apparently free from iron and lead. As this rendered it unsuitable for the purpose in hand, white zinc carbonate had been substituted. On dissolution in acid, the coloured oxide gave a yellow precipitate with hydrogen sulphide which it was feared was arsenic sulphide.

"This information induced me", wrote Stromeyer, "to examine the oxide of zinc more carefully and I found, to my surprise, that the colour it assumed was due to the presence of a peculiar metallic oxide, the existence of which had not hitherto been suspected. I succeeded by a peculiar process in freeing it from the oxide of zinc and in reducing it to the metallic state."

This metal Stromeyer named cadmium, since cadmia is an old name for calamine or zinc carbonate, derived from the Lat. *calamus* reed, in allusion to its slender stalactitic forms. To avoid confusion it should be mentioned that American mineralogists know natural zinc carbonate under the name of *smithsonite*, after Smithson, who founded the Smithsonian Institute at Washington, and who analysed the mineral in 1803. Unfortunately, the Americans use the term calamine to designate our hemimorphite, $Zn_2SiO_4.H_2O$ or more probably $Zn(OH)_2.Zn_3Si_2O_7.H_2O$, since one half of the

---

*STROMEYER, *Ann. Chim. Phys.*, 1819, (2), **11**, 76. *Gilbert's Annalen*, 1818, **60**, 193. *Schweigger's J.*, 1818, **22**, 362.

total water content can be removed without destruction of the crystal, but not more than half.

The pure metal is used in the cadmium and Weston standard cells, invaluable for the accurate determination of E.M.F's. It is sprayed on to steel to protect against corrosion; sometimes it is plated on to steel prior to chromium plating. Alloys of cadmium with 2 per cent of Ni, or of 2·25 Ag plus 0·25 Cu are used in automobiles etc, as handles, and for other purposes.

Many alloys melting at low temperatures contain cadmium; these are useful as fusible metals. Thus, Wood's alloy contains 4 Bi, 2 Pb, 1 Sn and 1 Cd; it melts at about 70° C. (p. 88). Extensive use is made of cadmium in bearing alloys, the other metals being nickel, nickel + silver, copper + silver, or copper + magnesium. These alloys have low coefficients of friction, greater resistance to fatigue, and are harder than the tin-base Babbitts. Unfortunately, they are easily attacked by organic acids in lubricating oils. To improve their resistance to these they are first plated with indium and then heated to permit diffusion of indium into the lloy. Such alloys are known as *cadmium base white bearing metals* (p. 166).

Both the metre and the yard have now been measured in terms of the cadmium red spectral line (p. 308).

CHAPTER 13

THE ALUMINIUM GROUP

THE aluminium group comprises aluminium, indium and thallium.

Aluminium

The Romans used the term *alumen* to denote substances of an astringent taste. One of these was a crystalline substance well known to Geber (died A.D. 765) and the later alchemists, who classed it with the vitriols. This was our "alum".

The production of alum is an industry of great antiquity. Until about 1450 most of the alum used in Europe came from Asia Minor, the trade being mainly in the hands of the Genoese. In 1451 Henry VI, being "hard up", confiscated all the *Allom foyle* belonging to the Genoese merchants at Southampton to the value of £8000 — a very considerable sum in those days. Presumably Henry sold this alum to English purchasers and thus obtained the needed ready money*.

The alum trade in those days was a most important one; it even formed the subject of papal bulls and interdicts, and entered into the correspondence of kings, popes and cardinals.

It was during the fifteenth century that several alum works were established in Italy. The most famous of these was at Tolfa near Civitavecchia, the seaport of Rome, and the ancient *Centum Cellae*, whose harbour was planned by Trajan about A.D. 100. Tolfa is the chief place among volcanic mountains of the same name which, although extinct, still emit vapours. In this district the manufacture of so-called "Roman alum" was for centuries an industry of great importance. Baedeker summarises the present position somewhat laconically in the words "The mines are no longer of great importance, but the scenery is picturesque."

Pope Pius II described the origin of this industry. He stated that in May 1462, Giovanni de Castro, of Padua, whilst travelling over the mountains of Tolfa, observed a plant which he knew also grew on the alum mountains of Asia Minor. This led him to look

---

*A detailed account of the alum trade is given by RHYS JENKINS, *Trans. S.E. Union of Scientific Societies*, 1914, p. 57. *Science Progress*, 1915, **9**, 488.

for alum and he found some white stones with a salt-like taste which proved to be of a similiar nature to alum. It was *alunite*, or *alum rock*, a basic double sulphate of aluminium and potassium usually formulated as $K_2SO_4.Al_2(SO_4)_3.4Al(OH)_3$. It was only necessary to leach with water and crystallise the alum from the clear solution.

It is better, of course, to calcine and treat the product with dilute sulphuric acid. This gives a solution containing excess aluminium sulphate, and addition of potassium sulphate enables all the aluminium salt to be converted into alum. This has long been the recognised procedure.

De Castro hastened to acquaint His Holiness with his discovery and the latter, after a little initial scepticism, saw in this discovery the hand of God. With true Christian charity he "determined to employ the gift of God to His Glory in the Turkish War and exhorted all Christians henceforth to purchase alum only from him and not from the Turkish infidels." The mine was soon in operation and by 1463 some 8000 persons were engaged, and the papal treasury was enriched to the tune of some 100,000 ducats per annum. The following year Pope Paul II, who succeeded Pius II, launched a Bull excommunicating all who purchased alum from the unbelievers and thus set up a papal monopoly of alum in Europe. There was a rise in price and Charles the Bold decided in 1467 to allow his people to buy their alum anywhere they liked. This annoyed the Pope who threatened Charles with personal excommunication, and he capitulated.

The Tolfa alum was markedly superior to that brought from the east and was largely purchased by dyers and the demand rapidly increased. Despite the papal Bull, however, our Kings, with characteristic British independence reserved the right to purchase alum where they chose, and one Pietro Aliprando, writing in December 1472 to the Duke of Milan, was very outspoken in his views of the obstinate British. "In the morning", he wrote, "they are as devout as angels, but after dinner they are like devils, seeking to throw the Pope's messenger into the sea." In 1545, King Henry VIII arranged to take papal alum in exchange for lead, of which he had immense quantities presumably as the result of spoliation of the monasteries. The alum was brought by sea from Cadiz and stored in the "late dissolved house of Fryer Augustynes". This was regarded as a good transaction because alum was necessary for the dyeing industry.

Alum was also produced from alum shale at an early date. Alum shales contain pyrites which on prolonged weathering, disintegrate and oxidise to sulphuric acid, which attacks the clay — essentially aluminium silicate — yielding aluminium sulphate and other substances. Both Agricola (1494 to 1555) and Libavius (1540 to 1616) knew that, in order to obtain crystals from the solution obtained by leaching the weathered shales, it was necessary to add an alkali. Both writers mention the practice of adding decomposed urine for the purpose. The salt obtained would thus be essentially ammonium alum, whereas the papal alum was obviously the potassium salt. It was not until 1797 that Chaptal and Vauquelin showed that ammonia and potash are vicarious in alum. This explained why alum could be obtained from alunite without addition of alkali, since the potash was already present as sulphate, whereas it was not present in the Whitby shales.

The discovery of the alum shales in the Upper Lias in the N. Riding of Yorkshire was due to Thomas Chaloner who, with others, obtained a joint patent for the manufacture of alum in England for 31 years in 1607. The work was so successful that King James I (1603 to 1625) became interested and decided that the Crown should share the profits. In 1609 Chaloner's monopoly was transferred to the Crown and, to stifle competition and thus counter the adverse effects that might follow through any rise in price due to maladministration, the importation of alum from abroad was prohibited. The usual result of "nationalisation" accrued; for many years the industry was not a success; by 1637 things had improved and the Yorkshire industry reached its zenith in the latter half of the eighteenth century; it then gradually declined to extinction.

In 1754 Marggraf showed that alumina and lime are two distinct earths and that alumina is the earth present along with silica in clay. Davy, after his brilliant success in isolating the alkali and alkaline earth metals by electrolysis, endeavoured in a similar manner to obtain aluminium, but failed. But Oersted, discoverer of the magnetic action of the electric current, succeeded in 1825 by acting on aluminium chloride with potassium amalgam. The resulting aluminium amalgam was then distilled in the absence of air, leaving a residue of metallic aluminium, which in colour and lustre was stated to resemble tin. In 1827, Wöhler, who found himself unable to repeat Oersted's experiment, obtained the metal by decomposing the anhydrous chloride with metallic potassium. In both cases the products were impure.

The French chemist, Henri St. Claire Deville was the first to obtain pure aluminium. In 1854, he prepared the double chloride NaCl.AlCl$_3$, and, by heating this with sodium, succeeded in isolating pure aluminium.

In June 1881, James Fern Webster patented a process for producing aluminium and erected what is claimed to be the world's first factory at Solihull Lodge, near Birmingham. The output was about 20 tons weekly and in 1883 a large consignment was sent to the Calcutta Exhibition, where it was awarded two gold medals. Although one or two patents were taken out the main process was secret.

In 1886, Charles Hall, an American, and the Frenchman, Paul Héroult, solved the problem of producing aluminium electrolytically from alumina in a bath of molten cryolite. Hall died in 1914, leaving a fortune of nearly £6 million. Héroult died the same year; both men were only 51 years of age at the time of their decease.

The first authentic article of aluminium was a rattle for the infant destined later to become Emperor Napoleon III. In 1854, an aluminium medal was struck and presented to him, and he both authorised and financed experiments to manufacture the metal on a larger scale. He had visions of supplying his troops with helmets and breastplates of aluminium, but its price of over £100 per lb. rendered the proposition hopeless. After the invention of the Hall-Héroult electrolytic process the price fell to about £85 per ton in 1914. The world consumption in 1938 was 550,000 tons, and by 1941 it was close upon one million tons. It was stated in October 1939, that bullet-proof duralumin armour was among Germany's new methods of warfare on the Western Front.

Owing to its low density, 2·7 (tin is 7·3) aluminium and its alloys, also of low density, are particularly valuable for aircraft production. Small quantities of certain alloying elements increase the tensile strength to that of mild steel. Thus *duralumin*, containing up to 5 per cent copper and small amounts of magnesium, manganese, silicon and iron, may have a tensile strength of 30·5 tons per sq. in., and will weigh only one third as much as corresponding steel plates.

Cooking utensils are made of aluminium, and elaborate experiments indicate that, if any aluminium thereby enters the system, it soon leaves the system and does no harm.

Aluminium is used in electric transmission in place of copper; it is added to molten steel prior to casting to prevent blow holes. It

163

is useful as a reducing agent in the production of certain metals, and in the manufacture of *thermit*. The action of this latter is due to the enormous heat of union of aluminium with oxygen, namely, 399,040 gram calories per 54 grams of metal.

In 1938 an aluminium wire was on exhibit at the Glasgow Empire Exhibition, of diameter 0·0001 in. It was calculated that 1 oz. of this wire would cost some £5 million and would encircle the earth at the equator 1200 times. Some 600 of these hairs would be equivalent to a human hair.

Although it readily combines with oxygen, aluminium is resistant to atmospheric corrosion because a thin film of closely adherent oxide is formed which protects the underlying metal from attack. Aluminium powder is therefore used as a pigment in anti-corrosive paints.

In 1936 sen coins in Japan were made of aluminium.

The excessive wear of aluminium pistons in internal combustion engines has been traced to oxidation with production of amorphous oxide, Al_2O_3, which hardens to corundum, which is strongly abrasive. To prevent this, magnesium is added to the aluminium; this on oxidation gives spinel, $MgO.Al_2O_3$, which is amorphous, stable and not abrasive. This is termed "spinelising".

The surface of aluminium may be allowed to undergo superficial oxidation and then dyed with various dyes to give beautiful effects. The explosive *ammonal*, used in mining, consists of 4 to 6 parts of aluminium the remainder being ammonium nitrate.

Aluminium yields many valuable alloys. *Magnalium* consists of aluminium with 1 to 2 per cent of magnesium; *duralumin* contains up to 5 per cent of copper with small amounts of Mg, Mn, Fe, and Si; it has a low coefficient of expansion with rise of temperature, and plates of duralumin are only one-third the weight of equally strong steel ones. There is a growing interest in aluminium bronzes, alloys of aluminium and copper which are resistant to seawater and certain concentrations of sulphuric acid. Alloys of aluminium and silicon are also becoming important.

The first bridge of aluminium alloy was opened at Sunderland in 1948. It has a span of 95 feet and is designed to carry road and rail.

Indium

In one sense the discovery of thallium led to that of indium as did the discovery of caesium to that of rubidium. Ferdinand Reich*, professor of physics at Freiberg, was examining some local zinc ores and in 1863 obtained a yellow precipitate (In_2S_3) on passing hydrogen sulphide into an almost neutral solution, arsenic, etc, having been previously removed from the ore by roasting. He concluded that this contained a hitherto unknown element and asked his assistant Hieronymus Theodor Richter to examine the precipitate spectroscopically as he himself was colour blind. Richter noticed a brilliant line $\lambda 4512$ in the dark blue region which did not coincide with either of the caesium lines 4555, 4593. This was taken to confirm the existence of a new element, and it was appropriately decided to call it *indium* from *indigo*. The element was studied in detail by Winkler† a few years later.

Indium occurs in widespread association with both zinc and tin ores. It seems improbable that this can be due to chemical segregation, for isomorphism of indium and tin compounds, for example, appears to be ruled out by their difference both in valency and atomic radius. It has been suggested‡ that the tin isotope 115 has gradually been transmuted into indium 115 by loss of an electron and a neutrino. The process is presumed to take place extremely slowly so that in finite time it escapes observation. Tin has eleven natural isotopes; of these Sn 115 constitutes 0·44 per cent. Indium comprises In 115, 95·5, and In 113, 4·5 per cent. The high percentage of isotope 115 in natural indium is in harmony with the above suggestion.

The chlorides of indium are of considerable historical interest. Kekulé regarded valency as a fundamental property of the atom, as unchangeable and invariable as the atomic weight. This view he retained to the last. Apparent exceptions certainly existed. Carbon monoxide could, however, readily be explained on the assumption that the two unused valencies of the carbon atom saturate each other; mercurous salts, such as the chloride, possessed the double formula, Cl-Hg-Hg-Cl, and so on. In 1888, however, Nilson and Pettersson§ showed that three distinct chlorides of indium can exist in the vapour state. To these they gave the formulæ InCl, $InCl_2$ and

---

*REICH and RICHTER, *J. prakt. Chem.*, 1863, **89**, 441; 1863, **90**, 172; 1864, **92**, 480. RICHTER, *Compt. rend.*, 1867, **64**, 827.

†WINKLER, *J. prakt. Chem.*, 1865, **94**, 1; 1865, **95**, 414; 1867, **102**, 273.

‡EASTMAN, *Physical Review*, 1937, **52**, 1226. But AHRENS dissents from this view (*Nature*, 1948, **162**, 414).

§NILSON and PETTERSSON, *Trans. Chem. Soc.*, 1888, **53**, 814. *Zeitsch physikal Chem.*, 1888, **2**, 657.

$InCl_3$, respectively. This was the first clear example of an element showing three valencies; these could not be explained away by association or self-neutralisation in Kekulé's manner, and were regarded as definitely establishing the principle of multiple valency. No one doubts this principle to-day, though indium may not of necessity be divalent in $InCl_2$; it may perhaps be a complex, such as $In[InCl_4]$ or indium tetrachlorindiate, the indium atoms functioning with valencies of one and three, respectively.

On account of its relatively low melting point ($156 \cdot 4°$ C) and high boiling point ($2087°$ C) indium has an unusually large liquid range; its use in high temperature thermometry has been advocated. An alloy of 18 per cent of indium with Wood's metal (p. 159) melts at $46°$ C. Small amounts up to 5 per cent are added to jewellery to increase the hardness. A 42 per cent alloy with silver is untarnishable; but the cost is high and the alloy is difficult to work. It is more usual, therefore, to plate silver with indium and then by suitable heat treatment to induce the formation of a thin surface layer of untarnishable alloy. Indium is also used in dental alloys; it is also plated on to cadmium base white metal bearing alloys, and heated to $340°$ F ($170°$ C) to diffuse it inwards whereby resistance to corrosion by organic acids in lubricating oils is enhanced.

Thallium

Thallium was discovered independently by Sir William Crookes* in England and by the Belgian chemist M. Lamy. Crookes was the first to make the discovery. He was the founder and editor of the now defunct *Chemical News* which, in its day, was a valuable contribution to scientific literature. In March 1861 he was engaged in extracting selenium from a deposit obtained from a sulphuric acid factory at Tilkerode in the Harz. Bunsen and Kirchhoff had just announced their discovery of caesium and rubidium with the aid of the spectroscope (p. 147), so Crookes tested his material in a similar manner.

He noticed a new line in the green portion of the spectrum and in accordance with the Bunsen-Kirchhoff rule then recently enunciated, concluded that a new element was present to which he gave the name thallium from Greek *thallos*, a young shoot or green twig.

---

*CROOKES, Chem. News., 1861, **3**, 193, 303. Phil. Mag., 1861, (4), **21**, 301. FOURNIER D'ALBE, "The Life of Sir William Crookes" (Unwin, 1923), Chapters 7, 8 and 13.

At first Crookes thought the new element was probably a metalloid like selenium. His early work was hampered by lack of material, but eventually he found that thallium was a metal and in May 1862 was able to exhibit a few grains in powder form.

In April 1862, Claude August Lamy* independently observed the same green line due to thallium in the spectrum obtained from slime from a sulphuric acid works at Loos, where Belgian pyrites were used. More fortunate than Crookes he had considerable quantities of material at his disposal and soon established the metallic nature of thallium. In May of the same year he was able to display a lump of the metal and before the end of the year he isolated several hundred grams and gave a fairly complete account of the physical and chemical properties of the metal.

For some time the question of the priority of these two chemists was an unfortunate cause of dispute. There can be no doubt, however, that Crookes was the first to observe the green line and it appears highly probable, too, that he was also the first to obtain the metal; he claimed to have obtained it as a black powder as early as 1st May 1862.

At this time the Periodic Classification had not been formulated and it was difficult to decide to which group of elements thallium should be assigned. The metal resembles lead in many of its physical properties and a number of thallous compounds likewise resembled those of lead. Other thallous salts were found to be isomorphous with those of potassium and the spectrum of thallium was simple like the spectra of the alkali metals. To add to the uncertainty, thallic compounds resembled those of aluminium. For these reasons Dumas referred to thallium as "the paradoxical metal" and "the ornithorynchus of the metals". Mendeléeff, with characteristic courage, classed thallium with the aluminium metals in his Periodic Table in 1869, and subsequent research has fully justified this arrangement. With an atomic number 81 it lies between mercury (80) and lead (82) and whilst in the monovalent state it shows analogy with the alkali metals, in the trivalent state it is a true congener of indium.

---

*Lamy, *Compt. rend.*, 1862, **54**, 1255; 1862, **55**, 836. *Ann. Chim. Phys.*, 1863, (3), **67**, 385.

CHAPTER 14

MENDELÉEFF'S PREDICTEES

MENDELÉEFF's predictees include scandium, gallium and germanium.

When once the Atomic Theory, as enunciated by John Dalton, *circa* 1803, had been accepted, numerous attempts were made by chemists to discover some method of grouping together those isolated portions of matter known as elements.

In 1816 Doebereiner directed attention to the curious fact that certain triads of elements existed in which the elements showed both a peculiar regularity in their atomic weights and a close similarity in chemical properties. For several years, however, the subject was allowed to drop into abeyance until Dumas in 1851 again brought it to the fore; both he and other chemists added to the examples. Sulphur, selenium and tellurium were typical; the atomic weight of selenium was practically the mean of those of sulphur and tellurium. Five such triads were found, namely —

	Atomic Weights	Means		Atomic Weights	Means
Lithium	6·940		Sulphur	32·06	
Sodium	22·997	23·018	Selenium	78·96	79·84
Potassium	39·096		Tellurium	127·61	
Calcium	40·08		Chlorine	35·457	
Strontium	87·63	88·72	Bromine	79·916	81·19
Barium	137·36		Iodine	126·92	
Phosphorus	30·98				
Arsenic	74·91	76·37			
Antimony	121·76				

At first it was hoped that all the elements might ultimately be grouped into these triads and that in this way a complete system of classifying might be evolved, for the Periodic Classification had not then been introduced. These hopes were, however, doomed to failure and a severe blow was struck at the utility of the triads when Cooke showed that some of them actually broke into natural groups of four or five closely related elements, as in the case of the halogens and the alkali metals respectively.

A second group of triads was also known in which the atomic weights of the constituent elements were closely similar; these were the iron and platinum metals. In the accompanying list the modern atomic weights are used as in the previous table.

Iron	.. 55·85	Ruthenium..	101·7	Osmium	.. 190·2
Cobalt	.. 58·94	Rhodium	.. 102·91	Iridium	.. 193·1
Nickel	.. 58·69	Palladium ..	106·7	Platinum	.. 195·23

Some years later, when the atomic weights had been revised by Cannizzaro, Chancourtois observed that certain remarkable regularities were brought out by arranging the elements in the order of increasing atomic weights, and in 1862 he arranged them in a spiral round a vertical cylinder divided into 16 vertical sections known as the *Telluric Screw*. The elements in any vertical section were seen to possess analogous chemical and physical properties.

About this time Newlands was working along similar lines and in a series of papers from 1864 to 1866 introduced his generalisation known as *The Law of Octaves*. In a series of short papers he showed that when the elements are arranged in order of increasing atomic weights, similarities between their properties become apparent periodically between the first and last of every eight elements. Thus lithium, sodium and potassium resembled each other; counting lithium as 1, sodium was 8; with sodium 1, potassium was 8, and so on. Hence the term octave. At first Newlands' papers were ridiculed and the coincidences ascribed to chance. In 1866, at a meeting of the Chemical Society when a paper entitled "The Law of Octaves and the Causes of the Numerical Relations among the Atomic Weights" was being discussed, one cynic inquired if Newlands had ever examined the elements according to their initial letters and suggested that such a study might prove profitable. Newlands, however, did not pursue the subject.

In 1869 and in subsequent years Lothar Meyer and Mendeléeff independently made similar observations and these generalisations came to be known as the Periodic Law.

Mendeléeff's Periodic Table in 1871

Row	Group I R₂O	Group II RO	Group III R₂O₃	Group IV RH₄ RO₂	Group V RH₃ R₂O₅	Group VI RH₂ RO₃	Group VII RH R₂O₇	Group VIII RO₄
1	H = 1							
2	Li = 7	Be = 9·4	B = 11	C = 12	N = 14	O = 16	F = 19	
3	Na = 23	Mg = 24	Al = 27·3	Si = 28	P = 31	S = 32	Cl = 35·5	
4	K = 39	Ca = 40	— = 44	Ti = 48	V = 51	Cr = 52	Mn = 55	Fe = 56, Co = 59, Ni = 59, Cu′ = 63
5	(Cu = 63)	Zn = 65	— = 68	— = 72	As = 75	Se = 78	Br = 80	
6	Rb = 85	Sr = 87	?Yt = 88	Zr = 90	Nb = 94	Mo = 96	— = 100	Ru = 104, Rh = 104, Pd = 106, Ag = 108
7	(Ag = 108)	Cd = 112	In = 113	Sn = 118	Sb = 122	Te = 125	I = 127	
8	Cs = 133	Ba = 137	?Di = 138	?Ce = 140	—	—	—	— — —
9	(—)	—						
10	—	—	?Er = 178	?La = 180	Ta = 182	W = 184	—	Os = 195, Ir = 197, Pt = 198, Au = 199
11	(Au = 199)	Hg = 200	Tl = 204	Pb = 207	Bi = 208	—	—	— — —
12	—	—	—	Th = 231	—	U = 240	—	— — —

Can any good come out of Nazareth? Prophets often remain unrecognised in their own country. As soon as Meyer and Mendeléeff recognised the periodicity of the elements, the British began to think that after all there might be something in Newlands' observations. At that time, however, not only was the number of elements known to the chemist relatively small but the values assigned to their atomic weights were often faulty, even when their equivalent weights were known with reasonable accuracy. Thus the atomic weight assigned to beryllium was 14, indium 76 and uranium 120, and these values threw them out of their true positions. As more elements were discovered and their atomic weights correctly determined, the general truth of the Periodic Law came to be appreciated and attempts were made to bring the recalcitrant elements into line.

The periodic table drawn up by Mendeléeff in 1869, as it appeared when published in English in 1871, is shown on p. 170. It is much the same as the modern *Ideal Periodic Table*, shown on page 5, in which the elements are arranged in the order of the increasing electric charge on the atomic nucleus, which is much the same as the order of increasing atomic weights. There is one important difference, namely the inclusion of the inert gases in column "o" by William Ramsay; these gases were of course unknown in 1869. This scheme was an enormous advance on anything which an arrangement based on the Doebereiner triads could hope to be. The vertical groups held not only all the triads but the other elements associated with them, so that natural groups were no longer dissected. Thus the 5 alkali metals and the 4 halogens fell into groups I and VI respectively. There were, however, certain difficulties; but Mendeléeff, believing in the real existence of periodicity, felt that these were due to incorrect data and sought means of harmonising all the discrepancies.

Taking the three elements mentioned above, Mendeléeff suggested that, as their equivalent weights were well known, it might well be that the valencies assigned to them were incorrect. Thus from its resemblance to aluminium, beryllium was regarded as trivalent and its atomic weight was in consequence taken as $4 \cdot 7 \times 3$ or $14 \cdot 1$; if, however, the analogy were mistaken and beryllium ought really to be compared with magnesium and calcium, its valency would be 2 and its atomic weight in consequence $4 \cdot 7 \times 2$ or $9 \cdot 4$. In that event there was room in his table. Mendeléeff therefore assumed that this was correct and boldly placed beryllium at the head of group II. Similarly he assumed that indium was trivalent, resembling aluminium rather than zinc, so that its atomic weight became 113 instead of 76; he also assumed that uranium was hexavalent like sulphur, not trivalent like iron, thus raising its atomic weight from 120 to 240. These three recalcitrant elements then fell into line. Subsequent work has fully justified these manœuvres.

Even so there remained three important gaps in the fourth and fifth rows of the table. Mendeléeff again took his courage in both hands and suggested that these pointed to the existence of three elements as yet unknown to science. He named them *eka*-boron, *eka*-aluminium and *eka*-silicon respectively; moreover he went so far as to indicate the general properties these elements would be found to possess when discovered.

In due course these elements were discovered and christened *scandium, gallium* and *germanium* respectively. They were found to possess properties remarkably close to those predicted by Mendeléeff, and their discovery removed all lingering doubts as to the importance of the Periodic Law.

Scandium

In 1879 Nilson was extracting ytterbia from euxenite — a complex niobo-titanate of yttrium and uranium — and from gadolinite — a basic ortho silicate of iron, beryllium, and the yttrium earths named after Gadolin, the Finnish mineralogist. He used the method adopted the previous year by Marignac, the discoverer of ytterbia, and obtained some 63 grams of "earth" which he converted into nitrate and fractionally decomposed by heat — a favourite method of fractionation, first adopted by Berlin in 1860. To his surprise he found that it contained a small amount (actually only 0·3 gram) of an entirely new earth characterised by feeble basicity, a very low chemical equivalent, and a new spark spectrum. To this new earth he gave the name *scandia* in honour of his native Scandinavia. A little later Nilson obtained a further supply of scandia, described some salts, and determined the atomic weight of the metal, scandium. It was Cleve who, in the same year (1879), pointed out that the properties of the element agreed with those predicted by Mendeléeff for *eka*-boron.

In many respects scandium resembles the rare earth metals, but not so closely as does yttrium (p. 178). Like the rares it is found in small quantities in many minerals, it is trivalent yet yields neither an alum nor alkyl or aryl derivatives; its oxalate is insoluble in water and dilute acids and it yields double platino-cyanides. Nevertheless, it is not now usually regarded as a true rare earth, since in many ways it presents notable contrasts. Thus, for example, its acetyl acetonate sublimes without decomposition, like that of thorium; its fluoride, ScF_3, again like that of thorium, ThF_4, is insoluble in mineral acids and affords a convenient method of separating scandium from the rare earth metals whose fluorides are soluble. A further difference lies in the tendency for scandium sulphate to yield complex ions in aqueous solution. Addition of barium chloride does not at once precipitate all the sulphate ion as barium sulphate. It is concluded that the salt has the constitution $Sc[Sc(SO_4)_3]$, that is, it is scandium sulphato-scandiate, analogous to cadmium iodo-cadmiate, $Cd[CdI_4]$. In each of these and in many other ways the scandium derivative behaves differently from the corresponding rare earth one.

For many years an atomic weight of 44·1 was accepted for scandium, but in 1923 Aston showed that the element had no isotopes and that its atomic mass relative to oxygen 16 was 45. As a result of fresh chemical investigation, the atomic weight 45·1 was accepted by the International Committee in 1925, and this value is accepted to-day (1950).

Gallium

In August 1875, Boisbaudran observed a pair of violet lines in the spark spectrum of some material he had separated from zinc blende from the Pierrefitte mine, from which he concluded the presence of a new element. This he named *gallium* in honour of his native country. Later in the year he obtained a small quantity of the free metal by electrolysis of a solution of gallium hydroxide in caustic potash. It was Mendeléeff himself who, in November 1875, suggested the identity of this element with *eka*-aluminium, and further study of its properties and those of its compounds confirmed this view.

Gallium has a very wide range of liquidity; it melts at 30° and boils at 1600° C, and may therefore be used as the liquid indicator in a quartz thermometer at temperatures much higher than the ordinary mercury thermometer.

Germanium

Towards the close of 1885 Welsbach discovered a new mineral in the Himmelsfürst mine near Freiberg, Saxony. This he called *argyrodite* from its metallic lustre and the fact that it contains silver (Greek *arguros*, silver). On the assumption that the mineral was essentially silver sulphide, which a qualitative analysis by Richter had indicated, Winkler (1838 to 1904) was requested by Welsbach to make a quantitative analysis. He did so, but, as in Plattner's examination of polluxite (p.147), his analysis only added up to some 93 per cent. For several months he puzzled over this, but at last was able to isolate a new base from which, in 1887, he prepared a new metal. In honour of his fatherland he called it *germanium*. Argyrodite is $4Ag_2S.GeS_2$. It was at first thought that the new metal would fill in the supposed gap between antimony and bismuth, but it was soon recognised as Mendeléeff's *eka*-silicon.

For a long time germanium was very rare, but in 1916 a new mineral, *germanite*, was discovered in S. Africa. It is a complex copper pyrites and contains some 8 per cent of germanium and 1 of gallium, together with varying amounts of nearly twenty other elements. It is the only mineral known to contain both gallium and germanium in appreciable amounts.

Germanium has at present few uses in industry. With the extension of radio communication to ultra-high frequencies the use of point-contact crystal rectifiers in telecommunication circuits has become an established practice. Both silicon (p. 70) and germanium crystal rectifiers are in use. The germanium crystals are obtained from ingots formed in vacuo and slowly cooled.

CHAPTER 15

THE RARE EARTH OR LANTHANIDE SERIES

THE rare earth metals constitute a group of fifteen contiguous elements, numbers 57 to 71 inclusive, in the Periodic Classification to which is added yttrium (No. 39) because of its very close analogies generally and particularly with those with the higher atomic numbers. For reasons already given, scandium (21), although a congener of yttrium and belonging to the same vertical group of the Periodic Table, is not included amongst the rare earths proper.

The modern acceptation of the term "earth" was discussed in connexion with the alkaline earths. The so-called rare earths are of peculiar interest. They even attracted the attention of H.I.H. Prince Louis Lucien Bonaparte who prepared pure ceria and several salts of cerium in 1843. It is convenient to retain the specific adjective "rare" although it is well recognised that many of the earths are quite plentiful although others may be extremely scarce. Indeed their distribution is remarkably uneven. It has been estimated* that they, all told, constitute only 0·001 per cent of the earth's crust. Cerium is relatively abundant; it rivals tin and is three times as plentiful in the earth's 10-mile crust as lead, as is evident from the table on page 176†.

Yttrium, neodymium and lanthanum are more plentiful than lead, and all are more so than silver, with the single exception of illinium with regard to the existence of which considerable doubt now exists.

Although the figures shown are always liable to modification as our knowledge of the composition of the earth's crust is extended, they are probably of the right order. One feature is very pronounced, namely that the metals of even atomic number are invariably more plentiful than their immediate odd congeners. This is clearly shown in Fig. 6.

---

*WASHINGTON's estimate, quoted by HOPKINS, *Trans. Amer. Electrochem. Soc.*, 1935, **66**, 49.
†Numerous estimates have been published. The data in the Table are substantially the same as those given by GOLDSCHMIDT, *J. Chem. Soc.*, 1937, p. 656.

Rare-earth Metals in the Earth's crust

Atomic No.		Grams per ton	Atomic No.		Grams per ton
29	*Copper* ..	100	66	Dysprosium ..	4·3
			70	Ytterbium ..	2·6
58	Cerium ..	44	68	Erbium ..	2·4
50	*Tin*	40	67	Holmium ..	1·2
			63	Europium ..	1·0
39	Yttrium ..	31	65	Terbium ..	1·0
60	Neodymium ..	24	71	Lutecium ..	0·7
57	Lanthanum ..	19	69	Thulium ..	0·3
			61	(Illinium) ..	?
82	*Lead*	16			
62	Samarium ..	6·5			
64	Gadolinium ..	6·3			
59	Praseodymium	5·6			

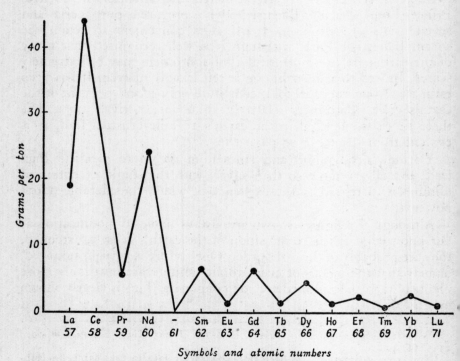

Fig. 6—Abundance of rare earth metals

In their chemical properties the rare earths resemble one another very closely; there is a gradual change in properties as we pass along the series from lanthanum (57) in order of increasing atomic number towards lutecium (71), and although it is easy to distinguish between and to separate elements of widely removed atomic numbers, like the two mentioned, it is sometimes extremely difficult to separate two contiguous elements. It can be done qualitatively in most cases by repeated fractionation of one kind or another, usually by fractional crystallisation, but the method cannot give quantitative results. Two contiguous elements frequently resemble each other much more closely than the platinum metals and in this respect lie between these and some isotopes, notably hydrogen and deuterium.

The reason for this similarity is not difficult to find. The chemical and optical properties of atoms are mainly decided by the outermost electrons, as we have already seen. The arrangements of the electrons round the nuclei in yttrium, scandium and the rare earth elements are shown in the accompanying table.

Shell	K	L	M	N	O	P
Maximum No. of Electrons	2	8	18	32	50	72
20 Calcium	2	8	8	2		
21 Scandium	2	8	8 + 1	2		
38 Strontium	2	8	18	8	2	
39 Yttrium	2	8	18	8 + 1	2	
56 Barium	2	8	18	18	8	2
57 Lanthanum	2	8	18	18	8 + 1	2
58 Cerium	2	8	18	18 + 1	8 + 1*	2
59 Praseodymium	2	8	18	18 + 2	8 + 1*	2
60 Neodymium	2	8	18	18 + 3	8 + 1*	2
61 (? Illinium)	2	8	18	18 + 4	8 + 1*	2
62 Samarium	2	8	18	18 + 5	8 + 1*	2
63 Europium	2	8	18	18 + 6	8 + 1*	2
64 Gadolinium	2	8	18	18 + 7	8 + 1	2
65 Terbium	2	8	18	18 + 8	8 + 1	2
66 Dysprosium	2	8	18	18 + 9	8 + 1*	2
67 Holmium	2	8	18	18 + 10	8 + 1*	2

N

Shell	K	L	M	N	O	P
Maximum No. of Electrons ..	2	8	18	32	50	72
68 Erbium ..	2	8	18	18 + 11	8 + 1*	2
69 Thulium ..	2	8	18	18 + 12	8 + 1*	2
70 Ytterbium ..	2	8	18	18 + 13	8 + 1*	2
71 Lutecium ..	2	8	18	18 + 14	8 + 1	2
72 Hafnium ..	2	8	18	32	8 + 2	2
73 Tantalum ..	2	8	18	32	8 + 3	2

According to a more recent view* the starred electrons in the O-shell are held in the N-shell. For reasons explained later Seaborg has suggested (p. 311) that the series of elements ranging from lanthanum (57) to lutecium (71) be termed the *lanthanide series*, a term that calls attention to the *actinide series*, ranging upwards from actinium (89) in which the O-shell gradually fills up.

It has already been mentioned (p. 172) that scandium bears a resemblance to the rare earth metals and the electrons in the M and N shells of the former certainly resemble those in the O and P shells in the latter. But for reasons already given scandium is not regarded as a true rare earth metal.

The structure of yttrium approaches even more closely that of the rare earth metals, for like these latter its M shell is complete, and in its chemical properties it so closely resembles those with the higher atomic weights that elements 63 to 71 are frequently classed as belonging to the yttrium group. We shall observe this classification in the present section.

The characteristic valency of the elements is 3, but a few of them can function in other capacities; they then show marked differences in the physical properties of their derivatives and can often be separated very completely from their congeners in this way. For example, oxidation of cerous (trivalent) compounds to ceric (tetravalent) enables cerium to be separated. It yields, for example, beautiful orange crystals of ceric ammonium nitrate, $Ce(NO_3)_4.2NH_4NO_3$, insoluble in concentrated nitric acid, whereas the nitrates of its congeners are soluble. Similarly upon reduction europium and ytterbium yield insoluble sulphates, $EuSO_4$ and

*Yost, "The Rare Earth Elements and Their Compounds", p. 3 (Chapman & Hall, 1947).

$YtSO_4$, corresponding to barium sulphate, whereas the sulphates of their congeners gadolinium, $Gd_2(SO_4)_3.8H_2O$, and dysprosium, $Dy_2(SO_4)_3.8H_2O$, are soluble and cannot be reduced. Such methods are a very great help, for fractionation is slow and tedious; thus, in preparing a very pure lutecium, Urbain in 1911 submitted his material to fractionation some 15,000 times (p. 232).

In discussing the history* of these elements it is convenient to discuss them in two groups, namely, the cerium earths, comprising elements 57 to 62, and the yttrium earths 63 to 71 with yttrium (39) itself.

The yttrium group

Let us be scriptural and take the last first. The story begins with a Swedish mineralogist, by name Lieutenant Arrhenius, to be distinguished from Svante Arrhenius who, a century later, evolved the theory of electrolytic dissociation. In 1788 Lt. Arrhenius found a black mineral in a quarry at the little town of Ytterby, near Stockholm, and regarding it as new to science he called it *ytterbite*. Six years later, in 1794, the Finnish mineralogist Gadolin, a native of Helsinki, examined this mineral and concluded that it contained a new earth. This was confirmed in 1797 by Ekeberg, destined later to be the discoverer of tantalum. He showed that the mineral contained beryllia, which had just been discovered by Vauquelin although the result was not published until 1798, and a new earth which he called yttria. In recognition of Gadolin's original observation, the original ytterbite came to be known as *gadolinite*, and to-day we assign to it the formula $3BeO.FeO.Y_2O_3.2SiO_2$. This new earth yttria, however, proved to be complex, and in 1843 Mosander separated three earths from it to which he gave the names *yttria*, erbia, and terbia. The yttria was essentially the earth known by that name to-day. The erbia gave a brown higher oxide on ignition whilst the terbia was pink. In 1860, however, Berlin introduced a method of fractionation depending upon the partial decomposition of rare earth nitrates by heat; experimenting with the crude yttria he failed to obtain the brown earth and most unfortunately called the pink earth, the existence of which he was able to confirm, erbia.

In 1873 a mineral known as *samarskite* was found in quantity in Mitchell County, North Carolina. This mineral had been found in Russia many years previously by von Samarski and handed to

---

*Full references to the early histories of these elements are given in FRIEND'S "Textbook of Inorganic Chemistry", Vol. IV. H. F. V. Little (Griffin, 1917).

Heinrich Rose for analysis. It is a complex niobo-tantalate containing numerous rare earth elements and Rose named it after its discoverer. The finding of the mineral in Carolina enabled chemists by 1877 to obtain fairly large amounts of raw material for the study of the now "less rare" earths, and the work entered on a new phase. In 1877 Delafontaine confirmed the existence of Mosander's brown oxide-forming earth in samarskite, and owing to Berlin's unfortunate action, he had perforce to call it terbia. Thus a most distressing confusion arose. The following year (1878), Marignac confirmed the existence of this terbia in gadolinite as Mosander had claimed. But it was only present to a minute extent, its deep staining powder being characteristic. It was only many years later that the brown higher-oxide forming earth was obtained in a state of purity.

About this time Laurence Smith and Delafontaine obtained what they believed to be two new earths, which they called mosandra and phillipia respectively. Moseley's method of determining atomic numbers had not then been dreamed of, and it was extremely difficult not merely to ascertain whether or not an earth was simple, but also how many separate earths were to be expected, as the Periodic Table gave no help at all. Suffice it to say that Smith's mosandra and Delafontaine's phillipia were mixtures.

Returning now to Marignac, in 1878 he fractionated the earths from gadolinite, and Soret examined the absorption spectra of the erbia fractions with the result that he concluded that at least two earths were present. He suggested retaining the name erbia for the earth which gave the absorption bands characteristic of the crude erbia and designated the new element giving other bands, particularly $\lambda 6404$ and 5363 as X. He also observed a band $\lambda 6840$ which did not appear to belong to either. Marignac meanwhile fractionated the crude erbia and isolated a new earth which he called ytterbia, which was shown to be complex by Auer von Welsbach and Urbain many years later. In 1905 Welsbach announced that it consisted of two earths which he called Aldebarania and Cassiopeia; but Urbain in 1907 named them neoytterbia and lutetia, the latter name being the Latin for Urbain's native city *Lutetia Parisiorum*. The International Atomic Weights Committee, however, adopted the names *ytterbium* and *lutetium* for the elements. It should be mentioned that Charles James of New Hampshire University, U.S.A., simultaneously discovered lutecia, but delay in publishing his results caused him to lose priority to Urbain.

The order of discovery of the yttrium earths is summarised in the following scheme —

History of the yttrium earths

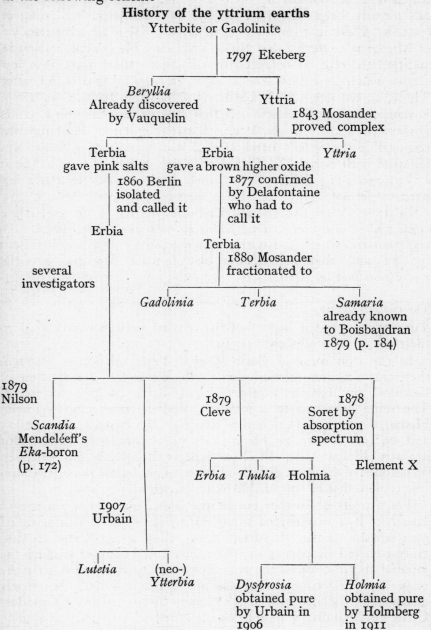

Ytterbite or Gadolinite

1797 Ekeberg

Beryllia
Already discovered
by Vauquelin

Yttria

1843 Mosander
proved complex

Terbia
gave pink salts

Erbia
gave a brown higher oxide

Yttria

1860 Berlin
isolated
and called it

1877 confirmed
by Delafontaine
who had to
call it

Erbia

Terbia

1880 Mosander
fractionated to

several
investigators

Gadolinia

Terbia

Samaria
already known
to Boisbaudran
1879 (p. 184)

1879
Nilson

1879
Cleve

1878
Soret by
absorption
spectrum

Scandia
Mendeléeff's
Eka-boron
(p. 172)

Erbia *Thulia* Holmia

Element X

1907
Urbain

Lutetia

(neo-)
Ytterbia

Dysprosia
obtained pure
by Urbain in
1906

Holmia
obtained pure
by Holmberg
in 1911

181

Nilson, in 1879, obtained still another oxide from crude erbia which he called *scandia*, in honour of his native Scandinavia. This has already been discussed as one of Mendeléeff's Predictees (p. 168). Cleve in 1879 also fractionated crude erbia after removal of Marignac's ytterbia and Nilson's scandia. He concluded that in addition to *erbia*, as characterised by Soret, there were two new earths which he called *holmia*, after Stockholm, and *thulia*, after Thule, an old name for Scandinavia or possibly Iceland. In 1886, however, Boisbaudran showed that holmia was complex as its absorption spectrum characterised two elements. Thulium was responsible for Soret's band $\lambda 6840$, whilst the new *holmium* was identical with Soret's X. The third element, which gave bands at $\lambda 7530$ and 4515 Boisbaudran named *dysprosium* (Greek *dysprositos* hard to get at).

In 1880 Marignac showed that the "terbia" from samarskite contained in addition to true *terbia* at least two other earths. One was Samaria, which had been discovered in 1879 by Boisbaudran (p. 183), and the other was a new earth to which Marignac gave the name *gadolinia* in 1886.

The cerium group

Turning now to the history of the cerium earths we hark back to the close of the eighteenth century.

In the iron mine at Bastnäs, near Vestmanland, in Sweden, there was a mineral of high density known as the "heavy stone of Bastnäs", or "Bastnäs tungstein", *tung* being Swedish for heavy. The mine belonged to a wealthy Swedish family and Wilhelm Hising, a member of the family who later was raised to the nobility and became known as Hisinger, sent a sample to Scheele for analysis. This was in 1781. Now Scheele expected to find tungsten on account of the great density of the mineral, but in vain. He therefore replied that he was unable to find anything new in it.

For a while no further notice was taken, but in 1803 Klaproth examined it and concluded a new earth was present which he called *terre ochroite*, because it turned dark yellow when heated. Simultaneously and independently Berzelius and Hisinger studied the mineral and discovered the same new earth to which they gave the name *ceria* in recognition of the minor planet Ceres, then newly discovered (in 1801) by Piazzi and named after the Sicilian goddess Ceres Ferdinandea, who is to be identified with Ceres, the Roman goddess of corn. The mineral itself became in consequence known as *cerite*.

In 1839 Mosander showed that the ceria obtained by Berzelius was not a simple earth but a mixture. When suspended in potash and chlorinated, a yellow, insoluble residue was obtained, which Mosander regarded as true *ceria* and the earth present in the soluble portion he called *lanthana*, from the Greek *lanthano*, I lurk. Precipitation of the lanthana yielded a brownish earth; but Mosander rightly believed that it ought to be white and that its brown colour was due to impurity, and in 1840 he proved this to be the case by isolating a brown earth from it, leaving a colourless lanthana. This new earth he called *didymia*, from the Greek *didumos*, twin, regarding didymia as the twin brother of lanthana, the two always being associated. In 1879 Boisbaudran isolated a new earth from didymia extracted from samarskite and called it *samaria*. Six years later Auer von Welsbach observed that didymium freed from samaria was still complex, its salts on fractionation yielding green and rose-red portions. He therefore termed the earth yielding green salts *praseodymia* (Greek *prason*, leek) and the one yielding rose-red derivatives *neodymia* (Greek *neos*, new). Even now the tale was not quite complete. The presence of small amounts of a new earth was demonstrated by Demarcay in 1896, which he called *Europia*.

The method evolved by Moseley (1887 to 1915) of determining the atomic number enabled chemists to ascertain, as has already been seen, the maximum number of elements that can exist in serial order between any two selected ones. As the atomic numbers of lanthanum and lutecium are 57 and 71, it is clear that it is possible for 13 elements to exist of atomic numbers between these. Now europium was the twelfth to be discovered, but no element corresponding to 61 had been recorded. This should lie between neodymium (60) and samarium (62), and as early as 1902 Bohuslav Brauner had predicted its existence. In 1926 Hopkins, of Illinois, with his collaborators Harris and Yntema, announced the discovery of a new element in the neodymium extracted from monazite sand, the lines of the X-ray spectrum agreeing with those expected for element 61. He called it *Illinium*.

About the same time, Prof. Rolla, of the Royal University of Florence, announced that he had, a couple of years before, obtained evidence of the existence of the same element and called it *florentium*. The results had been deposited in a sealed package with the *Reale Accademia* in June 1924, and the contents were withheld from publication until November 1926 — a singular procedure, to say the very least.

Considerable doubt has been expressed as to whether element 61 has been detected in nature at all. As a general rule pairs of

---

The order of the discovery of the cerium earths is summarised in the following scheme —

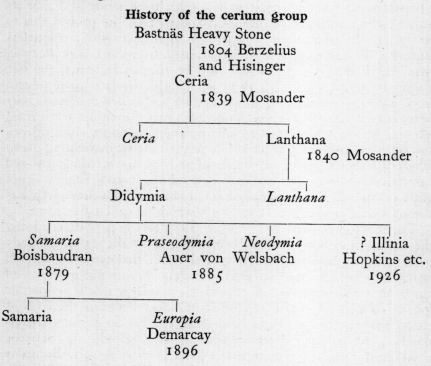

History of the cerium group

Bastnäs Heavy Stone
1804 Berzelius and Hisinger
Ceria
1839 Mosander

Ceria   Lanthana
1840 Mosander

Didymia   *Lanthana*

Samaria   *Praseodymia*   *Neodymia*   ? Illinia
Boisbaudran   Auer von Welsbach   Hopkins etc.
1879   1885   1926

Samaria   *Europia*
Demarcay
1896

---

stable isobares of adjoining elements are incapable of existence; one must be unstable. Now the known isotopes of neodymium and samarium are all stable, viz. —

(60) Nd .. 142 143 144 145 146   148
(62) Sm ..   144   147 148 149 150

There is thus no room for a stable element 61 between them. But an unstable 61 might exist. Evidence has been obtained of its production by bombardment of neodymium and praseodymium by deuterons, α-particles and protons, the products having half lives ranging from 2·7 hours to 200 days, possibly indicating the existence of various isotopes of varying stabilities. Also during bombardment of uranium with neutrons, element 61 of mass 147 has been obtained, its half life being about 4 years*.

Its properties are found to agree with those to be expected from its position in the Periodic Table. The names *promethium* and *cyclonium* have also been suggested for this element in view of its artificial production.

The position to be allotted to the rare-earth metals in the Periodic Table has been the subject of much discussion. They cannot be accommodated in the usual way and the present author has arranged them, purely for convenience, in a belt across the table (see page 5). They do not conform in their properties with the elements in the same vertical columns.

The rare earth metals are extracted from their oxides by the alumino-thermic process. An indefinite mixture of these metals obtained by reduction of the mixed earths is known as *misch-metall* and is used for the reduction of other refractory oxides. Alloys of cerium are used in automatic lighters, tracer bullets and luminescent shells. Those rich in cerium are used as reducing agents and for flashlight powders.

---

*See note, p. 5. Apparently even more stable is isotope 145, of half life approx 30 years (BUTEMENT, *Nature*, 1951, **167**, 400).

CHAPTER 16

THE HEAVY METALS
LEAD, TIN, AND MERCURY

Lead

OWING to its softness lead did not play an important rôle in the life of primitive man. His interest in metals was mainly confined to their uses as ornaments or as weapons yielding hard and sharp cutting edges. Lead is not suitable for either of these purposes. It can be hammered out into sheets and rolled into pipes, but of what use would these be to the cave man or even to his immediate successors? Only at a much later date would it occur to him that lead might be moulded into containing-vessels and by reason of its density used for sinking his fishing nets.

Primitive metallurgy of lead

The bright appearance of galena would attract early man, for it often lay on or very close to the surface of the soil. Having already learned how to reduce copper ores in his primitive furnace, he would experience no difficulty in reducing galena. It was sufficient merely to roast it in air, whereby the sulphur burned off and the molten metal sank into the hearth.

The early hunters in Missouri practised a crude version of this process; they threw pieces of galena into a fire made in the hollow of a fallen tree, or in an old stump, and scraped the resulting metal out of the ashes. Much of the metal was of course lost in the slag.

The Indians of the Mississippi valley obtained their lead in a somewhat more pretentious manner. They piled logs on the ground and laid smaller pieces of wood round them; lead ore was now thrown on to the heap. The fire was ignited in the evening and next morning the ashes were searched for lumps of lead.

The early French settlers in S.E. Missouri dug a hole in the ground in the shape of a large brick; in the centre of this a stick was fixed so that, when the ore was reduced in the fire, the molten lead collected in the cavity as an ingot with a hole. On cooling, a raw-hide rope was passed through the hole to facilitate transport when the ingot was swung either on the shoulder of a man or upon the back of a horse*.

Lead in Holy Writ

Lead is mentioned nine times in the Old Testament but, as with silver, not until after the Flood *circa* 4000 B.C. It was one of the metals traded in the fairs at Tarshish, probably our Andalusia, along with silver, iron and "tin" (*Ezekiel* xxvii. 12). The great density of lead was a matter of common knowledge; in the Song of Moses, which celebrated the flight of the Hebrews from Egypt and their escape from the pursuing troops of the Pharaoh, we read that the chariots "sank as lead in the mighty waters" (*Exod.* xv. 10).

An interesting passage in Job reads as follows—"Oh that my words were now written! Oh that they were printed in a book! that they were graven with an iron pen and lead in the rock forever!" (*Job* xix. 23, 24). This evidently refers to the use of lead sheets as writing material. The Book of Job was not all composed at the same time. It appears to have been finally compiled in the fourth century B.C., but portions of earlier MSS. were undoubtedly incorporated into the text. Astronomers calculate that the curious reference to Arcturus in *Job* ix. 9 probably dates back to 750 B.C. Even at that date the practice of inscribing on soft metals had already been long established for important documents. It was paralleled in ancient Assyria by the customary habit of writing on clay tablets which were afterwards baked to ensure permanency of the record.

Hesiod, next to Homer the earliest Greek poet whose works are still extant, lived during the eighth century B.C. and would thus be co-eval with the passage in Job above referred to. He wrote seven of his books on sheets of lead.

An inscription on lead has been found on the site of ancient Nineveh, and thin sheets of the same metal, bearing amulitic texts, have been unearthed at Babylon. The Phœnicians believed they could communicate with the dead by dropping little rolls of inscribed lead sheets into the tombs.

Lead and Egypt

Lead was known to the ancient Egyptians by whom it appears to have been regarded as an inferior kind of silver. It has been found

---

*RICKARD, *J. Inst. Metals*, 1930, **43**, 297.

in predynastic remains almost as early as those in which silver first occurs, being used for sacred figures and, in sheet form, as a cover for wood. Beads of galena frequently occur in predynastic tombs; the powdered ore was used as an eye paint almost as commonly as malachite (basic copper carbonate) both in predynastic and in First dynastic times.

Lead and galena were not plentiful in the early dynastic periods, but by the advent of the New Kingdom, *circa* 1580 B.C., the metal was fairly common; the fishermen used it regularly for weighting the edges of their nets as is done at present. By the sixth century B.C. it was used on a much larger scale as, for example, in making water tanks.

Lead ores occur in Egypt and were worked there; but when at the height of her power, Egypt received also much lead as "presents" or tribute from neighbouring countries.

Sheet lead was used as a damp course in the walls of ancient Babylon, and inscriptions were engraved by the Babylonians on sheets of lead.

Lead and the Mediterranean

Lead was known to the peoples of the Mediterranean at a very early date.

A hideous idol of metallic lead, evidently representing an ancient goddess, was found in the second ancient city of Troy dating back to *circa* 2200 B.C. Xenophon, writing *circa* 400 B.C., tells us that the Rhodian slingers used lead balls whereas the Persians used stone ones, as did David in combat with Goliath, about 1030 B.C. Roman and Greek sling bullets, made of lead, have been found in Cyprus. The Greek word for lead was *molybdos* (p. 53), but this word was also used to denote plumbago. It is difficult to say when the ancients learned to distinguish between lead and our modern tin.

Lead and the Romans

Pliny, writing at the beginning of the Christian era (see note p. 18) was familiar with both tin and lead; he referred to lead as *plumbum nigrum*, whilst tin was *plumbum album* or *candidum*. Nevertheless, he seemed to regard them as varieties of the same metal rather than as separate species. Plumbum by itself invariably meant lead; the word *stannum* or *stagmum* sometimes meant tin and sometimes an alloy of lead and silver.

The Romans used lead on an enormous scale for water pipes, cooking utensils, etc, and lead poisoning appears to have been frequent. They obtained much lead from Spain and later from Britain. Lead pipes of Roman origin have been found in Bath with walls nearly half an inch in thickness and of internal diameter from 4 to 5 in. Lead pipes were made by folding strips of sheet lead into the required shape, probably by beating round a wooden core or mandrel until the longitudinal edges of the sheet met. The edges were then either welded at the seam or joined with molten lead.

Rome in the first century of the Christian era had a remarkable water supply system administered by a body of officials comparable to the modern Water Board. The chief officer was the *Curator Aquarum;* the supply of water was taken from nine different sources, including springs and lakes from 10 to 60 miles from the city; supplies suitable for potable purposes were kept apart from less pure waters which were used for public fountains, baths and sanitation. Each length of pipe bore raised inscriptions formed by impressions in the sand bed in which the lead sheet was cast. The inscriptions indicated the person authorised to receive the water.

Pliny states that the Public Acts in his time (A.D. 23 to 79) were preserved on plates of lead. In 1699 Montfaucon purchased in Rome an ancient book entirely composed of lead. It measured about 4 inches long by 3 across, and not only were the two pieces that formed the cover and the six leaves made of lead, but also the stick inserted through the rings to hold the leaves.

Silver in lead

British lead ores invariably contain some silver; the average for Britain as a whole is some 4 to 5 oz. per ton of lead. Ores in Cornwall and Devonshire are very rich with some 30 to 70 oz. in the former county reaching to 170 oz. in the latter*.

Pre-Roman lead does not appear to have been de-silverised, but the Romans certainly knew how to abstract the silver by cupellation (p. 190) long before they invaded Britain. Probably they worked lead ores with the dual object of obtaining both silver and lead. Many Roman lead pigs bear the inscription *ex arg*, that is, silver extracted. Analysis of Roman pigs show their silver contents to have often been very low. The following silver contents from

---

*H. Louis, *loc. cit.* E. A. Smith, *J. Inst. Metals*, 1927, **37**, 74.

ancient samples of lead illustrate the great variation that has been found to occur* —

	Silver per cent
Sumerian lead from Al 'Ubaid, Imgig Relief, 3100–3000 B.C.†	0·0131
Egyptian net sinker, *circa* 1400 B.C.	0·0282
Assyrian lead 700–600 B.C.	0·011
Spartan lead 700–500 B.C.	0·0568
British lead net sinker from Meare Lake Village, Somerset, 250 B.C.–A.D. 50	0·0077
Roman lead from Bath, A.D. 44–100	0·0027
Lead from Merlin's Cave, Wye Valley, A.D. 100–400	0·0263
Lead from Glastonbury Abbey, A.D. 1130–1184	0·0327
Lead pipe from Rievaulx Abbey, A.D. 1131–1500	0·0084
Lead bullet from Marston Moor, A.D. 1644‡	0·0073
Ordinary commercial lead (1920)	0·0020
Ordinary commercial lead (1928)	0·0004

The low silver contents of Roman lead as compared with earlier eastern specimens and some of the western ones, notably those from Merlin's cave and Glastonbury Abbey are a tribute to the efficiency of Roman desilverisation processes.

Lead in Britain

There is no evidence that lead was produced in any quantity in Britain before the arrival of the Romans; on their arrival they found large quantities of surface ores, and lost no time in turning the mineral wealth of Britain to account. More than 50 Roman lead pigs have been found in Britain, some near the ancient mines where they were produced, others near the roads leading from them to Roman stations. As these were merely "strays" it is evident that enormous quantities of lead must have been produced during the Roman occupation. This conclusion is supported by the vast extent of Roman mining excavations and accumulations of slag and other

---

*FRIEND and THORNEYCROFT, *J. Inst. Metals*, 1929, **41**, 105.

†This Relief is described on p. 91. The antlers of the left hand stag, made of hammered copper bar, had been fixed into the head of the stag with lead poured into the root holes. The lead had in both cases corroded and burst open the head. Through the kindness of the British Museum Authorities a fragment of the lead was made available for analysis.

‡This was a genuine, authentic bullet, and its analysis confirms this.

debris*. In Mendip mines Roman lamps have been found made of lead.

It is evident that many of the pigs were cast very shortly after the Romans arrived here. As the pigs invariably bear inscriptions, often with the Emperor's name, they can usually be roughly dated; but only roughly, for news would travel but slowly to outlying posts and an Emperor might well be dead for some time before the miners became aware of it.

The mines were under the control of the state; the administrative officer who regulated a mining area was known as the *procurator metallorum*; although sometimes worked by the state the mines were usually farmed out by the procurator to private prospectors, called *occupatores*, from whom a royalty was demanded in the form of a percentage, sometimes amounting to 50 per cent, of the produce. This perhaps accounts for the fact that pigs of lead sometimes bear the name of some person other than the emperor, representing the portion kept by the private prospector. The miners themselves were largely slaves; but even so provision was made for pit-head baths, the Romans thus setting an excellent example in cleanliness†.

Among leaden articles belonging to the Roman period are pipes, coffins, cists, etc. The Romans also used articles of pewter (p. 211), at that time an alloy of lead and tin in the ratio of 1 to 4. Probably the two metals were deliberately mixed to produce the pewter, for the Romans were familiar with solder. It is possible, however, that pewter may have been produced in the first instance from a natural mixture of tin and lead ores, just as bronze resulted from a mixture of tin and copper ores (p. 91). Professor Louis has recorded such an occurrence in the Far East, where he found the Chinese smelting a natural mixture of lead and tin ores obtained by washing certain alluvials in the State of Patain in the northern part of the Malay Peninsula.

Large quantities of lead were used by the Romans in the construction of the baths in the Somerset town of Bath. It has been suggested that baths may have been there before the Roman occupation, but the evidence is slight and the need for them would appear to be even slighter, for the early British are usually

---

*GOWLAND, "Huxley Memorial Lecture for 1912", Royal Anthropological Institute of Great Britain and Ireland, p. 275.
†WHEELOCK, "Prehistoric and Roman Wales" (Clarendon Press, 1925), p. 269.

regarded as having belonged to the great army of the unwashed. The baths as we know them were founded by Vespasian or else by his son and successor, Titus, that is between A.D. 69 and 81. Originally there were two baths, divided by a street that ran from north to south, and in the centre of each was a hot spring rising at a temperature of some 113°F (45° C). The bottom of the bath was paved with sheet lead, the whole being built below street level so that pumps were not required. During excavations a unique lead consecration cross was discovered, believed to date from the seventh century A.D. It is worked on a plaque about 3 inches in diameter and bears the names of the four evangelists with a Latin inscription*.

When the Romans withdrew from Britain they left behind them a firmly established lead industry. No doubt this continued through the unsettled periods that followed, for the Venerable Bede or Bæda (672 to 735) wrote in his "Historia Ecclesiastica Gentis Anglorum", on which his literary fame rests, that *Venis metallorum, aeris, ferri et plumbi et argenti fecunda*, which means that Britain "is rich in veins of the metals copper, iron, lead and silver". This book was subsequently translated into Anglo-Saxon by Alfred the Great (849 to 901), the word plumbum being rendered "leade" (lead), this being the first recorded use of this English word.

Bede also stated that the Bishop of Lindisfarne removed the thatch from his church and covered the roof and the sides with sheets of lead. This would be *circa* A.D. 680.

Lead in Derbyshire

Lead was being worked at the time of the Norman invasion in 1066, for reference is made in the Domesday Book to the lead mines or *plumbaria* in Derbyshire and to the salt works and lead furnaces at Droitwich in Worcestershire†. The Normans used lead very largely for coffins, for church ornaments and for roofing churches.

Wirksworth, now a producer of limestone, was from very early days the chief centre of the lead industry of Derbyshire, but lead mining has almost died out now. The expense of freeing the deep workings from water raised the cost of production unduly and enabled foreign ores to swamp the market. The lead was regarded as amongst the finest in Britain.

---

*BADDELEY, "Bath and Bristol" (Nelson, 1908), p. 21.
†See A. BALLARD, "The Domesday Boroughs" (Clarendon Press, 1904), p. 62.

It is estimated that there are between four and five thousand derelict lead-mine shafts on the limestone uplands of Derbyshire; all now fenced round as a safeguard for wandering animals. The lead in the Wirksworth region was certainly worked by the Romans, and the late Professor Windle believed that their town of Lududarum was Wirksworth. Pigs of lead bearing Roman inscriptions have been unearthed in the vicinity, the first, found in 1777, bearing the mark of the Emperor Hadrian, about A.D. 120. In Saxon days the manor of Wirksworth belonged to Repton Abbey, and early in the eighth century an Abbess of Repton sent a coffin from her lead mines at Wirksworth to Crowland for the burial of St. Guthlac.

Defoe, who expressed little admiration for Derbyshire folk, wrote of Wirksworth about 1720—"There is no very great trade to this town but what relates to the lead works, and to the subterranean wretches, who they call Peakrills, who work in the mines . . . . The inhabitants are a rude boorish kind of people, but they are a bold, daring, and even desperate kind of fellows in their search into the bowels of the earth."

Any man was at liberty to prospect for lead and mark out his claim, and he had the right to a direct draw-way, three oxen wide, to the nearest highroad, provided it did not pass through churchyard, garden or orchard. A proportion of the ore was payable to the King or the lord of the manor, and the lead was measured in wooden dishes. These dishes had to be taken periodically to Wirksworth to be tested by a standard measure. The only ancient standard now known to exist is preserved in the Moot Hall at Wirksworth. It is in fine bronze and holds fourteen pints. Part of the inscription, in Old English characters, reads—"This dishe was made the iiij day of October, the iiij year of the reigne of Kyng Henry the VIII . . . This Dishe to Remayne in the Moote Hall at Wyrksworth hangyng by a cheyne so as the Merchauntes or mynours (miners) may have resorte to the same at all tymes to make the trw mesur after the same."

The fuel problem

The rapid disappearance of our forests in the attempt to supply the metallurgical industries with charcoal caused the authorities no little concern. Cardinal Wolsey attempted to reduce his lead ore with coal instead of with the more usual charcoal in his smelting furnace at Gateshead-on-Tyne; but as he subsequently disposed of the furnace, in 1527, to one Thomas Wynter, it would appear

193

O

probable that the attempt proved a failure. In the reign of Queen Elizabeth two Acts of Parliament were passed, one in 1558 and the second in 1584, with the object of preserving the timber (p. 278). In 1678 a patent was granted to Viscount Grandison for smelting lead ore in a reverberatory furnace with sea-coal. Fourteen years later the famous London Lead Company was founded under a charter of William and Mary "for smelting down lead with pit coal and sea coal". This company carried on lead smelting operations continuously until it was finally wound up in 1905.

Lead and the alchemists

The alchemists used the sign ♄ to denote lead, as has already been mentioned; the curved portion suggests a connection between lead and silver. Lead was under the influence of Saturn and the symbol was often called the scythe of Saturn. In consequence of the high density of the metal the term saturnine became synonymous with heavy, dense, or dull-witted. Minium or red lead was known as saturnine red.

A favourite experiment was the production of the "lead tree" or *arbor Saturni* by suspending a piece of zinc in a solution of some soluble lead salt such as the acetate, popularly known as "sugar of lead". The experiment is popular to-day.

Lead was often regarded as a debased form of silver and in the Middle Ages it was held that lead in progress of time became transmuted into bismuth and later into the more precious metal.

In A.D. 1121 Al Khazini, an Arabian philosopher, wrote a book on the physical properties of matter. He discussed the balance and gave the density of lead as 11·33, coincident with the modern value of 11·33 to 11·35.

Uses of lead

Commercial lead is a metal with a high degree of purity. The foreign metals generally present include copper, antimony, zinc and iron; less frequently bismuth and traces of tin and arsenic. Silver is almost completely extracted by desilverising processes. The total metallic impurities rarely exceed 0·1 per cent and may fall below 0·01.

Lead is used as sheets for gutters, spouts, etc. As strips for "leaded lights", in pipes for water, gas, electric wiring, etc. It was once used a great deal for roofing cathedrals and churches; but it was very heavy. Wren used it for the dome of St Paul's Cathedral (begun 1675) because his workmen were not equal to the task of using copper (p. 103). It is estimated that had copper been used the weight of the roof would have been reduced by some 600 tons. This would have greatly relieved the anxiety of those responsible for the safety of Wren's masterpiece.

Owing to its resistance to acids lead is in demand for chemical plants. As an example the lead chambers used in the manufacture of sulphuric acid may be quoted. They are constructed of sheet lead, about 3 mm. in thickness, the sheets being autogenously soldered — that is, lead is used as solder to prevent electrolytic action in contact with acid — or sealed by a blow-pipe flame. Chambers frequently exceed 40,000 c. ft. in individual capacity, and a series of three or four is commonly used, the gases being conducted from one to the other by lead pipes.

Thin sheet lead is frequently used as a lining for wooden cases or chests in which tea is imported.

Hardened with a little antimony it is used in storage batteries or accumulators, for cables, and occasionally for statuary. For this last, however, it is not really suitable; its dull colour is not prepossessing. Bullets, etc, are made of lead hardened with 4 to 12 per cent of antimony. Other important alloys are solder (p. 212), type metal (p. 197) and bearing metals, which contain also tin and antimony.

Pewter in Roman times contained 1 of lead to 4 of tin; in the Middle Ages 1 of Pb to 3 of Sn were used. The amount of lead was gradually increased until the alloy became too debased and fell out of favour. Modern pewter contains no lead (p. 212).

The density of lead makes it useful in making the builders' plumb lines and for "sounding" apparatus at sea. It is this latter use which has given rise to the expression "swinging the lead", which indicates a shirking of duty.

In "sounding" the lead must be "heaved". The lead weighs from 10 to 14 lb, therefore "heaving the lead" is not light work, even for a strong man. It is for this reason that a leadsman will make his "swing" last several minutes before finally "heaving". So to "swing the lead" became a recognised Navy term for an excuse for shirking; in some way it passed into Army parlance, and so into popular usage.

Archers were wont to carry heavy leaden mallets as part of their equipment and this was an important factor in winning, for example, the battle of Agincourt in 1415, the heavy mallets of the British archers crashing through the iron helmets of the French knights whose horses were held fast in the mud.

Lead shot

At one time lead shot was made by cutting sheet lead into small squares thus producing little cubes which were then rolled into little balls or shot—a laborious process, which has long since been discarded. The addition of a little arsenic to lead renders it less viscous in the molten state, and the alloy thus produced is now used in making shot by a more efficient and rapid process. The shot tower erected on the south bank of the Thames has long been famous. Fortunately, despite near misses, it escaped destruction by German bombs in both of the Great Wars; during World War II operations were carried on all the time, many thousand tons of lead shot being turned out as its contribution to victory. The tower looks like a tall chimney stack and has usually been regarded as such by the casual visitor; if one looks more closely, however, windows can be seen at various levels let into the wall, and near the top is a gallery. Probably the tower was deliberately designed to resemble a chimney stack in order to deceive the curious, as the process of making shot in this way was kept a secret for many years. The tower was taken over by the L.C.C. in 1948 and is now no longer used for shot making; at the moment, it is adding interest to the South Bank site of the 1951 Festival of Britain.

Molten lead passed as drops through a "card" or colander perforated with numerous holes — 1448 for the smallest shot — and fell into water which usually contained a little sodium sulphide. This coated the shot with a thin layer of sulphide of a lustrous black metallic colour which remained permanent in moist air. The size of the shot depended not only on the diameter of the holes in the colander, but also on the initial temperature and composition of the molten metal. The shot was sorted by sieves and by rolling down an inclined plane, the imperfectly shaped pellets remaining behind. Finally the shot was polished by rolling with plumbago in a barrel or rumble.

A curious story is told* of the invention of this process of making shot. One night, about the year 1782, William Watts, a Bristol plumber, dreamed that he was out in a shower, and the raindrops were not water but lead shot. On waking he argued that, by allowing molten lead to fall from a considerable height into water, the drops

---

*W. JONES, "The Treasures of the Earth" (Warne), p. 205.

would become spherical, and a great improvement might thus be effected in shot manufacture. The experiment was tried from the tower of St Mary Redcliffe Church, Bristol, and proved successful. Watts accordingly patented his idea, and erected a works which he ultimately sold for £10,000. But here his beneficent angel left him; he expended more money than he could afford in attempting to build houses at Clifton, for which considerable excavation work was necessary, and the half-finished parts of the buildings were for long known as "Watts's Folly".

A more modern method of producing shot embodies the use of centrifugal machines. The molten metal is poured in a thin stream upon a rapidly revolving metal disc which breaks it up into drops, the size of which depends on the rate at which the disc revolves. These drops are thrown off at a tangent by centrifugal force and are stopped by a screen.

Type metals

Probably the greatest single use of lead alloys is for type metals*. Long before these were introduced books were printed from engraved wood blocks, hard boxwood being a favourite. Each page of the book was cut laboriously in reverse by hand, an operation that took much time and required great skill. The Romans were accustomed to cast lead plates with raised inscriptions (p. 189); it is easy to be wise after the event, but it certainly seems curious that the world had to wait until the early years of the fifteenth century before a movable type became invented. The honour of this invention is usually given to Laurens Koster of Haarlem and to John Gutenberg of Mainz about 1440. In 1476 Caxton introduced the art into this country, having learned it when living abroad; he set up his press near the western entrance to Westminster Abbey. The following year was issued the first book ever to be printed in this way in England, entitled "The Dictes and Sayinges of Philosophres" — "Emprynted by one William Caxton at Westminster". The king, Edward IV, and his nobles used to visit and watch Caxton at work. To them it was a new toy.

In 1450 the whole Bible, in the Vulgate Latin, was produced.

At first leaden type was used; but it proved too soft and was later hardened by addition of a little tin. But the alloy still failed to give on casting a perfect type face, and subsequently antimony was added. This reduced contraction when the casting solidified so that

---

*"Printing Metals" (Fry's Foundries Ltd, 1936), p. 33.

the type had a good face and body. Early last century machines were invented which greatly accelerated the production of type, but even so each letter had to be set up by hand. Then came other machines, such as the linotypes and monotypes which reduced manual labour to a minimum and rendered possible the flood of newspapers and other printed matters with which we are inundated to-day. The alloy used for standard linotype metal is 86 Pb, 11 Sb and 3 Sn.

Tin*

It is, perhaps, unfortunate that the word "tin" should frequently be used in a derogatory sense, when the element itself is not under consideration. Thus a poor sounding bell is said to be "tinny" whilst another, possessed of beautiful tones, is described as "silvery". Money, the filthy lucre of *Titus* i. 7, is colloquially known as "tin". The reason for this disparagement appears to lie in the early belief that tin was not a genuine metal. Thus in Dyche and Pardon's "English Dictionary", dated 1744, we read that "tin by some is called an imperfect or compound metal, white and softer than silver, and harder than lead and so imagined to be made up of both . . ." As a debased silver, therefore, tin was not a genuine article. Although we know different to-day, the stigma remains; call a dog a bad name and it can never be any good.

The word "tinker" is also used in a derogatory sense; to tinker implies working in an inefficient or clumsy manner, and although often associated with a man who works in tin the word has nothing to do with that metal. It is derived from the Middle English *tinken*, to tink, tinkle or make a sharp, shrill sound.

"Tinsel", again, is an entirely different word derived from the Latin *scintilla*, a spark, and appears to be in no way connected with "tin", which is Anglo-Saxon. Tinsel originally meant something glittering, without any derogatory suggestion; but, apparently through false analogy with tin, it now implies cheapness if not indeed vulgarity. Thus Edmund Spenser (1553 to 1599) in his *Faerie Queen* wrote —

> "Her garments all were wrought of beaten gold,
> And all her steed with tinsel trappings shone"

There is no suggestion of paltriness here.

---

*A useful monograph "Tin through the Ages" by F. J. NORTH, was published by the National Museum of Wales on the occasion of a Temporary Exhibition in 1941.

Ancient Chinese philosophers had peculiar ideas anent tin. They believed that arsenic would generate itself in 200 years and after a further like period would become tin. The observation that wine kept in tin vessels sometimes became poisonous was regarded as confirming the idea, transmutation not being complete*.

Tin was not known in Egypt at a very early date; the earliest examples to be unearthed date only from the 18th Dynasty (1580 to 1350 B.C.). Tin is not even mentioned in the Ebers Papyrus† of 1550 B.C. although bronze has been found sporadically at a much earlier date. It would appear therefore that in Egypt tin was not *at first* reduced separately from its ore and added to copper to produce bronze, but that the mixed ores of copper and tin were smelted together, as usually elsewhere. Tomb pictures, however, indicate that by the 18th Dynasty the alloy was made by the former process. A tin vase dating back to *circa* 1200 B.C. has been found in upper Egypt and from 700 B.C. onwards tin foil was used in the wrappings of mummies.

Tin is not mentioned by name in Holy Writ before the Flood, *circa* 4000 B.C. The word occurs five times afterwards in the Old Testament and is mentioned along with silver, iron and lead as one of the metals traded in the fairs of Tarshish, the modern Andalusia of Spain (*Ezek.* xxvii. 12). As already stated, however, (p. 9) the so-called tin was an alloy of copper and tin, but containing a higher percentage of the latter metal than the ancient "brass" or bronze.

Both Homer *circa* 880 B.C. and Hesiod, who lived a century later, use the word *cassiteros* to denote tin. It is possible that it may have been borrowed from the Sanskrit *kastira*, tin, related to the verb *kas*, to shine. The Arabic word for tin is kāsdir, closely resembling the Sanskrit, although the two languages are not connected. On the other hand, Reinach has suggested that the name Cassiterides is Celtic, comparing it with Cassivellaunus, Cassignatus, Veliocasses, etc‡.

The Romans at the beginning of the Christian era were using considerable quantities of tin and clearly distinguished between it and lead. Much of their tin was undoubtedly obtained from Spain

---

*GOWLAND, "Huxley Memorial Lecture for 1912", *Royal Anthropological Institute of Great Britain and Ireland*, p. 247.

†Written during the reign of Amenhetep I and found reposing between the legs of a mummy.

‡"Guide to Early Iron Age Antiquities", British Museum, 1925, pp. 4–5.

where the metal was mined at a very early date. Pliny* called tin *plumbum candidum* or *album*, whereas lead was written as *plumbum nigrum* or simply *plumbum* (p. 188). He refers to the practice of tinning copper by dipping into molten tin (p. 205).

Tin in Britain

Diodorus Siculus, writing about 56 to 36 B.C. mentioned Britain as a source of tin. Herodotus *circa* 550 B.C. was the first to mention the *cassiterides* as such and it has been assumed by many that the Cassiterides were the Scilly Isles or, if Britain, Cornwall in particular was meant. Others have suggested the islands in Vigo Bay on the Atlantic coast of Spain. But this may be narrowing down the meaning of the word too much. Most of the passages in the ancient writers referring to these islands are quoted in Elton's "Origins of English History" and discussed at considerable length. Bailey† is of opinion that *Cassiterides* was originally a general name for the tin localities of Western Europe, covering a wide area much as we speak of the Middle East to-day without meaning Palestine in particular. The writers of those days had but a poor idea of the geography of the West and they were by no means helped by the Phœnicians themselves who did their utmost to conceal the goose that laid the tin egg; they not unnaturally wished to maintain their monopoly of the trade just as in the sixteenth century the Dutch and Portuguese guarded their secret of the discovery of Australia with the utmost jealousy (p. 125). Strabo, writing about 7 B.C. (p. 133), mentions that on one occasion a Roman vessel followed a certain Phœnician trader hoping to find the source of his tin. But the Phœnician purposely ran his vessel on to a shoal, leading his pursuers into the same disaster; he managed, however, to escape from drowning and subsequently received from the State the value of the cargo he had lost.

Pliny‡ states that there was a "fabulous story" of the Greeks sailing in quest of tin to the islands of the Atlantic and of its being brought in barks made of osiers covered with hides. There is nothing incredible in this as Pliny seems to imagine, for in an earlier book§ he had already mentioned that the British used boats of that kind —

---

*"The Natural History of Pliny", translated by Bostock and Riley (Bohn, 1857), Book 34, Chapter 48.

†BAILEY, "The Elder Pliny's Chapters on Chemical Subjects" (Arnold, 1932), Part 2, p. 193.

‡PLINY, Book 34, Chapter 37.

§PLINY, Book 4, Chapter 30.

but perhaps he had forgotten. The Greeks called these boats *coracles*, evidently a term borrowed or adapted from the Celtic *cren* or *croen* meaning skin*.

The Phœnicians themselves stated that the inhabitants of the islands where they traded were clad in black cloaks and in tunics reaching to the feet, with girdles round their waists, and that they walked with staves and were bearded like goats. So if these were indeed Cornishmen we now know what some of our ancestors were like.

In Cornwall, tin was mined in the bronze age; the tin trade† was already in existence at the time of Pythias, 325 B.C., and possibly the trade had been carried on since 450 B.C. It is possible that the Phœnicians sought tin in Britain as early as 1000 B.C. for it is certain they had even then passed through the Straits of Gibraltar and founded Cadiz. Irish gold work of about 1200 B.C. has been found at Gaza, so there must have been some connection between our Islands and the Mediterranean. The tin may have been shipped from St Michael's Mount or from the Isle of Thanet; possibly from both. It seems then to have found its way to the Loire or the Garonne, or to both these rivers, and thence overland to the Mediterranean. A Falmouth tradition holds that the Phœnician trade with Britain was first transacted on the Black Rock, a jagged islet at the entrance to the Carrick Roads.

Julius Cæsar and other Roman historians were rather prone to disparage the British whom they had defeated. This was foolish and belittled their own efforts, for their soldiers found the British very sturdy foes; warriors like Caractacus and Cassivellaunus were no mean antagonists. For many years it was supposed that our Celtic ancestors were barbarous folk, poor in physique and ill-clad, their bodies being stained with woad. This is an entirely wrong picture. British priests or Druids were a cultured and highly educated sect, possessing a high standard of scientific attainment. They had invented a water clock which enabled them to measure the passage of time beneath our leaden skies; sundials by day and clock-stars by night, so valuable in the East, were of little avail here. So great was the renown of the Druids that young men flocked over to Britain from the Continent to receive instruction at first hand from them. Britain was the university of Western Europe. In addition to this, Britain carried on an extensive commerce with

---

*A. TYLER, *Nature*, 1883, **29**, 84.
†BROMEHEAD, *ibid.*, 1940, **146**, 405.

the mainland of Europe, and must even have been a naval power, for the assistance she sent to the Veneti in Gaul evidently worried Cæsar and was made the pretext of the Roman invasion. Further, Tacitus, writing about A.D. 115, speaks of London after Cæsar's invasion as a city of great importance. This was obviously no mushroom growth that could spring up in a night.

There was a concentration of Roman roads at Venta Belgarum or Winchester, as a glance at the map in Fig. 7 shows. Such roads were clearly built mainly for military purposes but they must also have been designed with an eye to easy transport of metallurgical products. Of two roads to the north, one veered eastwards to

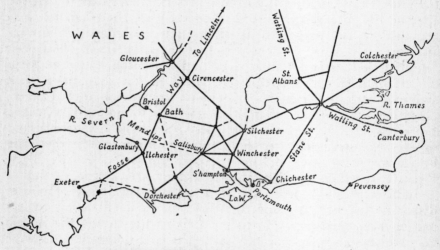

Fig. 7 — The Roman roads of Southern Britain

Silchester and thence to Londinium; the other turned westwards ending in *Fosse Way*, which connected Exeter and *Aquaesulis* or Bath with Lincoln. To the west lay a road passing through *Old Sarum*, that is Salisbury, and so to the Mendips, cutting Fosse Way a few miles south of Bath. Almost due south a road led to *Clausentum* the modern Bitterne, now included in the borough of Southampton. A second road more to the east joined that from Clausentum to Chichester at Porchester Castle. From Chichester the road, called *Stane Street*, passed through Bignor, Pulborough and Dorking to Londinium. It was thus an easy matter to transport on the backs of pack-horses, through Winchester to the Hampshire coast, Cornish and Dartmoor tin, lead and iron from the Mendips, iron from S. Wales and lead from the north. On the coast were several ports, notably Southampton and *Portus Magnus* or Portsmouth, from which the cargoes could be shipped to *Vectis*, the Isle of Wight, and thence to Gaul. The metals were never sea-borne from Britain to the Mediterranean, but followed an old trade route through St. Valery-sur-Somme and Chalons-sur-Saone.

At the beginning of the thirteenth century the tin miners of Cornwall began to make history of their own. Mining had been carried on, as we have seen, for more than 1,000 years, and the tinmen had formed a separate community. Their political position was unique. The tinman or "stannary" worker paid taxes not as an Englishman but as a miner. He lived, not by common law, but by miners' law, his courts were miners' courts, his parliament the Miners' Parliament. The parliament of the stannaries not only made its own laws but possessed the power to veto any national legislation that infringed the miners' privileges. These privileges were definitely confirmed by John in 1201.

When, in 1337, Edward III created his son the first Duke of Cornwall, it was done in order that the Black Prince might enjoy the revenues, derived chiefly from the tin mines of the county.

Tin and the alchemists

The western alchemists called tin *diabolus metallorum*, because of its peculiar crackling "cry" when bent due to the crystals crushing against each other. On account of its brightness coupled with its cry, tin was associated with the thunderbolt of Jupiter and about the sixth century received the sign ♃ (p. 13). Here again, as in lead, the curved portion indicates analogy with silver. The sign of the cross is once more in evidence. In ancient Persia tin was associated with the planet Venus.

A favourite experiment was the production of the "tin tree" by suspending a rod of zinc in a solution of tin chloride; tin deposited as the zinc dissolved yielding the *arbor Jovis*, analogous to the silver and lead trees already mentioned.

Tin plague

Aristotle, 384 to 322 B.C. was aware that, when kept very cold, tin undergoes a change which he described as "melting", for want of a better term. Since then attention has on numerous occasions been directed to this curious phenomenon. Thus in 1851 the tin organ-pipes in the church at Zeits were found to be attacked, the metal

203

crumbling to a powder. Some sixteen years later, after an extremely bitter winter in Russia (1867 to 8), blocks of tin stored in the Customs House at St Petersburg were found reduced to a greyish powder. This is variously known as *tin plague*, *tin pest* and *museum sickness*, and is due to the conversion of ordinary white tin into its grey allotrope, the transition temperature being 13° C, below which the grey tin is the stable form. As the temperature falls, white tin tends to change to grey at an increased rate, a maximum velocity being reached at −50° C. The white metal first tarnishes, then becomes covered with a number of grey warts, finally crumbling to a powdery mass. Fortunately, at the ordinary winter temperatures in Britain the rate at which this change occurs is very small. But the "disease" is contagious and if a "sick" piece of tin is allowed to remain in contact with white tin at a temperature below the transition point, the latter metal is more rapidly converted to grey than would otherwise be the case.

Tin is an important constituent of solder (p. 212). During Captain Scott's ill-fated expedition to the South Pole (1910 to 1912) the petrol tins were found to leak. It is believed that, exposed to the intense cold of the Antarctic, the solder disintegrated in consequence of the tin changing into its allotropic grey form and thus failed to keep the tins tight. Amundsen, who succeeded in reaching the South Pole a few weeks before Scott, recorded that his petrol tins required frequent re-soldering, presumably for the same reason.

It may well be that the tin plague is largely responsible for the paucity of ancient objects of pure tin. The addition of lead to tin appears to retard this change and it is worthy of note that of many hundreds of Roman tin objects that have survived until present times and have been examined all contain some lead. A soldier's button, which microscopic examination shows to have been cast, contained 0·84 per cent of lead; a jug from Glastonbury, 12·22; a cup 4·49; and a coffin from Ilchester, Somerset, 55·31 of lead, this last-named alloy being close to common solder in composition. On the whole, the Romans used a wide range of alloys of the two metals ranging from 4 : 1 to 1 : 4, and presumably determined by experience which alloys were best suited for any particular purpose*.

*J. A. SMYTHE, *Trans. Newcomen Soc.*, 1937–1938, **18**, 255. RICHMOND and SMYTHE, *Proc. Univ. Durham Phil. Soc.*, 1938, **10**, 48. A. WAY, *Arch. Journal*, 1859, **16**, 38.

The tin-plate industry

The largest consumption of tin occurs in the tin-plate industry, the history of which is extremely interesting.

Pliny* mentioned the application of protective coatings of tin to copper and iron to preserve the underlying metal from corrosion. "It was in the Gallic provinces", he wrote, "that the method was discovered of coating articles of copper with tin so as to be scarcely distinguishable from silver. Articles thus plated are known as *incoctilia*." The last term means "in-boiled", evidently referring to the practice of immersing the article to be coated in the molten tin. Pliny adds that this process was extended to coating base metals with silver and gold.

Apparently during Norman times iron was coated with tin in this country, but the application of the process was limited because sheet metal had to be made by the laborious practice of hammering out blocks of metal. The real tin-plate industry began in Bohemia *circa* 1240.

Subsequently the Duke of Saxony, learning of the wonderful properties of tin-plate and the great success of the Bohemian trade, determined to introduce the same into his country†. To this end he obtained the services of a Roman Catholic priest who, disguised as a Lutheran, went to Bohemia to pick up what information he could. Spying of this kind seems to have been popular in the Middle Ages, and it must be conceded that the priest did extremely well. He returned to Saxony with the necessary information and in a short time a thriving tin-plate industry was established. France now wished to emulate Saxony, and Colbert, Minister to Louis xiv (1643 to 1715), friend of the British King Charles ii, deputed Réaumur to visit Saxony and in his turn glean all the information he could. René de Réaumur (1683 to 1757) was a famous French scientist, chiefly remembered to-day, perhaps, for his thermometric scale (p. 226). As the result of Réaumur's visit, tin-plate works were set up in France, the labour being apparently carried out by German workmen; but the pay was regarded as insufficient, the workmen "struck" or withdrew and the trade died out.

Early in the reign of Charles ii (1660 to 1685) Thomas Allgood, a native of Northamptonshire, went to Pontypool to extract

---

*PLINY, *Opus cit.*, Book 34, Chapter 48.
†CHARLES WILKINS, "History of the Iron, Steel, Tinplate and other Trades of Wales" (Williams, 1903), Chapter 33. P. W. FLOWER, "A History of the Tin Trade" (Bell, 1880).

copperas and oil from the coal. An iron trade had already been established there, records of which date back to 1588. During the course of his experiments Allgood discovered a method of varnishing tin-plate so as to imitate the lacquered articles imported from Japan, then known widely as Japanware. The necessary tin-plate was accordingly imported from Saxony. To produce it in this country and thus make Britain independent of foreign trade was the aim of Andrew Yarranton*. In 1632, when a lad of 16, Andrew was apprenticed to a linen draper in Worcester. But the work was not to his taste and he ran away. When civil war broke out he joined the Parliamentary army, rising to the rank of captain. He distinguished himself by uncovering a Royalist plot to seize Doyley House in Herefordshire. For this he received the thanks of Parliament together with the substantial honorarium of £500. On sheathing his sword he started an iron works near Bewdley in 1652 and became interested in the development of canals and of river transport. He was one of the first to recognise the value of clover in agriculture.

On the accession of Charles II in 1660, people recalled that he had been of the opposite faction, charges were trumped up against him and he was thrown into prison. After an eventful escape, recapture and trial, he was released and in 1665 turned his attention to the possibility of manufacturing tin-plate in Britain. In 1667 he was sent out to Saxony, with a workman who understood iron, and an interpreter, by a number of interested gentlemen, so that he might learn the secrets of the process. "Coming to the works" wrote Yarranton "we were very civilly treated and, contrary to our expectation, we had much liberty to view and see the works go, with the way and manner of their working and extending the plates; as also the perfect view of such materials as they used in cleaning the plates to make them fit to take tinn, with the way they used in tinning them over when clear'd from their rust and blackness." When he had found out all he needed to know Yarranton returned to England and set up a factory in Worcester. In 1670 the Worshipful Company of Tinplate Workers was incorporated. Trouble, however, arose at Worcester in connection with patents, for his secret had leaked out, and Yarranton closed his factory.

John Hanbury now enters the picture. He was a Kidderminster man, destined for the bar. But he was more interested in mines and

---

*See "Dictionary of National Biography" edited by L. Stephen (London, 1888)

forges than in law. He was not without means which he made all the more substantial by a prudent marriage, and settled in Pontypool, Mon. Here he extended and "improved" the iron works to such an extent that a visitor, some years later, described the place as "A large, dirty, straggling town standing near the entrance of a once picturesque valley filled with ironworks and collieries."

At Pontypool the tin-plate was made as follows. Sheet iron was prepared by flattening out hot slabs of metal under a helve or tilt-hammer; the slabs, when reduced in thickness, were doubled over and piled, with other similarly thinned plates, under the hammer, their surfaces being sprinkled with powdered charcoal or coal to prevent welding. Hammering was continued until the resulting sheets were of the desired thickness. They were then pickled in dilute sour rye-water or vinegar to remove oxide and other surface impurities, and finally immersed in a bath of molten tin.

In 1728 Hanbury was joined by John Payne, and the same year they introduced the method of rolling the hot bars of iron into sheets between metal rollers. This was an enormous improvement. Not only could sheets be produced more rapidly but they were more uniform and even. The specification of the patent announced that "barrs, being heated... pass between two large mettall rowlers (which have proper notches or furrows on their surfuss) by the force of the inventor's engine or other power into such shapes and forms as required."

By 1740 the German imports of tin-plate were dispensed with, the plate produced in England being ample for home consumption. By 1776 England herself was exporting. It was not until 1885, however, that iron sheets were replaced by steel.

The fame of the Pontypool japanware lasted for 150 years and then decline set in. Meanwhile Wolverhampton (*circa* 1720) and other centres of industry had begun to manufacture the ware; even after Pontypool had ceased to produce it, the ware was still known as Pontypool ware.

The Old Hall at Wolverhampton, which occupied a site not far from the present library, was a remarkable mansion surrounded by a moat, built by the Levesons, a well-known county family, who acquired great wealth in the wool trade. The Hall was eventually let to the brothers Ryton, who had carried on the tin-plate trade in a small factory in Tin Shop Yard, North Street, and their enterprise made the Old Hall famous all over the world.

A further wave of prosperity followed the improvement in transport by the development of the Staffordshire and Worcestershire Canals, and then ensued a period when public taste demanded goods of high artistic merit, and japanned tea-trays, tea-caddies, coal-vases, and other goods were produced, cleverly decorated with hand-painted designs and scenes by artists of repute.

Edward Bird, R.A., was apprenticed to the japan trade at the Old Hall, and at one period Biblical scenes were the fashion. Then followed elaborate decorations in gold and colours, in Indian and Chinese designs, some splendid work being accomplished.

Another notable person associated with the Old Hall was Edwin Booth, who was a skilled workman before he became famous as a tragedian. He eventually emigrated to America and, sad to relate, it was his son, Wilkes Booth, who assassinated President Lincoln in the theatre at the close of the American Civil War.

One of the most far-reaching improvements on the manufacturing side of the industry was the introduction of Nasmyth's steam-hammer process *circa* 1840. It was on the suggestion of a foreman at the Old Hall works — Mr Pinson, afterwards of Pinson and Evans — that Nasmyth (1808 to 1890) made alterations in his steam hammer and adapted it for use in stamping articles of hollow-ware from steel and iron sheets. Originally all tin articles such as tea and coffee pots, saucepans and kettles, were made entirely by hand, but a slow and laborious method of stamping had been evolved just before Nasmyth's patent was applied. The hammer head was raised by hand by means of a winch, and later by steam, but Nasmyth's invention revolutionised the industry, and since then the machinery for the production of hollow-ware and pressed metal-ware generally has been continually improved by new inventions and adaptations.

Good may come out of evil. Military campaigns may stimulate research that ultimately proves to the good of man. Napoleon was anxious to feed his troops in regions where insufficient or even no food might be obtainable locally. He appealed to Nicholas Appert in 1808 to help him out. This man had already observed that food in airtight packages could be sterilised with heat and could then apparently be kept indefinitely. He thought that contact with air caused putrefaction. It was not until 1854 that Pasteur began those researches that culminated in the discovery that putrefaction was due to living micro-organisms.

Appert's first experiments were carried out with stout glass bottles as containers. In 1806 the French Navy tried out his preparations and apparently found them very successful. In 1809 Appert was awarded a prize of 12,000 francs in recognition of his work by the Bureau Consultatif des Artes et Manufactures.

In 1810 John Hall, founder of the Dartford Iron Works and his associate Bryan Donkin, a scientist and Fellow of the Royal Society, developed a similar process, evidently visualising an outlet for their products if iron containers could be used in place of glass. The same year patents were granted to Augustus de Heine and to Peter Durand for the preservation of food in "tin" containers. Although Durand is known both in this country and in America as the "Father of Tin Cans" neither he nor Heine appears to have engaged in canning on a commercial scale. By 1813 both the British Army and Naval authorities were interested in the scheme*. Evidently Wellington's attention had been drawn to the subject for a certain C. C. Smith wrote on his behalf a letter, dated 30th April 1813, saying that his Lordship (he was Lord Wellesley then) had found the preserved beef very good. Was it a sense of humour which made him add that his Lordship could not himself write owing to indisposition?

Captain Parry took some of Donkin's tinned foods with him on his three Arctic voyages of discovery (1819 to 1825) and found them invaluable. Some tins of meat were landed on the ice when one of his vessels, H.M.S. *Fury*, in the third expedition met her fate in August 1825; they were found several years later by Captain Ross during his voyages (1829 to 1833) and their contents were in excellent condition. Two tins brought back by Parry himself were opened as late as 1938 and the contents were still perfect — after 114 years.

Two tins of meat left over from the stores of H.M.S. *Blonde*, which went on a voyage of discovery to the Sandwich Islands in 1826, came later into the possession of Dr Alfred S. Taylor. In 1846 Taylor opened one of them before the chemistry students at Guy's Hospital, London, and noted that the meat seemed perfectly good. Unfortunately he was unable to analyse the food, for its savoury appearance and odour induced some hungry hospital assistants to sample it exhaustively. Nature did not exact any retribution for their unauthorised repast, so evidently it was

---

*"Historic Tinned Foods" (International Tin Research and Development Council, 1939). Publication 85.

P

still wholesome. In 1867 the remaining tin, then 41 years old, was opened, but the contents were bad; the tin had become perforated with rust. Taylor therefore recommended that the tins should be lacquered or painted as a protection against corrosion.

By 1820 the tin can had been introduced into the U.S.A. For 70 years the cans were made there by hand, and a tinsmith who could turn out 100 cans a day was a skilled workman indeed. Towards the close of the century automatic can-making machinery came in, and the "sanitary" top can was patented in 1904. To-day, as many as 300 cans per minute are produced by a single unit or "line" of can-making machinery in the modern plant.

The modern tin container, solderless, except for a small application on the outer edges of the side seam, represents a further improvement.

Equally great strides have been made by the canning industry in the methods used in canning foods. This improvement, together with scientific methods of sterilisation and processing, now in use by most canners, has practically eliminated "spoilage" of canned foods.

Tinned meats, fish, and fruits have long been on the market; since 1935 tinned or "canned" beer has been obtainable in the U.S.A. Some 40 per cent of America's tin consumption is absorbed by the tin-plate industry. The French call tin-plate *white iron*.

The industry consumes more tin than any other. It is stated that the quantity of tin-plate made in 1933 would suffice to form a belt round the earth at the equator 100 ft. wide.

Even cast-iron is now being tinned; cast-iron boxes required for the manufacture of penicillin have been tinned.

In medieval times sword blades were sometimes tinned to preserve them from rust, and analysis shows that inlaid inscriptions were sometimes executed in tin instead of silver.

South Wales is the centre of British tin-plate manufacture; more than 16,000 tons of tin and 1,000,000 tons of steel are consumed annually. The tin coating is very thin, usually about 0·0001 inch in thickness and less than 1·5 per cent of the weight of an empty tin, such as is used for meats, fruits, vegetables, etc, is really metallic tin. For this reason it has been suggested that our so-called "tins" should be called "cans". That would certainly be more logical, but we should lose the history.

Copper coated with tin is used in the dairy industry, the tin preventing the copper from flavouring the milk.

Copper wires coated with tin are used in the electrical industry. The tin prevents the sulphur in the rubber insulation from causing the copper to deteriorate.

Tin foil

The existing oriental custom of making lace by the laborious hand-beating of tin into foil and subsequent cutting into decorative design originated in dim antiquity. One lb. of foil will spread over some 11,000 to 14,000 sq. in., the usual thickness being 0·0035 to 0·0080 inch. Tin foil has in recent years been much favoured as a harmless wrapping for sweetmeats, tobacco, cheese, and other foodstuffs, although it is now displaced in considerable measure by aluminium. The mechanical weakness of tin imposes a limit on the thinness to which it can be rolled and yet retain its usefulness as a wrapper. Greater strength is obtained by addition of a little zinc and a trace of nickel and this alloy has proved useful for capping milk bottles.

Pewter

Tin is the essential constituent of pewter, which the Romans made by melting together approximately four parts of tin and one of lead (p. 191). This alloy dates mostly from the third and fourth centuries A.D. In 1348, The London Guild of Pewterers, founded in 1300, recognised this mixture as suitable, but three years later stipulated that the amount of lead should not exceed one part in seven of tin. Being relatively soft, malleable, ductile, and of pleasing appearance, pewter was largely used for vessels of all kinds including plates, flagons, tankards, salt cellars and the like. Even church plate, particularly on the Continent, was made of pewter. Edward 1 (1272 to 1307) is said to have possessed over 300 pewter vessels. The method of assaying was based on the fact that tin is less dense than lead, hence, by comparison of the weight of a cast disc of pewter with a similar one of pure tin, one could determine with ease whether or not the correct amount of lead was present. From the fifteenth to the eighteenth century pewter was largely used by the middle classes.

King Charles 1 (1625 to 1649) prohibited the import of tin, and directed "that all measures for wine and ale used in taverns, victuallers' houses, and shops should be made of pewter or tin and should receive the Royal stamp or seal." Unfortunately, after the Restoration this very law nearly ruined the trade, owing to the delay

211

in obtaining the Royal stamp. We hear similar complaints about the inertia of Government Departments even in this enlightened age. History repeats itself.

During the eighteenth century pewter became less popular for a variety of reasons. One lay in the increasing appreciation of glass, porcelain and pottery. Another was the debasing of pewter with increasing amounts of lead which gave it a dull grey or black appearance. This happened despite the attempt of the Pewterers in 1772 to regulate the quality of pewter by threatening members who disregarded their ruling with expulsion from the Guild.

Modern pewter contains no lead; it is roughly 95 per cent tin, with a little antimony (4) and a small amount of copper (1). It possesses a pleasing white lustre and is moreover very resistant to attack by comestibles. Hammered pewter with a highly polished facetted surface is popular in this country, whilst most Swedish ware is duller. *Britannia metal*, introduced by James Vickers towards the close of the eighteenth century and manufactured in Sheffield, also contained a little antimony; it was made by adding this element to high grade pewter, the product being harder, whiter and more resonant. At the present time several alloys are classed under the general name of Britannia metal. One of these comprises 93 of tin with 4·6 of antimony and 2 of copper.

Solder

Some 22 per cent of the world's tin production enters into the solders. The tinman's solder is 2 of tin and 1 of lead; the plumber's solder is just the reverse; formerly soft solders had equal amounts. The idea of the soft solder is that during soldering the lead will harden before the tin which remains molten in the interstices of the lead and thus keeps the whole plastic until the plumber has had time to "wipe the joint".

Other alloys are *type metal* (p. 197) and *fusible alloys* (p. 88).

In 1839 Isaac Babbitt prepared an alloy of tin with some antimony and copper which was more plastic than ordinary bronze and specially suited for reducing friction between moving parts of machinery. The alloy was white and was later modified until whole series of "antifriction alloys" or "bearing metals" had been produced. These are still known as *Babbitt's metal*. A typical alloy contains 83 of tin, 8·5 of antimony and copper each. Bearing metals with a high tin content are used in electrical generators and aeroplane engines, in the main bearings and big ends of connecting rods of steam engines and internal combustion engines and generally where risk of scoring shafts must be avoided.

Speculum metal (Latin *speculum*, a mirror) or *white bronze* contains 2 of copper and 1 of tin. It is whiter even than tin, extremely brittle, and takes a high polish. It was used in Roman days for making mirrors and in more recent times found application in reflectors for telescopes. Later it was, of course, replaced by the well-known silvering process (p. 116).

Collapsible tubes for paints, ointments, etc, are frequently made of tin. In 1841 John Rand brought out the first patent for making collapsible tubes, lead being used. By 1850 the lead was being replaced by the less poisonous tin. At the present time some 800 million collapsible tin tubes are produced annually.

Sources of tin

A century ago, two-thirds of the world's tin came from Cornish mines. Hot water welled up in the mines and was pumped out by the steam pumps of James Watt and later Trevethick. At the present time the two chief mines are at Geevor, near Land's End, and the South Crofty mine at Camborne.

Prior to World War II some 70 per cent of the world's tin ore came from S.E. Asia, including Malaya, Dutch East Indies and China. Other sources are Australia, Tasmania, Nigeria, the Belgian Congo and Bolivia.

The tin of Nigeria is extremely easy to work, for the deposits are all alluvial. It was secured in the early days of the industry by simply washing the sands and gravel. The resulting product, black tin, contained over 70 per cent pure tin.

The tin mining industry in Nigeria did not develop to any great extent until the price of the metal reached £150 per ton, when the mining world began to take an active interest in it. Since then it has gone rapidly ahead, and in 1928 Nigeria produced over 10,000 tons of tin concentrates.

The opening up of the railways has aided the development of the tin area by enabling modern machinery to be imported and by reducing the carriage of the raw material to the coast. While the shallower deposits are in some cases being worked out, the deeper ones are now being exploited. Hand labour is giving place to the hydro-electrical plant and steam shovels.

Prior to World War II nearly 40,000 natives were regularly employed in the tin fields and a real standard of living had been established. In half a century the slave-driver and his works have been forgotten.

In 1800 the world production of tin was less than 9000 tons; in 1900 75,000 tons and by 1940 238,000 tons, the increase being mainly due to the enormous consumption in the tin-plate industry.

Mercury or quicksilver

This was the latest of the seven metals to be discovered in pre-Christian times. The word quick means living and is used in this sense in the old expression "the quick and the dead" a modern version of which, since the advent of the motor car, is said to be "the quick *or* the dead". When held in the palm of the hand the surface of the metal is in constant motion, due to tremors caused by the blood coursing through the veins and arteries. It thus seems to be alive; this coupled with its bright silvery appearance, completes the aptness of its early name. The alternative name *mercury* is probably derived from the Latin *merx*, merchandise.

Mercury and the ancients

The metal has been found in Egyptian tombs dating back to some 1600 B.C. but is believed to have been introduced into these at a much later date by Arabs, who used small bottles or phials containing the metal as amulets. Mercury is not mentioned in the Ebers Papyrus, *circa* 1550 B.C. (p. 199) neither does the metal receive mention in the Old Testament. In *Numbers* xxxi we read of the spoil taken from the Midianites. This included (verse 22) gold, silver, "brass", iron, "tin" and lead. We are then told of the "water of separation" which the Lord commanded the Hebrews to use in purifying the spoil. "Everything that may abide the fire, ye shall make it go through the fire, and it shall be clean; nevertheless it shall be purified with the water of separation." Many have interpreted this passage as referring to the use of mercury, but more probably it merely refers to the usual "water of purification" used ceremonially and prepared by burning a red heifer whole, mixing the ashes with water and allowing to stand*.

The Greeks were already familiar with mercury before the Christian Era. Aristotle (384 to 322 B.C.) referred to it as "liquid silver"; this appears to be the first definite mention of the metal. Theophrastus, *circa* 300 B.C., mentions the manufacture of *chutos*

---

*PARTINGTON, "Origins and Development of Applied Chemistry" (Longmans, 1935), pp. 84, 193, 486.

argyros or quicksilver from cinnabar, saying that it can be obtained by rubbing the ore with vinegar in a copper vessel.

Mercury and the Romans

Pliny* has a good deal to say about mercury. It was apparently customary to distinguish between the native metal, that is *argentum vivum* or quicksilver, and the same element prepared from cinnabar, which was called *hydrargyrum* or "silver water". Pliny briefly described the preparation of this latter, which he somewhat disparagingly referred to as a "substitute" for the native metal. An iron pot, containing cinnabar, was placed inside an earthen pan and covered with a lid luted on with clay. The whole was then heated from beneath with a fire kept going with the aid of bellows. The vapour condensed on the lid to a liquid combining the colour of silver with the mobility of water.

Pliny knew that quicksilver could be used in the purification of gold for he states that "on being briskly shaken in an earthen vessel with gold, it rejects all the impurities that are mixed with it. When once it has thus expelled these superfluities, there is nothing to do but separate it from the gold."

In 1154 Al Idrîsi described a similar process as being carried out in his day in Central Africa. Auriferous sands were washed in wooden tubs and the gold mixed with mercury. On heating the amalgam over a charcoal fire the mercury volatilised leaving a residue of gold. This, of course, is the principle of the "amalgamation process" for the extraction of gold and silver, once extensively used. It was re-discovered by the Spanish about the middle of the sixteenth century, after having apparently been lost for several centuries.

Mercury and the alchemists

The alchemists placed a high value on mercury and their symbol for it has already been explained (p. 13). They were fond of experimenting with *amalgams*, that is alloys of various metals with mercury. The word amalgam, derived from the Greek *malakos*, soft, is believed to have been introduced by Thomas Aquinas, *circa* 1250, pupil of Albertus Magnus who introduced the term *affinity* into chemistry (p. 16).

---

*"The Natural History of Pliny". Translated by Bostock and Riley (Bohn, 1857), Book 33, Chapters 32 and 41.

Reference has already been made to the medieval conception of mercury as a constituent, along with sulphur, of all metals. An English MS. in the possession of the British Museum, dating back to the fifteenth century refers to mercury as "the mother of all metals with sulphur"*.

To the Indian alchemists† mercury was all-important. Their god, Siva, was the mercurial deity, and mercury was used not merely to transmute base metals into gold but also to prolong life beyond the normal.

In the sixteenth century liquid mercury appears to have been frequently prescribed as a medicine to be taken internally. Somewhat later Thomas Dover (b. 1660), a reputable physician, was a great advocate of its use; it is said that a patient of his, to wit Captain Henry Coit, took one-and-a-quarter ounces of metallic mercury daily until he had consumed more than two pounds. Dover claimed that mercury removed all vermicular diseases, opened all obstructions and purified the blood. But more gold could be accumulated in those days by piracy, for might was right and the weaker were thrust to the wall. So Dover threw up his medical practice and went aroving in the South Seas under a scheme engineered by a group of Bristol merchants, returning somewhat later with spoil estimated at £170,000. During his voyages he landed on the island of Juan Fernandez, where Alexander Selkirk was marooned in 1704 whose experiences are believed to have led Defoe to produce in 1719 his world-famous Robinson Crusoe.

The story of vermilion

Mercury occurs naturally as the sulphide *cinnabar* or *coral ore*. Both names refer to the colour. The word cinnabar is believed to come from India where it is used to designate the red resin known to us as dragon's blood. The crushed mineral was used as a pigment under the name *vermilion* and was much prized for its beautiful colour. The Egyptians used it as long ago as 400 B.C. for painting pictures of their gods. Its Roman name was *minium*, but it was so frequently adulterated with what Pliny‡ termed "a second-rate kind of minium", known to us as red-lead, that the name minium passed from vermilion to its adulterant, and still clings to it, thus

---

*See RODWELL, *Chem. News*, 1873, **7**, 206.

†P. C. RAY, "History of Hindu Chemistry" (Williams & Norgate), Volume 1 (1902); Volume 2 (1909).

‡Quoted from BAILEY, "The Elder Pliny's Chapters on Chemical Subjects", (Arnold, 1929), Part 1, p. 123.

perpetuating the memory of man's dishonesty. A nation's language bears the impress of the character of its people.

The quicksilver mines at Almaden in the province of Ciudad Real, Spain, are the richest and most valuable in Europe, normally producing about half the world's supply of the metal. They were worked at the time of the Punic Wars, 600 B.C., and the first actual excavations are believed to have taken place at this time. They cover an area of some 12 square miles, and as yet but a small proportion has been worked. In 1927 the output was 2,500 tons; in 1935 it was 1,227 tons, the output having been restricted in 1930; the present production is not known. Mercury mining is an unhealthy task, and in the early days it was allotted to slaves; later it was the duty of convicts, and the Spanish Government at one time granted exemption from military service to men who had been at Almaden for two years.

Approximately 2000 men normally work in these mines, but this number has often been exceeded. The present workings, which date from the seventeenth century, are 1,200 feet deep, with twelve galleries, one below the other. They are closed between April and October, when there is a lack of water for the distillation process.

In by-gone years, however, the conditions were ghastly. Slaves and criminals worked continuously throughout the seasons, through hot and cold, through summer and winter. They seldom survived three years of service, and as rapidly as they perished they were replaced by others. Stories are told of men whose bodies became so saturated with mercury that a piece of brass put into their mouths would become white.

In 1168 King Alfonso VIII granted the mines to the Knights of Calatrava who were, however, defeated by the Moors at the battle of Alarcos, with the result that Almaden became the property of the Caliphs of Cordova. The name Almaden is Arabic for *mine*, which suggests that the Moors worked the mineral in their turn. In 1212 the tables were turned, the Christians defeated the Moors at Las Navas de Tolosa, and the Spanish king again took over the mines. The Knights of Calatrava then reminded the king of their early rights and once more entered into possession, but this time they had to share their profits on a fifty-fifty basis with the Crown.

A few centuries later, with the discovery of the vast quantities of silver ore in Mexico and Peru (p. 109), the importance of Almaden grew enormously, for mercury was essential to the old Spanish amalgamation method of extracting silver.

The mines are still extremely valuable; in war time they possess a special interest, for mercury fulminate is then in huge demand as a detonator.

The cinnabar mines of Idria in Italy have been worked for several hundred years. A merchant noticed globules of mercury lodged in the hollows of a spring and thought that by excavating to a sufficient depth the source of the valuable metal might be discovered. He obtained a grant of the ground from the Government and began working; his efforts were to a large extent successful, but it became evident that much larger quantities of ore could be obtained at greater depths than he could afford to work. So he sold the works as a running concern to the Austrian Government and they are now known to be extremely rich. In some places free mercury is found in glistening globules, but of course the main bulk of the metal of commerce has to be extracted from the ore.

About the year 1566 Henry Garces, a Portuguese, examined a red earth used by the Indians for making paint. The colour reminded him of cinnabar and after making a few experiments he convinced himself that this red earth was indeed the same as that mined in Spain. This led to the opening up of the mines at Guancavelica in Peru, where thousands of workmen were subsequently condemned to forced labour amid the deadly fumes.

The mines run deep and it is said that in the abyss are seen streets, squares and a chapel where religious ceremonies are celebrated on festive occasions. Very rich mines are worked in California and elsewhere.

The Japanese were wont to utilise the antiseptic properties of cinnabar in preserving the dead. The rich and noble were buried in several square coffins, one inside the other, usually in a sitting position, the nose, ears and mouth being filled with cinnabar to arrest decay. In the case of the very wealthy the coffin might be completely filled with cinnabar*.

Pliny mentions the use of vermilion as a pigment; he states that in earlier days it had been customary on festive occasions to cover the face of the statue of Jupiter with the pigment, whilst victorious generals, returning triumphant from successful campaigns, likewise stained their bodies red — an emblem of blood and carnage!

Vermilion was expensive, and Roman artisan painters discovered an ingenious method of pilfering it; in the interest of cleanliness

---

*LORD REDESDALE, "Tales of Old Japan" (Macmillan, 1910), p. 75.

they would frequently wash their brushes when filled with pigment, which latter, owing to its great density, fell to the bottom of the water and was thus so much gained by the thief. Adulteration was common (p. 216). Pliny was aware that cinnabar is poisonous and mentions that "by Hercules" some physicians used it by mistake instead of Indian cinnabar, the resin now known as dragon's blood. Let us hope that it was by mistake only, and not of malice afore-thought. Pliny was fond of invoking Hercules when he wished to express himself forcefully.

The Chinese were long regarded as the best makers of vermilion; perhaps they took more pains with their work and thus produced a finer substance, for they are a gifted people and their patience is proverbial. The Chinese used vermilion as a royal colour in quite early times. Marco Polo (p. 55) states that the paper currency of Cublai Khan in the thirteenth century was stamped with the royal signature in vermilion.

The Hindoos knew how to make vermilion at an early date. In the *Rasarnava* tantra, *circa* A.D. 1200 a method of manufacture is given which is essentially the same as that long practised by the Chinese.

That mercury was a true metal was not generally admitted until 1759 when it was first frozen, its melting point being — 38·9° C. Solid mercury was then seen to resemble lead or silver in its physical properties. In 1849 Ross, when in Greenland, pierced a wooden plank an inch thick with a bullet of frozen mercury, so low were the temperatures he experienced.

Uses of mercury

Mercury is employed in thermometers, barometers and numerous other instruments. Priestley introduced the mercury pneumatic trough which enabled him to prepare and collect in a pure state such gases as ammonia, hydrogen chloride and sulphur dioxide, which are too soluble for collection over water.

Amalgams are of considerable importance. Some are at first so soft that they can be moulded in the hand like wax, but harden later; they are sometimes used by dentists for filling teeth.

As we have already seen, gold readily amalgamates with mercury, so does silver, and amalgamation processes for the extraction of these metals from their ores have long been practised, though they are now largely superseded by the cyanide process.

Gold amalgam is used in fire-gilding; the metal article to be gilded must of course be able to stand uninjured a temperature

219

close to that of boiling mercury, namely 357° C. It is first "pickled" or cleansed by dipping in acid, and then brushed with an acid solution of mercury nitrate. A little of the metal dissolves causing a thin layer of mercury to deposit, so that the article now appears whitish, and is ready to receive the gold amalgam which is applied with a stiff brush. The article is now heated to volatilise the mercury and leave a coherent coating of gold. The mercurial vapours are extremely poisonous and though fire-gilding yields the more durable coat, the process is being superseded by electro-deposition. Fire-silvering was also practised.

Tin amalgam was formerly used for "silvering" mirrors, but the process suffers from many disadvantages in addition to the poisonous character of the emitted mercurial vapours. It has therefor become virtually obsolescent.

Amalgams with the alkali metals are readily formed by plunging the latter into warmed mercury. They are of interest in that by using a mercury cathode, Sir Humphry Davy in 1807 was able to isolate both potassium and sodium by electrolysis of potash and soda (p. 144). Mercury is used to-day in the commercial manufacture of caustic soda and hydrochloric acid by the electrolysis of brine. It is used also as the raw material for the preparation of mercuric oxide, vermilion, mercurous and mercuric chloride, fulminate and other derivatives. The oxide is of special historical interest as it led 170 years ago to the discovery of oxygen (p. 21)

It has long been supposed that a loaf of bread loaded with mercury and thrown into a river or lake in which a dead body lay, would come to rest over the corpse and so reveal its presence. This ancient belief was tested with dramatic success at Bedworth, near Nuneaton, in October 1932 — on the *thirteenth* of the month, too. A girl of fifteen had disappeared four days previously. She had been last seen on a path leading towards the Coventry canal, on the banks of which her purse was afterwards found. Her uncle then decided to test the old belief, putting some mercury into a loaf of bread and launching it into the canal. Next morning, in company with the police he searched for the loaf and found it resting on the water at a spot a few yards from a bridge. Amid great excitement drags were thrown into the water — and the girl's body was located and brought to the side. A similar experiment had been tried on the Avon, near Amesbury, in May 1925, but without success. The sceptic declared that the loaf had not been properly baked; the true believer maintained that the girl had not been drowned!

Mercury vapour lamps are widely used for a variety of purposes, as for example in the sterilisation of water and the irradiation of milk to produce vitamin D. The use of mercury in making mirrors has largely been superseded by silvering.

By bombardment of metallic gold with neutrons in an atomic pile one of the isotopes of mercury has been produced and isolated in a pure state. Thus

$$Au\ (197) + n \longrightarrow Hg\ (198) + e$$

an electron being evolved. This is an inversion of the alchemists' dream. Hg(198) gives a pure monochromatic green light and its wavelength is being carefully measured so that eventually the yard and metre may be expressed in terms of wavelengths which are believed to be absolutely permanent (p. 308).

The thermometer*

Mercury has been for many years, and still is, employed widely in thermometry. It is curious that any serious attempts to measure temperatures were so long delayed in scientific history. One of the earliest written references to temperature differences occurs in the book of Daniel, written probably about 170 B.C. and purporting to give an account of events that had occurred several hundred years earlier in the reign of Nebuchadnezzar, King of Babylon 604 to 562 B.C. Annoyed at the uncompromising behaviour of three Hebrews, Shadrach, Meshach and Abednego, who refused to worship the golden image he had erected, the king ordered them to be thrown into a furnace heated "one seven times more than it was wont to be heated" (*Daniel* iii. 19). This appears to have been quite a usual method of inflicting capital punishment in Persia (*Jeremiah* xxix. 22) and was probably no more unpleasant than being flayed alive, the custom of the Assyrians a century before.

The word *thermometer* appears to have been first used by Father Leurechon, a French Jesuit, in his work entitled "Récréation Mathematique", dated 1624. The credit of inventing thermometers with a liquid indicator (actually spirits of wine) hermetically sealed in a glass tube is usually given to Ferdinand II about 1650; he was Grand Duke of Tuscany, a liberal patron of science and founder of the Accademia del Cimento at Florence. Prior to these, air thermoscopes or baro-thermoscopes had been used for comparing relative

---

*A detailed history with full references is given by FRIEND, *Nature*, 1937, **139**, 395.

changes in temperature. These were (probably) invented either by Santorio, professor of medicine at Padua and colleague of Galileo, or by Galileo himself, about 1592*. The utility of these thermoscopes was severely limited by their susceptibility to changes in atmospheric pressure. As no standard temperature scale was recognised, it was at first impossible, even with the Ferdinand or Florentine thermometers, to collate the results of different investigators. This very serious defect was soon realised, and steps were taken to find a remedy.

A single fixed point

It was regarded by some as sufficient to select a single fixed point at an easily reproducible temperature and regard that as the zero or null point. Other temperatures were measured by noting the percentage or other fractional changes in volume of the liquid indicator once the null point had been marked off on the thermometer.

Clearly the nature of the liquid medium was a matter of supreme importance, for, if the results of different investigators were to be collated, either the same liquid indicator must be used by all, or one possessed of an identical coefficient of expansion. Halley (1656–1742) directed attention to this, having observed that all liquids do not expand by similar amounts with rise of temperature. Further, the exact volume of the liquid in the bulb of the thermometer must be known in order that the fractional volume change may be calculated and the temperature evaluated.

Boyle (1627–91) proposed *water*. He recommended taking a vessel of water and noting the volume of the liquid at the boiling point. On cooling to a lower temperature, the latter could be registered in terms of the contraction of the water as parts per 10,000 of the boiling volume. But this suggestion did not find favour despite the abundance of water and the ease with which it could be obtained in a pure condition. Water was regarded as unsuitable for not only was its coefficient of expansion small, but also its freezing point was too high for many meteorological purposes, and it was for this kind of work that thermometers were then mainly required.

Sir Isaac Newton† (1642–1727) used *linseed oil*, noting its volume at the temperature of melting ice and, like Boyle, expressing

---

*BOLTON, "Evolution of the Thermometer, 1592–1743" (Chem. Pub. Co., U.S.A. 1900).

†NEWTON, *Phil. Trans.*, 1701, p. 824. The paper, entitled "Scala graduum Caloris", is anonymous and printed in Latin.

its change in volume as parts per 10,000. Martine* quaintly refers to his experiments as follows —

Sir Isaac Newton thought the settling [of] the degrees of heat and cold well worth his notice; and as he carried every-thing he meddled [sic] with beyond what anybody had done before him, and generally with a greater than ordinary exactness and precision, so he laid down a method of adjusting thermometers in a more definite way than had been done hitherto.

But although linseed oil has a low freezing point and a large range of liquidity, its use in thermometry did not become general, despite Newton's fame as an investigator and the fact that the oil could be used at temperatures far above the boiling point of water. This was probably due to the fact that, in consequence of its high viscosity, the oil drains very slowly, particularly at the lower temperatures, down the sides of the tube bearing the scale; the thermometer thus takes a long time to adjust itself to new conditions.

Ferdinand ordered his thermometers to be made with *spirit*; Boyle was quick to appreciate their merits and introduced them into England, and Martine says they "came immediately to be of universal use among the virtuosi in all the several countries, wherever polite learning and philosophy were cultivated." The scale divisions were approximately one fiftieth of the volume of the bulb. Sagredo used 360 divisions, like the graduation of a circle; hence the term *degree*, as applied to temperature.

The low freezing point and viscosity of spirit were excellent features, but a really serious difficulty lay in the fact that the co-efficient of expansion was found to vary greatly with the quantity of admixed water.

Fahrenheit favoured the use of *mercury* as well as of spirit; indeed he was the first to bring the mercurial thermometer into general use.

Two fixed points

Some investigators, Martine included, advocated the use of a thermometric scale based upon two fixed points. This had several great advantages. Any suitable liquid could then be used as

---

*MARTINE, "Essays on the Construction and Graduation of Thermometers" (New edition, Edinburgh, 1792). The first essay, from which these and succeeding quotations are taken, is dated 1738.

indicator, and the necessity no longer existed for determining with great accuracy the volume of the bulb of the thermometer. All that one had to do, and this was comparatively easy, was to note the levels at the two fixed points and divide the distance between them into as many parts or degrees as was held convenient.

The lower fixed point

Boyle* recommended the freezing point of oil of aniseed ($17°$ to $20°$ C) as zero, because it was not necessary to wait for frosty weather before it solidified. Halley thought a cave might be selected where summer and winter temperatures are alike; one such cave was known to Boyle, whilst Mariotte claimed that the cave under the Royal Observatory at Paris was also isothermal. Both Hooke and Newton chose the freezing point of water as their zero.

Boyle's suggestion is ruled out because oil of aniseed is a natural product and as such does not possess a fixed composition; its melting point is thus liable to vary. For geographical reasons, Halley's idea is impracticable, as a particular cave could not be visited by everyone desirous of checking his thermometer.

Ole Rœmer (1644–1710), the Danish astronomer famous for his measurement of the velocity of light from a study of the movements of Jupiter's satellites, used a mixture of ice and common salt or a similar one (ice and sal ammoniac) in obtaining his zero, which was regarded as the lowest temperature then attainable in the laboratory. This mixture was not entirely satisfactory and Fahrenheit later pointed out that a different result might be obtained in summer from that in winter (p. 226).

The suggestion of Hooke and Newton appears to be the simplest and most convenient. Why then was it not generally adopted? The reason appears to be that many believed the freezing point of water was not constant, but varied with the latitude, Halley and others asserting that, the farther north we go, the more cold is required to freeze the water — to use the then current phraseology.

Martine refers to this, and appears to have been the first to show that such is not the case. He rightly attributes the observed differences in the freezing point of water either to inaccurate observation or to the use of imperfect thermometers. He says that he marked the mercury level on a thermometer at Edinburgh, when immersed in snow and water, whilst a friend did the same with another thermometer in London. They then exchanged instruments

*BOYLE, "An Experimental History of Cold", 1665.

and tested them, finding them to agree perfectly. Evidently the difference in latitude between the two cities had not affected the freezing point. Later experiments as far south as Paris and Dijon yielded similar results.

The upper fixed point

For this Newton chose blood heat which was regarded as absolutely constant in a healthy person. Rœmer and Fahrenheit used this also.

Halley recommended the boiling point of spirit of wine, "only it must be observed" he wrote "that the spirit of wine used to this purpose, be highly Rectified or Dephlegmed for otherwise the differing goodness of the spirit will occasion it to boil sooner or later, and thereby pervert the designed exactness."

Carlo Renaldini in 1694 recommended the boiling point of water. He was the first to make this suggestion. Fahrenheit and others were aware that the boiling point varied with the pressure of the atmosphere but apparently this was not regarded as a serious drawback.

Newton's thermometer

As we have seen, Newton's fixed points were the melting point of ice taken as 0 and blood heat, which was designated as 12.

Rœmer's thermometer

In "Adversaria", which was printed in 1910, the MS having been mislaid for about 200 years*, Rœmer gives an account of the ways in which he made and standardised his thermometers.

For his upper fixed point he either used the boiling point of water, which he designated as 60, or blood heat, presumably when the thermometers were intended only for meteorological use as it would not then be necessary to graduate to so high a temperature. Blood heat was taken as $22\frac{1}{2}$. The thermometer was checked in ice-water, the reading being $7\frac{1}{2}$. How the zero was obtained is not definitely stated but simple calculation shows that it corresponds roughly to the temperature of a mixture of salt and ice. This, or a similar mixture, was Fahrenheit's zero, and he admitted to having copied Rœmer's methods.

---

*KIRSTINE MEYER, *Nature*, 1910, **82**, 296. "Adversaria" by THYRA and K. MEYER (København, 1910), reviewed in *Nature*, 1911, **86**, 4. Also KIRSTINE MEYER, "Temperaturbegrebets Udvikling gennem Tiderne" (København, 1909).

Q

Réaumur's thermometer

René de Réaumur (1683–1757), the French scientist*, found that the best spirits of wine of his day expanded by $87\frac{1}{2}$ parts per 1000 when warmed from the temperature of melting ice to that of boiling water. Equal parts of his spirit and water gave an expansion of $67\frac{1}{2}$. He therefore for simplicity chose such a mixture as expanded by 80 parts. Hence the Réaumur scale runs from 0° to 80° between those two temperatures. The choice was not accidental, as we frequently read, but by design.

The Centigrade thermometer

Celsius favoured the decimal system and in 1736 divided the temperature interval between the melting of ice and the boiling of water into 100, taking the former as 100 and the latter as 0. This meant that temperatures above the boiling point of water were negative, so the scale was inverted in 1743 by Christin of Lyons.

In 1948 a General Conference on Weights and Measures was held in Paris and Sèvres and the suggestion was made that the term Centigrade should be replaced by Celsius; this would bring the Centigrade scale into line with those of Kelvin, Fahrenheit and Réaumur.

The Fahrenheit thermometer

This was based on Rœmer's thermometer, as Fahrenheit candidly admits. His zero was the temperature obtained† "by the commixture of ice, water and sal ammoniac, or even sea salt". From the fact that he quotes sal ammoniac and sea salt as alternatives we gather that Fahrenheit supposed they yielded the same temperature with ice. We now know that their cryohydric points are $- 15°$ C (or $+ 5°$ F) and $- 22°$ C (or $- 8°$ F) respectively. Nevertheless, Fahrenheit did realise that there was a difficulty in reaching the true zero, for he naïvely remarks that "if into this mixture the thermometer be put, it descends to 0. This experiment succeeds better in winter than in summer"!

---

*Réaumur interested himself in spiders. He thought their "silk" might be used for textiles and sought to rear colonies of them. But they showed disgraceful cannibalistic propensities, the females being even more voracious than the males, and the experiments were not a success.

†FAHRENHEIT, *Phil. Trans.*, 1724, **33**, 78. Printed in Latin. This quotation is from Hutton's Abridged Edition, **7**, 22–24. See also ERNST COHEN and W. A. T. COHEN-DE-MEESTER, *Kon. Akad. Wet. Verhand.* (Amsterdam), 1936, XVI, No. 2, p. 1. *Chemisch Weekblad*, 1936, **33**, No. 24.

Fahrenheit's upper fixed point was blood heat. On Rœmer's scale this was $22\frac{1}{2}$, but he stated in a letter to Boerhaave* that in 1717 he felt Rœmer's scale with its fractions to be both inconvenient and inelegant; so instead of $22\frac{1}{2}°$ divided into quarters, that is, 90, he decided to take 96° as blood heat. Retaining the same zero, the melting point of ice became 32°, instead of $7\frac{1}{2}°$ divided into quarters or 30. This scale he continued to use and was using at the time the letter was written (that is, in 1729); he added that he had been confirmed in his choice because he found it to agree, by pure coincidence, with the scale marked on the thermometer hanging in the Paris Observatory.

Fahrenheit gave no reason for regarding the number 96 as more convenient than 90. Probably it was due to the fact that 96 is divisible not merely by 3 but also by multiples of 2 and hence by 12. The decimal system was not then in general use in scientific work, otherwise Fahrenheit would no doubt have fixed blood heat at 100°. In that case the freezing and boiling points of water would have been represented by numbers even more awkward and disconnected namely, 33·3° and 221° respectively. So let us be thankful.

Although we retain a Fahrenheit scale to-day, it is not quite the same as that which Fahrenheit used. The lower and upper fixed points adopted are those deliberately rejected by Fahrenheit, ice being taken to melt at 32° and water to boil under standard conditions at 212°.

---

*A few years ago there were found, in the Military Medical Academy at Leningrad, some letters sent by Fahrenheit to Boerhaave during 1718 to 1729. The letters were written in Dutch at Amsterdam and a literal translation of one of them into German, dated 17th April 1729, given by the Cohens, throws considerable light on Fahrenheit's procedure in graduating his thermometer. See *Nature*, 1936, **138**, 428. COHEN and COHEN-DE-MEESTER, *Kon. Akad. Wet. Verhand.*, Eersle Sectie, **16**, No. 2, pp. 1–37. Amsterdam, 1936.

CHAPTER 17

THE TITANIUM GROUP

THE titanium group comprises titanium, zirconium, hafnium and thorium.

Titanium

Years ago country clergymen were often keen students of nature and spent many hours of their free time in unravelling her secrets. In his parish of Menachan, Cornwall, the Rev. William Gregor noticed a black, magnetic sand, resembling gunpowder in external appearance, washed by a meandering stream whose principal source lay in the valleys of Gonhilly*. Analysis of the sand in 1791 showed it to contain, in addition to iron, a new element, the oxide of which was reddish brown and dissolved in acid to a yellow solution which became purple when reduced with zinc. These results were published in Crell's Annalen in 1791; the sand was called menachanite and the oxide menakine by Kirwan in 1829. They attracted but little notice, however. Can good come out of Nazareth? Can a country parson contribute anything of value to the scientific world?

In 1795 Klaproth† was examining a brownish red mineral then known as *red schorl* or *schorl rouge*, but later called *rutile*. From it he separated a red oxide which bore a close resemblance to that described by Gregor as obtained from his black sand, menachanite. Klaproth was fortunate in obtaining some of this latter mineral, which he playfully called "iron shot titanite", and confirmed the identity of the two oxides. Notwithstanding Gregor's priority, which should have been respected, Klaproth suggested the name *titanium* for the metal, although he did not isolate it, "borrowing" as he wrote "the name for this metallic substance from mythology and in particular from the Titans, the first sons of the Earth." Gregor did not live to see his metal isolated; he died in 1817 of tuberculosis, like his great contemporary, Karl Wilhelm Scheele.

---

*These place-names are given on the Ordnance Survey maps as Manachan and Goonhilly Down.

†KLAPROTH, "Analytical Essays towards promoting the Chemical Knowledge of Mineral Substances". Cadell and Davies (London, 1801).

Eight years later (1825), Berzelius, the renowned Swedish chemist, reduced potassium hexafluotitanate, K_2TiF_6, with potassium and obtained an impure amorphous specimen of titanium. In 1887, a 95 per cent pure sample was isolated by Nilson and Pettersson[*] by reduction of the tetrachloride, $TiCl_4$, with metallic sodium. By a similar method, Hunter obtained titanium of some 99·9 per cent purity in 1910.

Although titanium is surprisingly abundant in the Earth's 10-mile crust (p. 7), greatly exceeding copper and lead, the pure metal is not used commercially. In 1890 Rossi smelted titanium ores and from them made superior steels; from this the titanium alloy industry developed.

The alloy with iron known as *ferro-titanium*, is used in making titanium steels and in combating "weld decay" in stainless steels. It is used as final deoxidiser and denitrogeniser in steel manufacture. *Cupro-titanium* and *mangano-titanium* are used as deoxidisers in making brass and bronze castings. *Manganese-titanium* is also used as a scavenger for certain white metal alloys especially for alloys of nickel and chromium.

Zirconium

The *jacinth* or *hyacinth*, now also known as *zircon*, $ZrSiO_4$, has long been prized as a gem for its beautiful orange to red colour — whence the name zircon, from Arabic *zarkun*, cinnabar, and Persian *zargun*, gold coloured. Unfortunately, the colour tends to fade on exposure to light. The colourless, yellow and smoky varieties from Ceylon are termed *jargon*, a word possibly derived from the same root. The word jacinth occurs twice in the New Testament. In *Rev.* xxi. 19 to 20, we read that the foundations of the Holy Jerusalem "were garnished with all manner of precious stones", the eleventh being the jacinth. In *Rev.* ix. 17, the horsemen are described as "having breastplates of fire and of jacinth and brimstone." The "brimstone" here may well refer merely to combustibility, as explained in a previous chapter (p. 22), but the connection of fire and brimstone with jacinth is not clear. Possibly, however, the jacinth referred to is not the stone we now know by that name. If it were amber or some other organic substance it would naturally be combustible.

Although zircons had been analysed before, it was not until 1789, when Klaproth examined a specimen from Ceylon, that the presence

---

[*]NILSON and PETTERSSON, *Zeitch physikal Chem.*, 1887, **1**, 27.

of a hitherto unknown "earth" was suspected. Zircons had been regarded as merely aluminium silicates,. the base we now call zirconia being confused with alumina.

In 1808, Davy, having successfully decomposed potash, soda and the alkaline earths with the electric current, endeavoured similarly to isolate the metal from zirconia. He was not successful, however, but in 1824 Berzelius obtained an impure specimen of zirconium by heating potassium hexafluozirconate, K_2ZrF_6, with metallic potassium — the method he subsequently adopted in isolating titanium, as already mentioned. The product was impure; many years were to elapse before a really pure specimen was obtained by Lely and Hamburger*, who, in 1914, reduced the chloride $ZrCl_4$ with metallic sodium. The pure metal† is now obtained technically by heating crude zirconium and iodine in a vacuum and dissociating the vapour of the iodide on a zirconium wire at 1300° C. The zirconium "grows" on the wire in very pure form and can be drawn to wire or rolled to thin foil 20μ thick. It is also obtained by reduction of the tetrachloride with magnesium in an atmosphere of helium (Kroll's method).

Zirconium has always been a difficult metal for the chemist. Berzelius in 1824 gave it a valency of six, like that of sulphur and wrote the oxide as ZrO_3 — in modern nomenclature; later he altered this to Zr_2O_3 by analogy with alumina. But analogy is the fruitful parent of error, as Davy was wont to say, and it led Gmelin astray also, for likening zirconia to lime he wrote the formula as ZrO. In 1857, however, Deville and Troost‡ found the vapour density of the chloride to correspond to $ZrCl_4$, and therefore suggested that the metal was tetravalent. This was supported by Mendeléeff when he drew up his Periodic Table in 1869, and confirmed in 1873 when Mixter and Dane determined the specific heat as 0·066 and the atomic weight, by the application of Dulong and Petit's Rule, as 97.

Ferro-zirconium is made by alumino-thermal reduction in an electric furnace, and is used in steel manufacture for de-oxidising, desulphurising and denitrogenising purposes, as also for making zirconium steel, armour plate and projectiles.

---

*LELY and HAMBURGER, Z. anorg. Allg. Chem., 1914, **37**, 209.
†DE BOER and FAST, ibid., 1926, **153**, 1. MILLER, Industrial Chemist, 1950, **26**, 435.
‡DEVILLE and TROOST, Compt. rend., 1857, **45**, 821. FRIEND, COLLEY and HAYES J. Chem. Soc., 1930, p. 494.

Zirconium metal is used in flashlight powders and ammunition primers, and as a "getter" in valves and discharge tubes as it readily absorbs gas when warmed.

Several hard non-ferrous alloys are now in use. Mention may be made of *cooperite*, a zirconium–nickel alloy, non-corrosive and acid resistant. Being very hard it is useful for high-speed cutting tools.

Hafnium

For many years chemists suspected that ordinary zirconia contained varying amounts of a second earth mixed with it. But, as with the rare earths, chemists were floundering in the dark; the principle of the atomic number had not been evolved and there was no clear indication as to the possible number of elements that could exist.

In 1845 Svanberg* claimed to have found a new earth in zircons which he called *noria*, the oxide of norium. The chloride, double sulphate and oxalate of norium differed from those of zirconium and the atomic weight of the metal was less. In 1853 Sjögren believed he had found the same element in catapleiite, a complex metasilicate of sodium, calcium and zirconium, and stated that the density of noria (D = 5·5) was greater than that of zirconia (D = 4·3). Both of these densities, however, are lower than that of pure zirconia (D = 5·73) and several investigators who repeated the experiments were unable to detect the presence of a second earth.

In 1864 Nylander† reported the presence of two earths in zirconia. Two years later A. H. Church‡ described unusual bands that he had observed in the absorption spectra of certain zircons, notably those from Ceylon and Norway. He hazarded the suggestion that they might be due to Svanberg's norium.

Unaware of this work H. C. Sorby§ in 1869 published an account of the absorption spectra of jargon from Ceylon and other zircons from which he concluded that a new element was present for which he suggested the extremely ugly name of *jargonium*. On hearing of this Church very properly directed attention to his earlier paper, stated that he had been continuing the research and felt convinced that ordinary zircons usually contained a new element. He suggested the name nigrium‖.

---

*Svanberg, *Ann. Phys.*, 1845, **65**, 317.
†Nylander, *Acta Univ. Lund.*, 1864, 11. Quoted by Venable, "Zirconium and its Compounds" (N.Y., 1922), p. 16.
‡A. H. Church, *Intellectual Observer*, 1866, **9**, 201.
§H. C. Sorby, *Chem. News*, 1869, **19**, 121, 181; 1869, **20**, 7, 104.
‖Church, *ibid.*, 1869, **19**, 121.

In 1901 Hofmann and Prandtl* claimed that a specimen of zirconia extracted from euxenite contained the oxide of a metal of high atomic weight. Euxenite is a very complex niobotantalate of uranium, yttrium and the rare earth metals in which Nilson had found scandia in 1879 (p. 172). But Hauser and Wirth† could not confirm the presence of a new element.

It is easy to be wise after the event. Looking back with our present knowledge of the existence of hafnium an invariable associate (usually in small quantity) of zirconium, it appears quite within the bounds of possibility that some of these investigators did actually observe slight differences due to this element. But the evidence of the existence of a new element was far from conclusive, and we must leave it at that.

The ultimate discovery of hafnium is an outstanding tribute to the value of modern scientific theory. When Moseley, in 1913 (p. 3) made it possible to ascertain by X-ray methods the serial order of the elements it became obvious that an unknown element should exist of atomic number 72, lying between the rare earth element lutecium, No. 71, and tantalum, No. 73. The question then arose as to whether or not this element would be the last member of the rare earth series.

Langmuir, whose scheme for the arrangement of the electrons round the atomic nucleus was based on Rydberg's formula, predicted that element 72 would end the rare earth series. Urbain‡ had already in 1911 fractionated lutecium residues some 15,000 times in an endeavour to isolate No. 72 and obtained some new lines in the spectrum which he took to indicate its existence; but they were really fresh lutecium lines not observable with the less pure specimens. He named the supposed element *celtium*.

According to the Bohr-Bury§ theory of 1921, however, the number of electrons in the various shells round the nucleus are given by $2n^2$, where n is the shell number. Accordingly the innermost or K-shell has 2 electrons, the second or L-shell has $2 \times 2^2 = 8$, and so on.

Arranging the rare-earth elements as shown in the table below, it will be seen that the N-shell of lanthanum contains only 18

---

*HOFMANN and PRANDTL, *Ber.*, 1901, **34**, 1064.
†HAUSER and WIRTH, *ibid.*, 1909, **42**, 4443; 1910, **43**, 1807.
‡URBAIN, *Compt. rend.*, 1911, **152**, 141; 1922, **17**, 1349.
§BURY, *J. Amer. Chem. Soc.*, 1921, **43**, 1602. BOHR, "The Theory of Spectra and Atomic Constitution", 1922.

electrons although it is capable of holding 32. Now it is the outer-most electrons that are mainly concerned with the chemical and optical properties of atoms; by filling up the N-shell, we can pass from lanthanum to lutecium without appreciably altering the chemical properties. But once we reach lutecium the N-shell is full up and any further electrons can only be added to the O or P shells, with a corresponding change in chemical properties. Element 72 therefore will have different properties from the others and can no longer be regarded as a rare-earth metal.

Shell	K	L	M	N	O	P
Maximum No. of electrons	2	8	18	32	50	72
57 Lanthanum	2	8	18	18	8 + 1	2
58 Cerium	2	8	18	18 + 1	8 + 1	2
70 Ytterbium	2	8	18	18 + 13	8 + 1	2
71 Lutecium	2	8	18	18 + 14	8 + 1	2
72 Hafnium	2	8	18	18 + 14	8 + 2	2

Coster and Hevesy were thus encouraged to search amongst the zirconium minerals for the elusive element and in 1923 announced its presence as evidenced by its X-ray spectrum*. They called the metal *hafnium* after Hafnia or Copenhagen. It was found to be present in varying amounts in most zirconium minerals, being about one-tenth as abundant as zirconium. *Alvite* (Zr, Hf, Th) SiO_4 was found to be particularly rich.

The metal was first isolated by Hevesy by reducing K_2HfF_6 with sodium. As the atomic weight of hafnium is double that of zirconium it now became obvious why different investigators had obtained such varying results for the atomic weight of zirconium. The two elements resemble each other as closely as do adjacent members of the rare earth series and are as difficult to separate. For most industrial purposes it is unnecessary to separate them. Hafnium is about one-tenth as plentiful as zirconium in the earth's crust, its amount being estimated at about 3·2 ppm. Van Liempt in 1925 recommended the use of the oxide, HfO_2, with tungsten in filament lamps, as it has a high melting point and low vapour pressure, in order to reduce the tendency of tungsten to "off-set" or crystallise. At present silica and thoria are used.

---

*COSTER and HEVESY, *Nature*, 1923, **111**, 79, 182, 252. *Chemistry and Industry*, 1923, **42**, 258, 929. *Chem. News*, 1923, **127**, 33, 353. *Ber.*, 1923, **56**, 1503. See also HEVESY, "Das Element Hafnium" (Springer, Berlin, 1927).

Thorium

Thorium is sometimes regarded as a rare earth element; but it is wise to restrict the term to yttrium and the elements lying between and including lanthanum and lutecium — for these are trivalent and closely similar, whereas thorium is tetravalent and presents many other contrasts. In many ways it resembles scandium, which we have already seen to differ in several important ways from the rare earth metals. Thus, like scandium, thorium yields an insoluble fluoride, an acetyl-acetonate that sublimes without decomposition and a basic thiosulphate. The rare earth metals do none of these things.

In 1817 Berzelius* examined the Swedish mineral now known as gadolinite and isolated from it what he believed to be a new earth, the oxide of a metal which he called thorium after the Scandinavian god Thor. Subsequently, however, he concluded that his earth was a basic phosphate of yttrium, an element that had already been discovered by Gadolin in 1794. Eleven years later, however, in 1828 Berzelius examined a black mineral from the island of Lövön near Brevig in Norway and obtained from it a new earth somewhat resembling his previous product, so he called it thoria. The mineral is now known as thorite, $ThSiO_4$, and is isomorphous with zircon, $ZrSiO_4$. Berzelius isolated the metal by heating the hexafluo potassium double salt, K_2ThF_6, with metallic potassium.

In 1851 Bergemann† announced the discovery of a new metal in orangite, the gem variety of thorite, and named it *donarium*. Subsequently, however, this was shown to be identical with thorium. In 1862 Bahr‡ thought he had discovered in a mineral from Rönsholm a new metal which he named *wasium*, but two years later he himself showed that it was thorium. From experiments on the fractional distillation of thorium chloride Baskerville§ concluded in 1901 that two other elements were present, which he named *berzelium* and *carolinium*. In this he was mistaken.

The radio properties of thorium are discussed later (p. 321).

The gasmantle industry

It was known more than a century ago that certain oxide earths emit an intense light when heated in non-luminous flames such as

---

*Berzelius, *Afhandl. Fys. Kem. och. Min.*, 1817, **5**, 76. *K. Svenska Vet.-Akad. Handl.*, I, 1824, p. 315; 1829; p. 1.
†Bergemann, *Pogg. Annalen*, 1852, **85**, 558.
‡Bahr, *ibid.*, 1862, **119**, 572; *Annalen*, 1864, **132**, 227.
§Baskerville, *J. Amer. Chem. Soc.*, 1901, **23**, 761; 1904, **26**, 922.

we now obtain from a Bunsen burner. In 1829 it was known to Berzelius that zirconia and thoria yielded a particularly brilliant light in these circumstances. The earliest application was the *Drummond light* or "lime-light" invented by Drummond in England in 1826. A cylinder of quicklime was heated in an oxyhydrogen flame and proved excellent for magic lanterns, for which it was used for very many years, the lime being often replaced by zirconia after 1867. In 1846 mantles of platinum were used in the ordinary gas flame; but they soon wore out and were, moreover, too expensive.

In 1880 Dr Carl Auer, later von Welsbach, experimented with cotton fabrics impregnated with nitrates of many metals yielding upon ignition refractory oxides; these included zirconium and lanthanum, and his success encouraged him in 1884 to apply for patents. In 1886 his experiments were extended to include thorium nitrate. In efforts to obtain a maximum illumination thorium salts were subjected to increasing purification and in 1891 the curious discovery was made that the highly pure oxide gave a much less intense light than the less pure. This was soon tracked down to the catalytic activity of ceria, CeO_2, addition of one per cent of which to pure thoria increased by seven times the illuminating power of the latter.

The main difficulty in commercialising the gas mantle lay in the shortage of thorium which was only known to occur as the relatively scarce mineral *thorite* or *orangite*, $ThSiO_4$, the price of which rose to £13 10s 0d per lb. avoirdupois. This was prohibitive so an intensive search was made for fresh sources. Sands were soon found in Carolina containing one per cent of monazite, which consists essentially of thorium phosphate, $Th_3(PO_4)_4$, associated with the phosphates of the rare earth metals. These were worked for a time by the Welsbach Light Co. of New York. Deposits were also found on the Pacific side of Idaho and a Company was formed in 1906 to extract the monazite from the residues left after removing the gold; the process was short-lived for a disastrous fire in 1910 ended the work .

In the meantime sands had been found in Brazil with a high thorium content lying near the coast so that transport was easy. By 1910 the two above-mentioned American firms had been ousted and the Brazilian sands, worked under German control, supplied the world demand until 1913 when a formidable rival source was found in the sands of Travancore, India. These were very rich in monazite, containing some 46 per cent with a thoria content of from 8 to 10 per cent. At the outbreak of war in 1914, shipments from Brazil fell off and the Travancore sands, under British control, were shipped to Britain and America.

The fabric mantles are constructed of cotton, ramie fibre or artificial silk, the last named being best but most expensive. The fabrics are soaked with nitrate solution, dried, branded with a didymium nitrate solution, shaped on wooden models and burned off, the nitrates being converted to oxides. The fragile mantle is now dipped in nitrocellulose and oil and dried. This renders it sufficiently strong for transport. When burned off the usual composition is 98 parts of ThO_2, 1 of CeO_2 and 1 of some suitable binder, such as CaO, Al_2O_3 or MgO. Beryllium nitrate is added to the impregnating solution to increase the strength of the finished mantle when destined for use with high-pressure gas, as in lighthouses.

CHAPTER 18

THE VANADIUM GROUP

THE vanadium group comprises vanadium, niobium and tantalum.

Vanadium

In 1801 a specimen of *brown lead* from Zimapan was examined by Andres Manuel del Rio, a Spanish professor of mineralogy in the Colegio de Mineria, Mexico City. Del Rio concluded that it contained a new metal similar to chromium, to which he gave the name *erythronium*, in recognition of the red colour acquired by its salts when ignited. The mineral is known to-day as *vanadinite*, $PbCl_2.3Pb_3(VO_4)_2$, and the red colour obtained on ignition, for example, of ammonium vanadate is due to formation of vanadium pentoxide, V_2O_5.

Second thoughts are not always best. On further study of the mineral, del Rio concluded that he was mistaken in assuming the presence of a new element and that the brown lead was merely basic lead chromate. In this he was supported by Collet Descôtils, and there the matter rested for many years.

But "truth will out". In 1830, Nils Gabriel Sefström*, a Swedish chemist, established the presence of a new element in an unusually tenacious and ductile specimen of wrought iron prepared from ore from the Taberg mine in Smaland. Upon dissolving the iron in hydrochloric acid, a black insoluble powder was formed, which contained an element that was neither chromium nor uranium. To this he gave the name vanadium, in honour of Vanadis, also known as the Scandinavian goddess Freia or Frigg, the wife of Odin (p. 14), it being customary to name planets and elements after heathen deities.

Now it so happened that Friedrich Wöhler† was, at this time, interested in del Rio's brown lead and had found something new in it when he was compelled, by temporary indisposition, due to inhalation of hydrofluoric acid vapour, to set the problem on one side. In 1831 he established the identity of Sefström's vanadium

---

*SEFSTRÖM, *Pogg. Annalen*, 1831, **21**, 43.
†WÖHLER, *ibid.*, 1831, **22**, 1.

with the erythronium of del Rio. He greatly blamed himself for not having pursued his study of brown lead, although, as he afterwards added, "Even if I had charmed her (*i.e.*, vanadium) out of the lead mineral, I would have had only half the honour of discovery, because of the earlier results of del Rio on erythronium. But Sefström, because he succeeded by an entirely different method, keeps the honour unshared."

Like Stephen Hales, the worthy Vicar of Teddington, who, in 1728, allowed the discovery of oxygen to slip between his fingers (p. 21), and Liebig, who had bromine on his shelves unhonoured and unrecognised at the time that Balard discovered it in 1826 in Montpellier brines (p. 49), Wöhler had narrowly missed a great discovery.

Berzelius examined a number of derivatives of vanadium and concluded that the element was allied to chromium and uranium. Berzelius, however, had been handling the oxide, VO, or the nitride, VN, when he thought he was dealing with the free metal. The same kind of error occurred with uranium (p. 312). Roscoe, however, corrected this error in the course of his classical researches during 1868 to 1870. He isolated the metal by reducing the dichloride, VCl_2 at bright red heat in a current of hydrogen, every precaution being taken to prevent the entry of moisture and oxygen into the apparatus. The product was 95·8 per cent pure metal.

Rammelsberg in 1856 had shown that vanadinite and pyromorphite are isomorphous. Roscoe pointed out that if Mitscherlich's Law of Isomorphism applied, the two minerals ought to possess analogous structures. This could only be the case if vanadium had the same valency as phosphorus. In that case vanadium would be pentavalent like nitrogen and phosphorus, not hexavalent like chromium and uranium. The two minerals would thus be represented as follows —

Vanadinite, $3Pb_3(VO_4)_2.PbCl_2$
Pyromorphite, $3Pb_3(PO_4)_2.PbCl_2$

This was accepted by Mendeléeff who, when he drew up his Periodic Table in 1869, placed vanadium in Group V along with nitrogen and phosphorus.

Vanadium is not used commercially in the pure state. More than 90 per cent of it is marketed as ferro-vanadium and used in the manufacture of steels; ferro-vanadium contains from 30 to 40 per cent of vanadium. The metal enhances the toughness, tensile strength and elasticity of steel. Thus a good carbon steel containing some 1·1 per cent of carbon has an elastic limit of about 30 tons per sq. in.; addition of 0·3 per cent vanadium increases this to 43 tons, whilst 0·6 per cent raises it to 65 tons. Vanadium steels are in consequence used in the construction of piston rods, axles, bolts, gears, motor car and aeroplane parts, rock crushers, dredgers, and in tools for punching, shearing and drawing. Vanadium is used along with tungsten and molybdenum in the manufacture of high speed tools. Chromium–vanadium steel is used for armour plate, torpedo tubes, gun shields, etc. Vanadium is also added to cast-iron. It is used to a limited extent in non-ferrous alloys; thus copper–vanadium and aluminium–vanadium alloys are used in aeroplane construction; they contain up to about 0·5 per cent of vanadium. Vanadium oxides are used to impart to glass an amber colour. The pentoxide is used as a catalyst in the manufacture of sulphuric acid, replacing the more expensive platinum catalyst used in oxidising SO_2 to SO_3.

The world production of vanadium averages some 3000 tons per annum.

Niobium and tantalum

John Winthrop the Younger (1606 to 1676) was fond of minerals and made a hobby of collecting them. In a spring near his home in New London, Connecticut, he found a black rock, now known as *columbite*. His grandson sent this to Sir Hans Sloane (1660 to 1753) in London, who handed it over to the British Museum. There it lay until 1801 when Charles Hatchett* examined it. Hatchett was the son of a prosperous London coach-builder in Long Acre, a well-known mineralogist and chemist, and one of the Founders of the Animal Chemistry Club (1809) which met alternately at the houses of Sir Everard Home and of Hatchett himself. He was working on some chromium minerals in the British Museum and concluded that this black mineral contained a new element, which he called *columbium*; the mineral in consequence was later called columbite, as mentioned above. It subsequently transpired, however, that the columbium was not a simple element, but a mixture of two. The discovery was made in this way.

In 1802 Anders Gustav Ekeberg† found what he thought was yet another new element in two minerals, one being *tantalite* from

---

*HATCHETT, *Proc. Roy. Soc.*, 1802, **92**, 49.
†EKEBERG, *Ann. Chim.*, 1802, **43**, 76.

Kimito, Finland, and the other *yttro-tantalite* from Ytterby, Sweden. To this element he gave the name *tantalum* partly because it was then the fashion to name new elements after heathen deities and partly because the name was particularly appropriate in view of the "tantalising" difficulty he experienced in effecting the dissolution of the metal oxide in acid.

At first, the impression gained ground that columbium and tantalum were identical, but in 1844 the famous German pharmacist and mineralogist Heinrich Rose* followed up the observation that many columbites and tantalites, together with the oxides produced from them, showed marked differences in density. He showed that columbite from Bodenmais in Bavaria contained a new element in addition to tantalum, to which he gave the name *niobium*, since Niobe was the daughter of Tantalus. Thus Hatchett's columbium was a mixture of niobium and tantalum. Columbite may therefore be written as $(Fe,Mn)O.(Nb,Ta)_2O_5$ whilst tantalite is essentially $(Fe,Mn)O.Ta_2O_5$. There is no definite line of demarcation between the two minerals; they merge, like iron and copper pyrites, into one another. If niobium is in excess the mineral is called columbite; if tantalum, tantalite. In 1846 Rose thought he had obtained evidence of the presence of yet another metal in columbite; this he called *pelopium*†, but later concluded that it was merely niobium. Nevertheless in 1925 Noddack and Tacke did discover at least one new element in columbites and tantalites, namely *rhenium* (p. 250) and believed they had obtained evidence of the existence of another metallic element, No. 43, which they named masurium (p. 251).

In 1903 von Bolton‡ of Charlottenburg showed it was possible to convert tantalum powder, the only form in which the metal had then been obtained, into ductile filaments which rendered possible its industrial application. The powder was pressed into rods, melted in the electric arc, rolled and drawn.

In 1905 niobium and tantalum received commercial attention, as possible material for electric lamps filaments to replace the fragile carbon then in use. Niobium was soon found to be useless, but tantalum with a melting point of 2850° C proved valuable, and was extensively used during 1905 to 1911. In 1910 the National

---

*Rose, *Pogg. Annalen*, 1844, **63**, 307, 693; 1846, **69**, 118.

†Gmelin devoted a chapter to this "element" and its compounds in his "Handbook of Chemistry". Translated by Watts (Cavendish Society) 1850, Vol. 4, Chap. 17B.

‡von Bolton, *Zeitsch. Elektrochem.*, 1905, **11**, 45.

Electric Lamp Association of the U.S.A. used 5 million feet of tantalum wire weighing less than 100 lb. Each 1 lb. of wire yielded some 20,000 lamps. After some 100 million lamps had been made and used, tantalum was largely superseded by the more efficient tungsten, melting only at 3382° C. Tantalum lamps are still used, however, when required to resist more than ordinary vibration, as on railways. But only D.C. lamps are possible, for with A.C. tantalum undergoes progressive crystallisation.

Tantalum is extraordinarily resistant to acid attack and is being used in ever-increasing amounts in the building up of chemical plant. Its special field of usefulness appears to be in plant for halogens, aqua regia and hydrochloric acid. For use in the manufacture of the last named a tantalum absorption tube 6 ft. 6 in. in height and 6 in. in diameter has been described*. Tantalum dishes can be used for evaporating aqua regia and they are resistant to hydrofluoric acid. For the same reason tantalum can be used as cathode in electrolytic analysis as the deposited metals do not alloy with it and gold and the platinum metals can be dissolved off with aqua regia. In the U.S.A. tantalum is used in plant for concentrating acids and resisting the corrosive action of acid vapours; tantalum nozzles are used in chlorinating water, and in dental and surgical instruments, although for these latter stainless steels are also in demand. The metal is biologically "acceptable" and is used in wire for repairing bones and in plates for skull injuries; tantalum "wool" and gauze are used in replacing muscular tissue and as bridges for the overgrowth of new tissue.

Tantalum tends to oxidise above 150° C and cannot therefore be used for crucibles except in a reducing atmosphere and it cannot be used, either, in place of platinum as anode owing to oxidation. It is useful as a "getter" for traces of unwanted gases.

Tantalum is a white metal similar to platinum but being much less expensive is sometimes used as a substitute in jewellery; it takes an iridescent oxide film which is attractive. It yields a very hard and dense (D = 13·96) carbide, TaC, which is used in dies.

Niobium, now also known as *columbium*, enjoys a much more restricted use in industry. It finds application in the refining of the grain of aluminium alloys; it is present in certain stainless chromium steels and weldable high-speed steels.

---

*HUNTER, *Ind. Eng. Chem.*, 1938, **30**, 1214.

R

CHAPTER 19

THE CHROMIUM GROUP

THE chromium group comprises chromium, molybdenum and tungsten.

Chromium

In a letter to Buffon in 1762 Lehmann described a new mineral from the Berezov mine near Ekaterinburg, now of tragic memory. From its ruddy colour it was known as Siberian red lead, but is now called *crocoite*, Greek *krokos* saffron, $PbCrO_4$. A specimen reaching Paris was analysed by Vauquelin and Macquart in 1789, who found it to contain lead, iron and alumina. Bindheim of Moscow, however, believed that several other elements were also present, including the then newly discovered molybdenum. Accordingly Vauquelin* re-examined the mineral in 1797. On boiling the powdered specimen with potassium carbonate solution he obtained an insoluble residue of lead carbonate with a yellow solution (of potassium chromate) which gave a red precipitate with mercury chloride (mercuric chromate) and a yellow one with lead nitrate. He rightly concluded that the yellow solution contained the potassium salt of a new acid. The following year Vauquelin obtained the metal itself; he decomposed the mineral with acid, reduced the liberated oxide, CrO_3, with charcoal and obtained a mass of interwoven metallic needles, weighing about one-third as much as the original oxide.

Fourcroy and Haüy suggested chromium as a suitable name for the element in recognition of the various colours shown by its derivatives, Greek *khroma* colour. The same year Vauquelin detected chromium in the spinel ruby while Taessert showed it to be an essential constituent of chrome iron ore or chromite, $FeO.Cr_2O_3$ — now the main source of chromium compounds. The colour of the ruby is now usually attributed to its chromium content and artificial rubies are manufactured by fusing pure alumina with a little oxide of chromium, to "colour" it, in an

---

*VAUQUELIN, *Ann. Chim. Phys.*, 1798, **25**, 21, 194; *Crell's Annalen*, 1798, i, 183, 276.

oxyhydrogen flame. It should be mentioned that, about this time, Klaproth* independently discovered chromium in crocoite.

Chromium is now used to a considerable extent in plating. It yields a pleasing, non-tarnishing coat, which is greatly appreciated domestically and in other realms. Hard deposits can now be obtained, so they are used on cycle wheel rims, and for "making up" after wastage. Its most important use is in the production of ferro-chrome — an alloy with iron containing 43 to 80 per cent of chromium. This is used largely in the manufacture of special irons and steels. *Stainless steel*, for example, contains 13 to 14 per cent of chromium and is very resistant to atmospheric corrosion and attack by vinegar and other vegetable acids. It is used in cutlery, etc. A chromium steel containing, say, 1 to 1·5 of carbon and 2·5 to 4 of chromium is intensely hard and is useful for burglar-proof safes, railway couplings, etc. Chrome vanadium steels find application in axle shafts and locomotive wheels; chrome nickel steels containing 2 to 3 per cent Cr and some nickel are used for armour plate, whilst high-speed tools are manufactured from chrome tungsten and chrome molybdenum steels. Staybrite steel may contain about 18 per cent Cr and 8 of Ni.

Amongst the non-ferrous alloys of chromium, *nichrome*, *cochrome*, *stellite* and magnet steels (p. 245) may be mentioned.

Molybdenum

This word, derived from the Greek *molybdos*, lead, was used rather widely in the eighteenth century to designate graphite and substances resembling it in appearance, such as the mineral known to-day as *molybdenite*, MoS_2, and some compounds of antimony. The distinction between graphite and molybdenite was established by Scheele in 1778, and he found it necessary in the opening words of his thesis to make clear what the precise nature of his material happened to be.

"I do not mean", he wrote, under the title *Experiments with Lead-Ore*: *Molybdæna*, "the ordinary lead ore that is met with in the apothecaries shops, for this is very different from that concerning which I now wish to communicate my experiments to the Royal Academy. I mean here that which in Cronstedt's Mineralogy is called *Molybdæna membranacea nitens*, with which Quist and others probably made their experiments."

---

*See ROSCOE and SCHORLEMMER, "Treatise on Chemistry" (Macmillan, 1907) Vol. 2, p. 995.

Scheele observed that although nitric acid is without appreciable effect on graphite, in contact with molybdenite it yields sulphuric acid and a white insoluble residue. This he called *terra molybdænæ*, and regarded it as an acid, whence molybdic acid.

"Earth of molybdæna is of an acid nature. Its solution reddens litmus; soap solution becomes white and liver of sulphur is precipitated."

Bergman suggested that it might be the oxide of a hitherto unknown metal. Scheele desired to effect its reduction and, having no suitable furnace of his own, induced his friend Peter Jacob Hjelm* to undertake the work. Incidentally it may be mentioned that shortly after, namely, in 1782, Hjelm was appointed Assay Master of the Royal Mint at Stockholm. A paste of the powdered residue was made with linseed oil, heated in a closed crucible as strongly as possible, and, on cooling, metallic molybdenum remained, albeit impure. Some years later, namely, 1817, Berzelius† obtained a pure metal by reduction of the oxide in hydrogen.

Molybdenum has a fairly wide industrial application. Ferro-molybdenum is manufactured as an intermediary in steel production as it enhances the tensile strength, toughness and fineness of grain. Molybdenum steel, since about 1917, has been used for making high-speed tools (associated with tungsten), rifle barrels, rollers, in high-pressure work, and in the motor industry in place of nickel steel. It contains up to 0·5 per cent Mo. Some of the alloy steels are exceptionally resistant to acid and are useful in making chemical plant steels with 3 to 4 per cent. Molybdenum and 1 to 1·5 of carbon are used for permanent magnets. An alloy of iron, copper and molybdenum, known as *toncan*, is very resistant to corrosion.

The pure metal, reduced in hydrogen, is softer than tungsten and more ductile so it is used as a fine wire or filament for screens for radio valves; thicker wire for winding electric furnaces; hemispherical cups and sheets for X-ray and vacuum tube work.

Tungsten

There were two dense minerals, now known as *scheelite*, $CaWO_4$, and *wolframite*, $FeWO_4$, which, in the eighteenth century, were regarded as varieties of tin ore, for tin-stone is a very dense mineral $(D = 7)$. Scheelite was then known as *tungsten*, which is Swedish for "heavy stone" and in 1781 Scheele wrote a short paper on its

*HJELM, *Crell's Annalen*, 1790, i, 39; 1791, i, 179, etc.
†BERZELIUS, *Schweigger's J.*, 1817, **22**, 51.

examination. Scheelite was, of course, later named after Scheele himself. Wolframite was so called because it caused loss in tin smelting, just as antimony was known as the wolf by the early alchemists because it devoured the base metals in refining gold; it can be separated magnetically from tin stone which is not magnetic.

"The constituents of this variety of stone", wrote Scheele "seem probably to be still unknown to chemists. Cronstedt enumerates it amongst the ferruginous varieties of stone, under the name of *Ferrum calciforme, terra quodam incognita intime mixtum.* That which I used for my experiments is pearl coloured and taken from the iron mine of Bitsberg; and as I made many experiments upon it and have ascertained its constituents, I take the liberty of presenting the following to the Royal Academy."

Scheele then proceeded to give an account of his experiments from which he concluded that scheelite is a compound of lime and "tungstic acid".

In 1782 Bergman found the same acid in wolframite. The following year, 1783, two Spanish brothers, Don Fausto d'Elhuyar and Don Juan José, extended Scheele's observations and also showed that wolframite likewise contains "tungstic acid". This they proceeded to reduce by ignition with pulverised charcoal in a crucible and were rewarded by finding metallic globules of tungsten in the residue, some of which were as large as a pin's head. In 1847 Oxland patented a method for manufacturing sodium tungstate, tungstic acid and metallic tungsten from cassiterite. In 1857 he took out a second patent for manufacturing iron-tungsten alloys, the basis of modern tool steel production.

Some 90 per cent of the world's production of tungsten is absorbed in the manufacture of steel. The old Mushet steel of 1859 contained tungsten. Ferro-tungsten is largely made for this purpose. Some 2 to 8 per cent of tungsten increases the hardness, toughness and tensile strength of steel, and the alloy is much used in armour plate, projectiles, etc; 15 per cent of tungsten enables steel to retain its hardness at a high temperature and renders it valuable for high-speed tool production.

The alloy known as stellite retains its hardness at high temperatures. It comprises Co 55, Cr 33 to 35, W 10 and C 1·5 to 2 and stellite bits are often used in rock boring instead of diamonds. It is used cast as it is too difficult to work. Magnet steels contain iron alloyed with the above four elements. A typical steel suitable for good, permanent magnets, contains Co 35, Cr 6·0, W 4·0 and C 0·75, the remainder being iron.

Prior to the European War of 1914 to 1918, wolframite was mostly sent to Germany, and in August 1914 we had barely a four months' stock of metallic tungsten in the country. A Government inquiry was instituted, works were erected, arrangements were made with the Dominions to furnish us with ore, and in the course of a single year we were producing 98·5 per cent tungsten, fully 1 per cent better than the best that Germany had ever sent to Sheffield. That illustrates very graphically what *can* be done when necessity arises. On account of its resistance to acids, tungsten is recommended as a platinum substitute in laboratory practice. Tungsten crucibles, lined with an alloy of Pt-Ir, are used for high-temperature work.

Tungsten has an unusually high melting point, 3382° C. This, indeed, is higher than that of any other known element. Its vapour pressure is extremely low and the metal finds useful application for electric wiring for furnaces, targets of X-ray tubes, contacts, arcing points, thermionic valves, wiring for electric furnaces and also for thermocouples in a reducing atmosphere; thus a W-Mo couple can be used up to 2000° C.

Owing to its high electrical efficiency tungsten has since 1911 almost completely ousted tantalum for ordinary lamp filaments, except when lamps are required to resist unusual vibration (p. 241). Usually the wire is mechanically drawn through a die at 2000° C. A rod the thickness and length (7 inches) of an ordinary pencil will give 100 miles of filament; fewer than two tons of metal are required to supply filaments for 100 million electric bulbs.

As a matter of historical interest, it should be mentioned that Edison was not the inventor of the filament lamp, although this has been frequently urged. Actually, in 1860, Sir Joseph Swan obtained a glow in a carbon filament *in vacuo* and by 1878 he had perfected his filament lamps and placed them on show in this country. At this time Edison's lamp was only in the laboratory stage. This is not to minimise in the slightest Edison's work. But fact is fact.

What is reputed to be the largest molybdenum and tungsten works in Europe was recently opened in Kabardino-Balkaria in the heart of the Caucasian mountains. The plant lies at the foot of Mount Tyrny-Auz. Prospecting began in 1934 and at a height of 9850 ft ores of both metals were found, together with rich beds of gold, tin, antimony, arsenic, copper and lead. Meteorological difficulties are immense, fierce blizzards rage, and the extraction of the ores presents many problems. But, *persevera*, *per severa*, *per se vera*.

CHAPTER 20

THE MANGANESE GROUP

THE manganese group comprises manganese, masurium and rhenium.

Manganese

The dioxide was known to the ancients, but until the close of the eighteenth century was confused with oxide of iron. Pliny, for example, distinguished two lodestones, one of which was magnetic, namely, Fe_3O_4, whereas the other was not and is usually thought to have been manganese dioxide. This mineral was used in Roman times for decolorising glass, whence the name *pyrolusite* from Greek *pyr*, fire and *luo*, I wash. Excess manganese gives a violet glass; amethystine glass has been found at Memphis, Egypt, as well as in Roman specimens. Such glass, resembling port-wine in colour, was regarded as protecting the drinker from becoming drunk and would naturally be popular; indeed the word amethyst is derived from the Greek *a*, not and *methein*, to be drunk. Cleopatra's famous amethyst ring was believed, in accordance with the doctrine of signatures (p. 293), to protect its fair wearer from becoming intoxicated should she be tempted to indulge too freely in Eastern wines. The amethyst is quartz tinted with manganese, presumably as silicate. Other names for pyrolusite were *manganese* and *magnesia nigra* (p. 151).

In 1740 J. H. Pott expressed the view that pyrolusite contained a metal unknown to science.

Scheele during 1771 to 1774 spent much time examining the mineral under the name of *manganese* and was led to the discovery of chlorine by acting on it with marine acid air (p. 46). He pointed out that although the mineral contained a little iron, silica and lime there was also "some of a new species of earth, which so far as I know, is as yet unknown." This was a barium compound; he further observed that the mineral as a whole behaved like a calx or oxide. His friend Johann Gottlieb Gahn, who had in 1769 recognised phosphorus as a constituent of bones (p. 77), ignited an oil paste of pyrolusite and charcoal and obtained a button of metallic manganese in 1774.

For a considerable time the position to be given to manganese in the Periodic Table was a matter of dispute. Mendeléeff in 1871 put it in Group VII immediately beneath fluorine and between chromium and iron in the first long horizontal series. But as no other metal was known to belong to Group VII, it was sometimes bracketed with iron in Group VIII. Those who supported its position in Group VII pointed to the isomorphism of potassium perchlorate and permanganate. The determination of its atomic number by Moseley's X-ray method confirmed this view and it was further shown that vacancies occurred in the list of atomic numbers that would lead one to expect the existence of two more elements in Group VII, namely, numbers 43 and 75, lying between molybdenum and ruthenium in the second long horizontal period and between tungsten and osmium in the fourth long period respectively. Mendeléeff's original scheme was thus supported.

Manganese by itself is seldom, if ever, used commercially. Alloys with iron rich in manganese are extremely important. Ferro-manganese contains upwards of 20 per cent of the latter metal, whilst spiegel irons range from 20 downwards. They are used in steel manufacture. Small quantities of ferro-manganese are added to the steel before teeming into ingots to de-oxidise and desulphurise. Almost all of the manganese enters the slag, leaving perhaps 0·4 per cent as sulphide disseminated throughout the steel. Steels containing about one per cent of alloyed manganese are commonly used for rails and structures. Those containing some 12 to 15 per cent manganese are very hard and tough and are used for tramway points and crossings and numerous other purposes where high resistance to shock and wear is essential.

Many alloys with non-ferrous metals are well known, such as manganese bronze, manganin, cupro-manganese, Hensler's alloy, and manganese German silver.

Elements 43 and 75

Amongst the claims to the discovery of elements that might have been No. 43, the *eka-manganese* of Mendeléeff, the following may be mentioned —

> *Ilmenium*, by Hermann, 1846, in ilmenite and also accompanying niobium and tantalum in various minerals; it was closely allied to them in its general characteristics and to it he ascribed an atomic weight of 104·6. Several years later he relinquished his claims, but brought them forward again in

1877, together with the announcement that a second element, which he called *neptunium*, occurred in tantalite from Haddam, Connecticut, belonging to the same series — presumably referring to element 75. Owing to the minute quantities of the supposed elements obtainable and the lack of modern X-ray methods of identifying them, no confirmation appeared possible.

Nipponium, by Ogawa, 1908, in molybdenite and thorianite, with an atomic weight of approximately 100. Nippon is the Japanese name for Japan.

In addition to Hermann's neptunium mentioned above there are three claims to elements that might have been No. 75, the *dvi-manganese* of Mendeléeff —

Ruthenium, by Osann in 1828, from platinum ores. This is not to be confused with the element now recognised by that name, discovered by Claus in 1845.

Uralium, by Guyard in 1869, again from platinum ores; it had a density of 20·25 and an atomic weight of 187; these are in general accord with those of rhenium D = 21·04 and At. Wt. 186·31. But in its chemical and other physical properties there was less similarity.

Davyum, by Sergius Kern* of St Petersburg, in 1877, in residues obtained from platinum ores after removal of the noble metals. He named it, as he says, in honour of Sir Humphry Davy. The density was 9·385, very low for rhenium (21·0). The atomic weight could not be determined with accuracy as the quantity of the material available was too small but a preliminary investigation suggested a value of about 154; that of rhenium is 186·3. It is of special interest to note that the solution of its chloride gave a red precipitate when heated with potassium thiocyanate — a reaction that is also given by rhenium. In 1899 Mallet† confirmed Kern's reactions and it would appear quite possible that Kern's material did actually contain a little rhenium.

Rhenium

Three young chemists, Walter Noddack, Ida Tacke and Berg‡,

---

*Kern, *Chem. News*, 1877, **36**, 4, 114; 1878, **37**, 65. *Nature*, 1878, **17**, 245.

†Mallet, *Amer. Chem. J.*, 1898, **20**, 766. Friend and Druce, *Nature*, 1950, **165**, 819.

‡Noddack and Coworkers, *Naturwissenschaften*, 1925, **13**, 567.

working in Nernst's laboratory, claimed in 1925 to have discovered two new elements. This was not a so-called "chance" discovery, but, like that of hafnium (p. 232), the result of a direct search in likely quarters. It was considered that the congeners of manganese should be found, if they exist at all, in platinum ores and certain other minerals such as molybdenite, niobite, and tantalite. After removing most of the known elements, residues were obtained and submitted to X-ray analysis with the result that the lines calculated for elements 43 and 75 were found, thus indicating the existence of the two elements in question. Element 75 was called *rhenium* — a very appropriate name for Germans to give it in honour of their national river the Rhine; but the choice of *masurium* for element 43 was a stupid psychological blunder, which no civilised scientist should make. It commemorates the crushing defeat inflicted on the Russians by the Germans in the Masurian district during the Great War of 1914 to 1918, and thus tends to perpetuate racial hatred in a realm where such should be forgotten in noble attempts to serve mankind.

Simultaneously Loring and Druce* were examining pyrolusite and crude manganese compounds for indications of a trans-uranian element, No. 93. In the course of the work evidence was obtained of the presence of dvi-manganese, No. 75. This was supported by X-ray analysis in collaboration with Messrs Adam Hilger in the latter's research laboratory in London and confirmed by Heyrovský and Dolejšek†.

Pure rhenium and rhenium compounds are now quite well known and are obtainable by purchase. As yet they have no industrial applications. The most important source of rhenium appears to be molybdenite, MoS_2, particularly Norwegian and Japanese ores.

Does element No. 43 exist in nature ?

The existence of a stable isotope of this element seems unlikely on theoretical grounds, and the claim of Noddack and Tacke to have detected its presence in the minerals they examined has not been substantiated.

In 1937 a molybdenum target that had been bombarded for many months with deuterons in a cyclotron showed radio-activity

---

*Loring and Druce, *Chem. News*, 1925, **131**, 273, 337. See also Druce, "Rhenium" (C.U.P. 1948).

†Heyrovský and Dolejšek, *Nature*, 1925, **116**, 782.

characteristic of isotopes of element 43, for which the name *technetium* or *technicum*, Tc, has been suggested*.

---

*See SEGRÈ and his co-workers, *J. Chem. Physics*, 1937, **5**, 712; 1939, **7**, 155. *Physical Review*, 1937, **52**, 1252; 1938, **54**, 772; 1939, **56**, 753. EMELÉUS, *Nature*, 1949, **163**, 624.

CHAPTER 21

THE IRON GROUP

THE iron group comprises iron, cobalt and nickel.

Iron

Iron, like copper, occurs native in many parts of the world and has in consequence been known to man from very early times.* Unlike gold and silver it is not particularly prepossessing in appearance and its contribution towards the growth of civilisation has lain in its industrial applications rather than in its artistic merits, although many primitive peoples have used iron for personal adornment, and as late as the nineteenth century steel jewellery was fashionable in Britain (see Plate 3).

The metallurgical discovery of iron, like that of copper, was a truly epoch-making advance. Using the term iron in its broadest sense to include cast and wrought irons and steels, we are still in the iron age.

It is generally accepted that most native iron is of meteoric origin, but in certain cases there can be no doubt as to its terrestrial source. Iron has been found in the coal measures of Missouri at depths of 30 feet and more below undisturbed strata, which precludes a meteoric source; it is extremely unlikely that iron meteorites of Carboniferous age ($c.\ 3 \times 10^8$ years) would have survived in metallic form. Furthermore, the metal was soft and free from nickel, whereas the meteoric metal is nickeliferous. Probably it was formed by reduction *in situ*.

Meteorites

Meteoric iron was known to primitive man and both worshipped and used by him during the stone age. Numerous meteorites have been found in different parts of the world; they vary greatly both in size and in composition. The largest known is the Hoba West meteorite which lies where it was found at Grootfontein, S. W. Africa. It is a roughly rectangular mass, $3 \times 3 \times 1$ cu. metres,

---

*A detailed account of the history of iron is given in the Author's "Iron in Antiquity" (Griffin, 1926).

weighing approximately 60 tons. Allowance for iron in the rocks immediately surrounding the meteorite suggests that its original weight was over 80 tons. Its nickel content of 16 per cent is unusually high, and it is a particularly hard and malleable specimen. Two natives required two full days, and a great supply of hack-saw blades, to cut a surface only 8 cm. × 13 cm.*

The second largest known is the Ahnighito meteorite brought by Peary from Western Greenland in 1895; it weighs 36·5 tons and now reposes in the Hayden Planetarium, New York. In February 1947 an enormous meteorite fell in Russia†, in Eastern Siberia, and the noise of its fall was heard 200 km. away. It was probably the largest that has struck the earth within historic times and may indeed have been a minor planet. A preliminary estimate of its mass is about 1000 tons and its temperature due to friction with the air was probably about 5000° C. On striking the earth it broke up into thousands of fragments. Had it fallen in a populous district like London the damage would have been irretrievable. On the other hand, by way of contrast, the famous Rowton meteorite of 1876 (p. 256) weighed only 7 lb. (3109 grams).

In former days a fall of stones or "thunderbolts" from the sky was regarded as heralding events of prodigious importance, and ancient literature contains many references to such phenomena. One of the earliest is that recorded in Holy Writ, in *Joshua* x. 11, early in the fourteenth century B.C., where we are told that "the Lord cast down great stones from heaven" upon the enemy of the Hebrews, more being killed by the stones than by the sword. Diana of the Ephesians (*Acts* xix. 35) — "the image which fell down from Jupiter" — was undoubtedly a meteorite.

Livy (59 to 18 B.C.) tells of a shower of stones that fell on Mount Albanus about 652 B.C. The Senate were so impressed that a nine-day solemn festival was decreed.

An interesting legend enshrouds a large black meteoric stone found in ancient Phrygia and taken to the shrine of the Mother Goddess Cybele to be worshipped as her image. It remained there for many generations. In 216 B.C., however, Hannibal, the Carthaginian general, defeated the Romans at Cannae and threatened Rome herself. The Sybelline books were consulted by the anxious Romans and appeals were made to the oracles by the City Fathers who were informed that Rome might yet be saved if Cybele could

---

*WATSON, "Between the Planets" (Churchill, London, 1945).
†*Nature*, 1949, **163**, 92.

be brought within her walls. An imposing embassy was sent to Phrygia to ask for the sacred image; naturally the king refused; but an earthquake conveniently shook the royal palace and the goddess herself spoke from her shrine stating that it was the will of the gods that she should repair to Rome and save the city. What king could resist so clear a command! The sacred pines were hewed by a thousand axes, a new vessel was built, fit for a divine passenger, and the image was duly taken to Rome, reaching there about 204 B.C. The ancient city was never taken; Hannibal left Italy for ever in 202 B.C. Thus were the oracles confirmed.

The behaviour of uncivilised races in analogous circumstances in modern times is closely similar*.

Built into the north-east corner of the Kaaba at Mecca is a very dark reddish-brown stone, believed to be a meteorite. It has been venerated by the Arabs for generations. When Mohammed captured Mecca, A.D. 630, he entered the sacred enclosure and with habitual iconoclasm destroyed the 360 idols within; but, strangely enough, he spared the stone; he even saluted it with his staff and kissed it. To-day that stone is the most sacred jewel of Islam. Towards it each devout Moslem is bidden to turn as he prays five times a day. It is called *The Right Hand of God on Earth* and is reputed to have dropped from Paradise when Adam was created. In the day of judgment it will be endowed with speech and will witness in favour of all who have touched it with sincere hearts; but woe to the unbeliever!

So rigidly obeyed is the injunction to Moslems to turn towards Mecca when making their devotions, that the Emir Abdullah, ruler of Transjordania, when on a flight over the Mediterranean towards this country in 1946, carried with him a compass so that he might know which way to turn at the hour of prayer even if his plane were lost in the clouds. There is something beautiful in such sincerity.

Meteorites may be roughly divided into three groups according to their composition, namely *siderites*, *siderolites* and *aerolites*†. The first named include those which consist mainly of iron (Greek *sideros*, iron), whilst the last consist almost wholly of stone, that is, silicates with interspersed particles of nickeliferous iron etc. (Greek *aer* air; *lithos*, stone). The siderolites are intermediate between the

---

*H. A. NEWTON, *Nature*, 1897, **56**, 355.

†L. FLETCHER, "An Introduction to the Study of Meteorites" (British Museum, 1908). Unfortunately the word siderite is also used to denote a natural carbonate of iron, namely chalybite or s pathic iron ore.

two. Some authorities connect the Greek word *sideros* with the Latin *sidus* a star, regarding this as an indication that meteoric iron was known and that it was recognised as the metal dropped from the sky.

It is interesting that most ancient folk designated iron by words indicative of celestial origin, but it does not necessarily follow that a meteoric origin was envisaged. Thus the natives of the West Indies, discovered by Columbus in 1492, were familiar with gold and copper but not with iron. The brass and iron introduced by the Spaniards intrigued them greatly; they called them *turey*, a gift from heaven. There was no question of meteoric origin; the natives may however have regarded their white visitors as gods — until they knew them better.

Analyses of numerous siderites indicate that the iron is invariably alloyed with varying amounts of nickel. The specimen from Rowton in Shropshire contains nearly nine per cent of nickel; it may be seen in the Natural History Museum, South Kensington, and is of special interest as its fall in 1876 is the first to be recorded by an eye-witness in Great Britain. Other siderites have been found to contain up to 60 per cent of nickel and as this metal tends to render iron more resistant to corrosion, it has helped to preserve the specimens from disintegration. On the other hand, a few meteorites have been observed to corrode rapidly upon exposure to the atmosphere, and this has been traced to the presence of small amounts of Lawrencite or ferrous chloride, $FeCl_2$, a salt which readily hydrolyses in moist air yielding free acid and stimulating corrosion; a three-ton specimen from Cranbourne, Australia, is now kept in a nitrogen-filled case for this reason[*]. Most iron meteorites contain a proportion of troilite (FeS) which also is readily erodible. Large specimens, after some years of atmospheric attack, are frequently deeply pitted owing to the dissolution of this constituent.

The lodestone

The richest ore of iron is magnetite or the lodestone, Fe_3O_4. According to an ancient legend a shepherd, Magnes by name, was crossing the slopes of Mt. Ida in Asia Minor, taking his flocks to pasture, when he felt his shoes fall to pieces, the nails having been drawn from the soles as he trod the magnetic soil. The mineral thus came to be known as *Magnes' stone* or *magnetite*.

It is always painful to destroy a pretty legend; let us do it gently. More probably the word magnetite is derived from Magnesia, a

---

[*]WATSON, *Opus cit.*

town in Lydia, destroyed by earthquake during the reign of Tiberius (A.D. 14 to 37).

In course of time the mineral was found to occur in other parts of the world, specimens possessing extra powerful magnetic properties being discovered in Siberia and the Hartz mountains.

The first iron miners in Greece appear to have been roving bands of Phrygians who, because of their skill in metallurgy, came to be regarded with awe. In due course tradition traced them back to the Idean Dactyls or "Fingers" of the Earth Goddess, Rhea. These miners settled in Samothrace where the ore was plentiful and exhibited to the wondering populace the magnetic properties of the lodestone by suspending from it rings of iron as in chains. They also demonstrated that the stone could impart its own magnetic properties to iron. The Samothracian rings were for long regarded as mysterious and were repeatedly mentioned by early authors from the time of Plato (427 to 344 B.C.) onwards. Lucretius* writing in the first century B.C. refers to the lodestone as still an object of wonder. "This stone men wonder at", he writes, "as it often produces a chain of rings hanging down from it. Thus you may see sometimes five or more suspended in succession . . . each in turn experiencing the binding power of the stone."

Some 500 years later St Augustine, Bishop of Hippo and most renowned of the Christian Fathers, wrote that he had been thrilled by a similar sight†. "When I first saw it I was thunderstruck", he wrote, "for I saw an iron ring attracted and suspended by the stone; and then, as if it had communicated its own property to the iron it attracted, this ring was put near another and lifted it up and, as the first ring clung to the magnet, so did the second ring to the first. A third and fourth were similarly added, so that there hung from the stone a kind of chain of rings with their hoops connected, not interlinking, but attached together by their outer surface. Who would not be amazed at this virtue of the stone . . .? Yet far more astonishing is what I heard about the stone from my brother in the episcopate, Severus, Bishop of Milevis. He told me that Bathanarius, once Count of Africa, when the Bishop was dining with him produced a magnet and held it under a silver plate on which he placed a bit of iron; then as he moved his hand with the magnet

---

*LUCRETIUS, "De Rerum Natura". Translated by Munro (Routledge, 1886), Book 6. Lucretius was born 95 B.C. and is believed to have committed suicide 51 B.C.

†P. BENJAMIN, "The Intellectual Rise in Electricity" (Longmans, 1895), p. 87. Quoted from Dod's translation of "De Civitate Dei".

S

beneath the plate, the iron upon the plate moved about accordingly. The intervening silver was not affected at all, but precisely as the magnet was moved backward and forward below it, no matter how quickly, so was the iron attracted above. I have related what I myself have witnessed. I have related what I was told by one whom I trust as I trust my own eyes."

During the later centuries the power of the lodestone grew apace. Mountains of it beneath the sea could draw the very nails out of the ships sailing above them so that they fell to pieces even in calm weather. Similarly their presence would disturb the compass and lead the mariner astray.

Being magnetic the mineral also possesses polarity, and an elongated specimen, when freely suspended, will place itself in a direction pointing to the magnetic north and south, whence the name lodestone, *lode* meaning direction.

The knowledge that the stone attracts iron presupposes a knowledge of the metal. But we can conceive the possibility that the polarity of the stone was known to man long before this. It is possible that it had been observed by man in the bronze age, and that the compass had already been invented before iron was intentionally reduced from its ores.

The power of the stone to transmit its properties to iron is clearly described in a fourteenth century MS. believed to contain the writings of one who styled himself William the Clerk, a monk of the twelfth century; an intriguing translation into English verse* runs as follows —

> "Who would of his course be sure,
> When the clouds the sky obscure,
> He an iron needle must
> In the cork wood firmly thrust.
> Lest the iron virtue lack
> Rub it with the lodestone black,
> In a cup with flowing brim,
> Let the cork on water swim.
> When at length the tremor ends,
> Note the way the needle tends;
> Though its place no eye can see —
> There the polar star will be."

To-day, all this and much more is taken for granted.

---

*By P. BENJAMIN, *Opus cit.*, p. 151.

Iron and primitive man

Whilst still in the stone age, man used both native copper and iron. The quantity of native iron known to science is much less than that of native copper and the chance that man would come across it was proportionately small. It has been estimated that some 246 tons of meteoric iron* are known to science, and in prehistoric times there were all the accumulations of previous ages for man to draw upon. As only about one per cent of the native metal is brittle and unsuitable for cold-working there would be sufficient malleable metal available to supply man with an appreciable number of implements. The Otumpa meteorite, discovered in the Argentine about 1783, and weighing more than half a ton, shows at least six places from which portions have been removed. The Descubridora meteorite (Mexico), already known in 1780, has a gap in which is wedged a broken copper chisel left by some primitive workman.

The metallurgical skill acquired by men of the bronze age paved the way for the discovery and rapid utilisation of iron in such areas as possessed suitable ores near the surface. Reduction of oxide or carbonate ores takes place quite easily in a primitive furnace; the metal does not melt, its melting point, $1535°$ C, being far too high to be reached in an ordinary fire. It is obtained as a spongy mass, more or less admixed with impurities but often very free from carbon and hence very soft. It could readily be hammered into shape, but would not retain a sharp cutting edge and would thus be useless as a sword. The introduction of a little carbon into the metal, however, would render it hard and capable of receiving a temper. The early worker would soon learn to test his product in some simple practical way and to work up those portions that gave promise of being suitable.

Unable to understand why his furnace sometimes yielded him good material and sometimes poor, the superstitious workman would tend to lay the blame on his gods. Thus in Japan, until recently, it was the custom of the armourers, when making the famous Samurai blades, to put on the cap and robes ·worn by nobles of the Mikado's court, close the doors of the workshop, and labour in secrecy and gloom†. A tasselled cord of straw, such as is hung before the shrines of the native gods of Japan, would be suspended between two bamboo poles in the forge, which would

---

*ZIMMER, *J. Iron and Steel Inst.*, 1916, No. 11, 306.
†LORD REDESDALE, "Tales of Old Japan" (Macmillan, 1910), p. 38.

for the time being function as a holy altar. The gods thus appeased, the work should be brought to a successful issue.

Once man had learned to produce good steel, its superiority over bronze for military purposes would be rapidly appreciated, and the conservative soldier proverbially slow to adopt new methods would be compelled by dire necessity to throw aside his bronze sword and shield and betake to himself weapons of steel (p. 275).

Iron in Egypt

Iron appears to have been known and prized by the pre-dynastic Egyptians some 4000 B.C., that is, if we are correct in assuming that the beads found in the graves, and now completely oxidised to rust, were originally specimens of the metal. But another explanation is possible, namely that the original beads were iron pyrites or marcasite, the latter being particularly liable to corrosion. This is by no means impossible, for the various forms of iron pyrites have long been admired for their golden colour*.

Iron did not come into general use in Egypt before about 1350 B.C. The period ranging from the earliest use of the metal down to this later date is aptly termed by Sir Flinders Petrie the *Sporadic Iron Age*. Considerable interest centres round the iron objects found by Howard Carter† in the tomb of Tutankhamen, the boy king who ruled over Egypt *circa* 1360 to 1354 B.C. Nineteen objects were found, including a dagger the blade of which was still bright though flecked with rust spots. It now reposes in the museum in Cairo.

By the time of Rameses II, *circa* 1300 B.C., iron was being used by the Mediterranean nations in fashioning weapons of war, and a letter is extant indicating that Rameses applied to the Hittite king for a supply of the metal; whether he received it or not we do not know, but iron gradually became more plentiful and the armies of Rameses III a century later appear to have been equipped with iron weapons, for these are painted blue on the monuments.

An interesting light is thrown upon the conditions prevailing in the time of Rameses II by the Egyptian Papyrus Anastasi I‡, popularly known as "The Travels of a Mohar". It is a collection of letters written by a professor of literature at the Court of

---

*See LUCAS, "Ancient Egyptian Materials" (Arnold, 1926), p. 97. WAIN-WRIGHT, *Revue Archeologique*, 1912, No. 1, 255.

†HOWARD CARTER, "The Tomb of Tutankhamen" (Cassell, 1927), Volume 2.

‡TOLKOWSKI, "The Gateway of Palestine" (Routledge, 1924), p. 21. From SAYCE, "Patriarchal Palestine" 1895, pp. 212–224.

Rameses II, giving a satirical account of the journeyings of a royal messenger. It appears that at Jaffa his arms were stolen from his side and the armour stripped from his unguarded chariot as he slept in a garden. In modern newspaper parlance this would be described as an "impudent theft" and it is noteworthy that the Mohar's prestige as envoy of the great Rameses was not sufficient to protect him from such indignity. The letters proceed —

"Thou comest into Joppa; thou findest the garden in full bloom in its time. Thou penetratest in order to eat. Thou findest that the maid who keepest the garden is fair. She does whatever thou wantest of her. Thou art recognised, thou art brought to trial and owest thy preservation to being a Mohar. Thy girdle of the finest stuff thou payest as the price of a worthless rag. Thou sleepest every evening with a rug of fur over thee. Thou sleepest deep sleep for thou art weary. A thief steals thy sword and thy bow from thy side; thy quiver and thy armour are cut off in the darkness, thy pair of horses run away ... Thy chariot is broken to pieces ... The iron-workers enter into the smithy; they rummage in the workshops of the carpenters; the handicrafts men and saddlers are at hand; they do whatever thou requirest. They put together thy chariot; they put aside the parts of it that are made useless; thy spokes are fashioned quite new; thy wheels are put on; they put the straps on the axles and on the hinder part; they splice thy yoke, they put on the box of thy chariot; the workmen in iron forge the (?); they put the ring that is wanting on thy whip and they replace the lashes upon it."

A truly human document.

It appears that even at this early date workmen could be found in Jaffa skilful in repairing chariots and familiar with the art of forging iron.

The earliest general group of iron tools in Egypt was found at Thebes and belonged to the time of the Assyrian invasion by Ashur-banipal, 666 B.C.

Iron in Holy Writ

The word iron occurs more than 60 times in the Old Testament. The first reference occurs in *Numbers* xxxv. 16, where the Lord lays down the law to be observed by the Hebrews when they entered the Promised Land. If a man smite another "with an instrument of iron, so that he die, he is a murderer; the murderer shall surely be put to death." The next time iron is mentioned is in connection with Og, the giant king of Bashan, a city of the Amorites. Og died about 1400 B.C. and his bier or sarcophagus, was of iron (*Deut.* iii. 11), "nine cubits was the length thereof, and four cubits the breadth of it, after the cubit of a man." As a cubit was roughly equivalent to 20·6 inches, the bier would measure 15 by 7 feet. Such large dimensions were no doubt worthy of note, but it is doubtful if they would have found their way into Holy Writ had it not been for the unusual fact that the bier was made of iron. Both in the Authorised and Revised Versions of the Bible the word *bier* is incorrectly rendered *bed*. Beds as we know them were not then in use. The account may, however, be a later addition to the MS. and it would be unwise to conclude from this alone that iron was in general use at that early date*.

The early Hebrews did not use war chariots and we are told† that in consequence they found themselves at considerable disadvantage when fighting the Canaanites who possessed large numbers of chariots plated or studded with iron.

The oldest specimens of iron hitherto found in Palestine are two wedge-shaped lumps discovered at the bottom of the sloping part of the water-passage at Gezer‡. The passage had been sealed up prior to 1250 B.C., so that the pieces of metal evidently date back to a time many years anterior to that at which iron came into general use in the country.

The Philistines who entered Palestine from the Mediterranean about the same time as the Hebrews from the desert, were a cultured, non-semitic race, familiar with iron. They wisely retained the monopoly of working the metal, refusing to teach the Hebrews lest they should equip their armies with iron swords (1 *Sam.* xiii. 19-22). In consequence the Hebrews had no smiths of their own and only Saul and Jonathan possessed iron swords. The petty skirmishes between the Hebrews and the Philistines are easily understood when one has visited the country and traversed the bleak and barren heights occupied by the Hebrews and compared them with the fertile maritime plains below owned by the Philistines. It was the have-nots versus the haves.

---

*RIDGEWAY, "The Early Age of Greece" (C.U.P., 1901), Volume I, p. 617.
†*Joshua* xvii. 16. *Judges* i. 19.
‡MACALISTER, *Palestine Exploration Fund, Quarterly Statement*, 1908, p. 1.

As Macalister* quaintly puts it "the promise of a land flowing with milk and honey was not made to a crowd of beef-fed excursionists, coming from cultivated and developed lands of the modern west, but to tribes of half starved wanderers, fighting their way from oasis to oasis over sterile sands." Hence, if the barren heights of Judah seemed to flow with milk and honey, how much more so would the maritime plain.

The break up of the Philistine domination removed the embargo on iron, and when David ascended the throne about 1000 B.C. the use of iron had become more general. By the time of Amos† (760 B.C.), the herdman of Tekoa in Southern Judah, iron was in general use among the Hebrews, and the later Hebrew writers were evidently familiar with smelting furnaces‡.

In 1925, when in Jerusalem, a dragoman informed the Author of a curious belief which he stated to be prevalent amongst the Jews, namely that if the crevices in the ancient wall at the famous Wailing Place are completely filled with iron nails, Jerusalem will once again be restored to the Jews. The authorities have very properly stopped the practice of plugging the walls with nails which had become a nuisance. A host of questions instantly suggests itself to the inquiring mind. Would copper nails be equally effective? If not, wherein lies the virtue of the iron?

There are but few references to iron in the New Testament. It is generally conceded, however, that the nails used in the crucifixion of Christ were of iron, and tradition says that these were subsequently welded into an iron band to which six golden plaques were affixed thus making the *Corona Ferrea* or the *Crown of Lombardy*. Tradition says that this crown was given by Pope Gregory the Great to Queen Theodelinda, who died A.D. 638, and it is known to have been used at many coronations since that of Henry of Luxemburg in 1311, who is the first who is known with certainty to have worn it§. In 1805 when Napoleon was crowned King of Italy in Milan cathedral he placed the crown upon his own head voicing the traditional formula "God gave it to me; woe to him who touches it." History adds pathetically that Josephine was present at the ceremony, but only as a spectator‖. The crown

---

*MACALISTER, "A History of Civilisation in Palestine" (C.U.P., 1921), p. 29.

†Amos may have witnessed the total eclipse of the Sun in Palestine in 763 B.C. (Amos viii. 9).

‡Jeremiah xi. 4. Written about 600 B.C.

§JONES, W., "Crowns and Coronations", p. 23 (1883, Chatto & Windus).

‖GEER, "Napoleon and his Family" (Allen and Unwin, 1928), p. 206.

followed the remains of King Victor Emmanuel to the Pantheon at Rome in 1878.

And what of the spear that pierced the Master's side so deeply that "forthwith came there out blood and water" *John* xix. 34? Traditions are unanimous that the spear-head was made of iron, but very different tales are told of its subsequent history. According to one story the spear-head was carefully preserved after the crucifixion and was ultimately blended into the huge sword *Joyeuse* of Charlemagne (742 to 814).

According to another legend the spear-head was found by Peter Bartholomew during the First Crusade in 1098. Antioch had fallen, but the crusaders who had taken it were themselves besieged in turn by the Turks. One night St Andrew appeared to Peter in a vision and showed him where the relic lay. "Behold" said he "the spear which pierced the side of Him who saved the world." On awaking, Peter communicated his vision to the authorities; digging was undertaken and the spear-head found — a piece of rusted iron. This was regarded by the crusaders as a sign that God was with them. Under Bohemund they sallied forth from Antioch with the spear-head bound to a standard; the Turks were routed. The spear-head was later encased in silver and given to the Byzantine emperor*.

Iron in India

It is claimed that iron was worked in India at a very early date, possibly some 2000 B.C. if early records are to be believed. This is quite conceivable. But the imagination of the Easterns is apt to run riot, and early traditions must be scrutinised with the utmost care.

Herodotus† states that the Indian troops in the army of Xerxes, King of Babylon 485 to 455 B.C., used arrows pointed with iron.

Several large masses of iron are to be seen in India made many centuries ago by welding together small blooms, obtained by the direct process and weighing several pounds each. That such huge masses could be constructed is a remarkable tribute to the skill of the early Indian metallurgists. The most famous of these are the Delhi Pillar, the Dhar Pillar‡ and the iron beams from the Black

---

*H. LAMB, "The Crusades" (London, 1930), Chapters 25 and 26. See also BESANT and PALMER, "Jerusalem" (London, 1908), Chapter 6.

†"The History of Herodotus", translated by G. Rawlinson, Book 7, Chapter 65.

‡V. A. SMITH, *J. Royal Asiatic Society*, 1898, p. 143. *J. Iron Steel Institute*, 1912, I, 158. GRAVES, *ibid.*, p. 187.

PLATE 2 [*Facing p.* 264

The Iron Pillar at Delhi

Height 22 feet, Upper Diameter 12½ inches, Lower Diameter 16½ inches, Weight 6 tons.
(*Reproduced by permission of the late Sir Robert Hadfield, F.R.S.*)

Pagoda at Konarak* in the Madras Presidency. It will suffice to give a brief account of the first of these, namely the Delhi Pillar, which dates back to about A.D. 300. According to Brahmin tradition it was erected after the stars had indicated the auspicious moment, and was embedded so deep in the earth that it pierced the head of the serpent god Schesnag, who supports the earth. The priests told the Rajah that this ensured that his kingdom would last for all time. But the Rajah could not be satisfied until he had confirmed what the priests told him. He dug the pillar up again and sure enough the end was covered with blood. On replacement the serpent refused to be caught and the pillar now merely rested in the soil without supernatural support. This of course was nothing like so secure a foundation and after a few generations the Rajah's kingdom was supplanted by another. The pillar is not now on its original site; it was placed in its present position in A.D. 1052 as an adjunct to a group of temples from the materials of which the Mahommedans later constructed the mosque†. Analysis‡ shows the metal to be an excellent type of wrought iron, somewhat high in phosphorus but low in sulphur, showing that the fuel used in its manufacture and subsequent treatment was very pure — it would most probably be charcoal. The pillar has resisted corrosion extremely well and it has been argued that this ancient metal is of better quality than that produced to-day. But the ancient custom of anointing the pillar with butter at certain religious festivals may have had something to do with this. The total height of the pillar is 23 feet 8 inches, of which only 20 inches lie beneath the ground. The upper diameter is roughly one foot, the lower $16\frac{1}{2}$ inches, the total weight being estimated at about 6 tons. The pillar is illustrated in Plate 2.

Legend hath it that Delhi owes its name to this pillar, the priests giving it that name from *dhili* loose or unstable. A Hindoo Judge has informed the Author that there is no connection between the two words. The word Delhi most probably means "Heart's Delight".

Iron in the Far East

In China the bronze age probably began about the time of the Emperor Ta-yü, that is, Yü the Great, *circa* 2200 B.C., and drew to

---

*FRIEND and THORNEYCROFT, *J. Iron Steel Institute*, 1924, II, 313. GRAVES, *loc. cit.*

†V. A. SMITH, "Early History of India" (Clarendon Press, 1924).

‡HADFIELD, *J. Iron Steel Institute*, 1912, I, 156. T. TURNER, *ibid.* p. 184.

a close about 500 to 600 B.C. For religious purposes bronze remained the favoured metal and the art of casting in bronze continued to improve, attaining its zenith in the magnificent and gigantic castings of the Northern Wei (386 to 535) and T'ang (618 to 907) Dynasties.

During the reign of the Emperor Chuang-Wang, 696 to 682 B.C., iron had come into general use, a tax on iron needles, knives and agricultural implements being instituted. This proved so profitable that later governments continued the tax and did all they could to increase the production of iron articles. But in the original tax no mention was made of swords or arms. This suggests that the metal was not as yet sufficiently reliable for military purposes. Some 300 years later the King of Ch'u is stated to have been interested in the production of iron swords possessing magical properties, which suggests that the Chinese had learned to carburise their iron and convert it into steel sufficiently hard and reliable to warrant the confidence of the soldier*; it was usual to attribute magical properties to swords that were specially efficient (see p. 276).

Japan has long been famous for her swords. The Samurai, a man belonging to the military class and entitled to bear arms, set much store by his sword, which was his constant companion and ally†. The price of the sword was high, particularly if made by a famous craftsman, the blade alone costing several hundred pounds. The swords were handed down from father to son as valued heirlooms, and the swordsmith, regarded as following a most honourable profession, was of gentle blood.

"The trenchant blade of the Japanese sword is notorious", wrote Lord Redesdale. "It is said that the best blades will, in the hands of an expert swordsman, cut through the dead bodies of three men, laid one upon the other, at a blow." The swords of the Shogun were wont to be tested on the corpses of executed criminals; it is said that the public headsman was entrusted with this duty and that for a "nose-medicine" or bribe he would substitute the sword of a private individual for that of his lord, and that the executioner earned many a fee from those who wished to see how their swords would cut off a head.

The blades of Muramasa‡ were reputed to be unlucky; and the

---

*F. HIRTH, "The Ancient History of China" (New York, 1908), pp. 203, 235.
†LORD REDESDALE,"Tales of Old Japan" (Macmillan, 1910), pp. 38, 61 and 93.
‡Ibid.

superstitious regard them as hungering after men's lives. The Sukésada was an ancient and famous family of swordsmiths whose blades fetched very high prices.

Iron and the Greeks

The Greeks and the Cretans appear to have been amongst the first European peoples to use iron; the Grecian iron age began about 1400 B.C., although for most of the Celtic and Teutonic peoples it did not commence until some 900 years later.

Homer, who lived about 880 B.C., was very familiar with the metal. The Homeric Age, however, as depicted in the "Iliad" and "Odyssey", was much earlier, being in the main coeval with the Third Late Minoan Period of Crete, that is about 1400 to 1200 B.C., and represents a transition period, during which iron and bronze weapons and implements were used side by side. In the Homeric age iron, though not regarded as a precious metal like gold, ranked amongst the treasures of the wealthy, and was used, amongst other things, in ransoming prisoners and as a prize in sporting contests. Thus Achilles awarded a heavy lump of iron to him who could hurl it the greatest distance. The swords and defensive armour of the Homeric Heroes were made of bronze, as this metal could be relied upon to resist reasonable force. Goliath of Gath was similarly armed. Heavy implements such as axes and plough shares, however, were frequently made of iron, as a solid block of metal would be less liable to deformation than the fine cutting edge of a sword. Thus we read of —

> Great Areithous, known from shore to shore
> By the huge, knotted *iron mace* he bore*.

The Greeks in Homer's time possessed a certain knowledge of tempering. This is hinted at in the Odyssey, in the story of the blinding of the one-eyed giant, Polyphemus, by Ulysses, who plunged a fiery stake into his orb†.

> As when the smith an hatchet or large axe
> Temp'ring with skill, plunges the hissing blade
> Deep in cold water (whence the strength of steel)
> So hissed his eye around the olive wood.

Herodotus, in his famous *History*, written about 450 B.C., makes numerous references to iron. It is curious that he refers to the metal

---

*"Iliad", Pope's translation, VII.
†"Odyssey", Cowper's translation, IX.

as having been "discovered to the hurt of man". The same idea runs through Homer and Virgil, whilst the Roman admiral Pliny moralises at length in the same strain. Even Mahomet, early in the seventh century, held a similar view; he is reported in the *Koran* as saying —

> And we have sent down iron. Dire evil resideth in it, as well as advantage to mankind.

Iron and the Romans

The Romans were skilled metallurgists and it is evident that already before the Christian era they were familiar not only with iron but with the tempering of steel. Virgil in his "Aeneid", written about 36 B.C. describes a smithy in full blast* —

> A flood of molten silver, brass and gold,
> And deadly steel in the large furnace rolled;
> Of this, their artful hands a shield prepare,
> Alone sufficient to sustain the war.
> Seven orbs within a spacious round they close,
> One stirs the fire, and one the bellows blows,
> *The hissing steel is in the smithy drowned.*

Ovid†, writing some 40 years later than Virgil, refers to the same metallurgical process in his description of the mythical fight between the Thessalian chiefs and the centaurs — half man, half horse. After the wedding of the beautiful Hippodame with Pirithoüs, the nuptial song was in full strain and the great hall smoked with fires. As the maiden entered, her surpassing beauty inflamed the wild centaurs, excited by the wine that had been flowing freely, and the hall was straightway in an uproar. Eurytus, the wildest of the centaurs, seized the bride, but Theseus rushed to the rescue, hurling an antique vessel full in the centaur's face, so that he fell, never to rise again. The centaur Rhoetus with a blazing torch struck Charaxus, whose hair caught fire and burned like a dry field of grain. The "blood, scorching in the wound, gave forth a horrid sizzling sound, *such as a bar of iron, glowing red in the fire,*

---

*VIRGIL, "The Aeneid". Dryden's translation (Routledge, 1884), Book VIII. The last line has been italicised by the present Author. Virgil was born 76 B.C., and was at work on the "Aeneid" when about forty years of age.

†P. OVIDIUS NASO, born at Sulmo, 43 B.C. and died A.D. 17. See OVID "Metamorphoses". Translation by Miller (Putnam, 1916), Book XII. The work was completed by Ovid in A.D. 7.

gives when the smith takes it out in his bent pincers and plunges it into a tub of water."

Pliny has much to say in reference to iron. One passage* is of special interest —

> It is a remarkable fact that, when the ore is fused, the metal becomes liquefied like water, and afterwards acquires a spongy, brittle texture.

This can only mean one thing, namely, that the Romans occasionally made small quantities of *cast iron*, possibly by the accidental overheating of their furnaces by extra draught. If so, the above passage is the earliest reference to cast iron in existence.

Like earlier writers (p. 268), Pliny laments the fatal uses to which iron is put, for "it is with iron also that wars, murders, and robberies are effected." But as a punishment for its evil propensities, iron is cursed with a tendency to rust. "Nature," he writes, "in conformity with her usual benevolence, has limited the power of iron by inflicting upon it the punishment of rust." Pliny knew also that some kinds of iron are more prone to rust than others. "There is in existence", he says, "at the city of Zeugma, upon the Euphrates, an iron chain by means of which Alexander the Great constructed a bridge across the river, the links of which that have been replaced having been attacked with rust, while the original links are totally exempt from it." This is the earliest recorded report on the relative corrodibilities of different specimens of iron†.

One cannot help smiling at the unconscious betrayal that human nature alters but little with passage of time. In Pliny's day, as in ours, the modern metal was inferior to the old. We are reminded of the man who complained that *Punch's* jokes are not now as good as they used to be; to whom *Punch* pithily replied "They never were".

As a sort of atonement, however, iron is accredited by Pliny with certain beneficial virtues. "For if a circle is traced with iron . . . it will preserve both infant and adult from all noxious influences; if nails, too, that have been extracted from a tomb, are driven into the threshold of a door, they will prevent nightmare." And so on.

---

*Pliny, "Natural History", translated by Bostock and Riley (Bohn, 1857), Book 34, Chapter 41.
†*Ibid.*, Chapter 43.

Iron in Pre-Roman Britain

Iron was known to the British at least a couple of centuries before Julius Cæsar visited our shores in 55 B.C. — one of the few dates we all remember. None of the earliest furnaces have been discovered but it is thought probable that the first iron furnace of the Britons was similar to those used so successfully in the extraction of tin; it would thus be a simple low hearth resembling the Catalan furnace of the Pyrennees which has been in use there from very remote times down to the present*.

At the time of the Roman conquest iron was in common use amongst the Britons. The wheels of their war chariots had iron tyres, and fragments of these have been found in the remains of chariot burials in various parts of the country. The wooden parts of the chariots have long since mouldered away. Some of the chariots, like modern motor cars, were fitted with iron mirrors to prevent the charioteer from being attacked unawares in the rear. Although Boadicea is represented on the Thames Embankment as riding in a scythed chariot, there is no evidence that such scythes were ever attached to British chariots, although they were used on the Continent.

Although coins were known, having been introduced from Gaul some 200 B.C. the British also used bars of iron as currency. Numbers of these bars have been found in various parts of the southern half of England, including the Isle of Wight, and were first recognised as such by Reginald A. Smith of the British Museum†. The bars somewhat resemble unfinished swords, a rude handle being formed at one end by folding over the edges. They are, however, of different sizes and weights, multiples or sub-multiples of about 309 grams or 4,770 grains. In the National Museum of Wales at Cardiff there lies a bronze weight, found near Neath in Glamorganshire amongst late Celtic relics, the weight of which approximates to the above. A similar weight, in basalt, once lay in the Mainz Museum; it weighs 4767 grains, and like the Neath specimen it bears the mark 1. These weights correspond to half an Attic commercial mina of the period 160 B.C. Evidently in their trade with the Continent the British used similar standard

---

*R. A. SMITH, "A Guide to the Antiquities of the Early Iron Age" (British Museum, 1925), p. 2.

†R. A. SMITH, *Archæological J.*, 1913, **19**, (2), 421. *Proc. Soc. Antiq.*, 1915, **27**, 69. FRIEND, *Trans. Worcestershire Nat. Club.* 1919. BULLEID, "The Lake Villages of Somerset" (Folk Press, 1924), p. 44.

weights. It is a thousand pities that we ever departed from this very sensible custom.

Various iron relics have been found in Wookey Hole, a cave in the Mendips some two miles from Wells in Somerset. A rocky path by the side of the Paper Mills leads up the hill to the famous cavern. The narrow entrance opens into a large cave some 80 feet in height carved out by nature in the limestone. The cave was inhabited in pre-Roman times as well as during the Roman occupation; it has been thoroughly explored by Balch* and his collaborators who found within it numerous implements in stone, bronze, iron and bone. The iron objects exceeded 60 in number and of particular interest are those dating from pre-Roman times. Amongst these was an iron dagger, now known as the Goatherd's dagger, for it probably belonged to the person whose skeleton was found near by, together with the remains of some goats. Judging from the size of the bones the goatherd was only about 5 feet in height, and may well have been a woman. As Balch suggests, it is just possible that this lonely occupant of the cave gave rise to the legendary Witch of Wookey, who was "laid" by a pious monk from the hard-by Abbey of Glastonbury. The ballad runs as follows —

> In anciente days tradition showes
> A base and wicked elfe arose —
> The Witch of Wokey hight;

In due course, however, a monk from Glastonbury came to exorcise the witch.

> He chaunted out his godlie booke,
> He crost the water, blest the brooke,
> Then — paternoster done —
> The horrid hag he sprinkled o'er;
> When lo! where stood a hag before,
> Now stood a ghastlie stone.

The first chamber entered by the curious visitor, and described above is known as the "Kitchen", and a lump of stalagmite is pointed out as the remains of the witch, a warning for all time to the godless. A strong imagination, assisted by the weirdness of the surroundings, enables the superstitious to detect a human profile in that shapeless mass of rock.

---

*H. E. BALCH, "Wookey Hole" (Oxford, 1914).

The cave was not always thus deserted. At times its walls echoed to the shouts of the hunter and the laughter of happy children. The hammer of the worker was also heard at intervals, for a piece of unworked iron weighing more than 6½ lb. was found near the door of the cave, indicating that it was usual to work up iron objects at the cave itself. Other pre-Roman iron relics included two Celtic saws, a bill-hook and sickle, a latch-lifter, awls showing remains of wooden handles and a currency bar. One of the saws had a handle of cleft antler, and the teeth of both were set in opposite directions alternately as with modern saws. The sickle indicates that the cave dwellers grew grain upon the land surrounding their home; a sickle of similar shape was used in Saxon times. The purpose of the latch-lifter was to lift a concealed latch in a palisade. It would appear therefore that the cave entrance was at times protected. An ox shoe had holes for nails just like a modern horse shoe.

Numerous iron objects have been found also amongst the remains of the Glastonbury Lake village which was probably inhabited from about 100 B.C. to 50 A.D. These include bill-hooks and latch-lifters similar to those found at Wookey.

The Mabinogion

Several references to iron occur in that curious collection of ancient Welsh literature known as the "Mabinogion"*. In the story of "Kulhwch and Olwen" we are introduced to the giant, Yspaddaden, father of Olwen whom Kulhwch wishes to marry. The name Olwen means *white footprints*, and the girl was so named because four white clover blossoms would spring up in her footprints wherever she walked. Kulhwch and his companions duly called upon the giant and stated their errand. 'Come here to-morrow, and I will give you some answer' said the giant. The young men rose and went their way, but as they left Yspaddaden "seized one of three poisoned *stone*-spears which were to hand, and hurled it after them; but Bedwyr caught it, and hurled it back, piercing the giant's thigh. 'A cursed savage son-in-law' roared the giant '. . . Like bite of gadflies has this poisoned *iron* pained me. Accursed be the smith who fashioned it and the anvil it was fashioned on, so painful it is'."

The stone spear, it will be observed, becomes one of iron when it is flung back. The episode was twice repeated; at the end of the

*See the translation by Ellis and Lloyd (Clarendon Press, 1929).

second visit the giant hurled his second stone spear after the young men but received it back as an iron one in the middle of his chest so that it came out in the small of his back. After the third visit the last of the three stone spears was flung back at the giant, the iron entering his eye.

This is not a mere idle tale. It represents the passage from the stone age to that of metals. The younger generation won the victory by using the more modern weapons.

Numerous Welsh stories tell of the dire result of allowing iron to come into contact with fairies*.

These stories have their modern counterpart in the belief that the gift of a knife or any cutting instrument will sever the bonds of friendship. Hence on receiving a present of this character it is usual for the recipient to give the donor a farthing or half-penny; the "gift" is then not a gift; it has been purchased.

The Manx saw displays much wisdom —

> Where folks believe in witches, witches are;
> And where they don't, the de'il a witch is there!

Iron in Roman Britain

With the advent of the Romans, the iron industry of our island was enormously stimulated; both Gloucestershire and Sussex became important centres. Large quantities of slag, known as *cinders*, were left in various places, and at one time were in demand for the repair of roads. That the word cinder is not modern is evident from its appearance on early documents, as also from the names of many early sites, such as *Cinderford, Cinderhill*, etc. In A.D. 120 the Emperor Hadrian founded an arms factory at Bath, where iron from the Forest of Dean was worked. From among the remains of ancient Roman towns many interesting iron relics have been taken. Mention may be made of an iron ring or ferrule unearthed during excavation on the site of Uriconium. The ring had been made by bending over on to itself a strip of sheet iron and "brazing" or, more correctly, "copper soldering" the ends together with some copper alloy. This appears to be the only duly authenticated sample of the kind actually done by the Romans†. The specimen cannot be

---

*T. Gwynn Jones, "Welsh Folklore and Folkcustom" (Methuen, 1930), p. 66. See also McPherson, "Primitive Beliefs in the N.E. of Scotland" (Longmans, 1929), p. 102.

†Friend and Thorneycroft, *J. Inst. Metals*, 1928, **39**, 61. Friend, *Nature*, 1925, **116**, 749.

T

dated very closely, but as Uriconium was destroyed about A.D. 380 it cannot be younger than this. It is now in the possession of the Birmingham City Museum. (See Plate 3).

Iron and Post-Roman Britain

With the coming of the Saxons we are beginning to escape from antiquity. The Saxons were, of course, quite familiar with iron, although references to it in the "Saxon Chronicle" are scanty. We do know, however, that, owing to shortage of weapons, some of the troops under Harold at the battle of Hastings were armed with stone hammers. The Normans required considerable quantities of iron for their armour. The metal was always made by the direct process.

In Anglo-Saxon times the smith was regarded as a person of great importance. In the royal court of Wales the smith sat in the great hall with the King and Queen, next to the chaplain, and was entitled to a draught of every kind of liquor that was brought into the hall. His duties were numerous, and the smith had to be proficient in all manner of ways. He was expected to make horse-shoes and the nails to fix them, as well as all sorts of military weapons including the forging of mail coats and armour for both knight and horse.

As the various uses to which iron could be put steadily increased, the smiths began to sort themselves out and specialise in certain types of work, some concentrating on horse-shoes and nails, others on swords and knives and so on. During the reign of Edward III (1327 to 1377), the pots, spits and frying-pans of the royal kitchen were classed amongst the king's treasures.

In Scotland likewise the smith was held in high esteem and a story is told of one of his craft who committed a crime for which he was found guilty and sentenced to death. But the chief of the clan could not dispense with his services and offered to hang two weavers instead!*

In the fifteenth century cannon were made by hooping wrought iron bars together; *Mons Meg*, in Edinburgh, made in 1455, is a noted example.

William Shakespeare in his various works makes reference to iron some 48 times and to steel 64 times. In his boyhood days the forge and smithy of Richard Horneby stood close to where he lived, and would be frequently visited by the youthful poet. They

---

*W. JONES, "Treasures of the Earth" (Warne), p. 167.

PLATE 3

[*Facing p.* 274

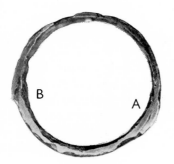

A Roman ferrule

The ferrule, here reproduced actual size, was found at Uriconium. The bottom view shows a copper join at *A* and a weld at *B*. (See page 273.)

A nineteenth century steel brooch

Steel jewellery was popular in the nineteenth century. (See page 291.)

adjoined a tailor's shop (now the Birthplace Ticket Office) which lay next door to Shakespeare's residence, in Stratford on Avon. In Shakespeare we find the expression "true as steel" ("Troilus and Cressida", act I, scene 3). The expression had also been used by Chaucer on several occasions; in the "Canterbury Tales" (c. 1388) the host uses it to describe his wife, and in the "Parlement of Foules" (1382) the royal eagle is described as "wys and worthy, secree, trewe as stel". The expression is first known in English literature from a MS. of c. 1300, which runs "Oure love is also trewe as stel". It is likely that from about Chaucer's time onwards the expression was a common enough compliment; a few centuries earlier, however, in Viking times, it would surely have been thought an insult (see p. 276).

For many centuries Sussex and Gloucestershire were most important centres of the iron industry. As the practice of metallurgy improved so did the size of the furnaces. At one time the Forest of Dean could boast the largest furnace in England; this was in 1724, the furnace measuring 28 feet in height. The ore was first dried by exposure to air and then calcined in heaps in the open using wood fuel; later this calcining took place in kilns. The ore was then smelted with charcoal in stout-walled furnaces built in the form of square, truncated pyramids which, by the advent of the seventeenth century measured some 22 feet square at the base. Inside they were approximately egg-shaped ending in a rectangular hearth of considerable depth. The blast was produced with bellows which, in 1323, were worked by water power for the first time, though of course hand bellows continued to be used for many years*.

Iron for swords

The soldier is naturally conservative. No doubt this is largely due to the natural working of the law of self preservation. The bronze age warrior was slow to discard his trusty sword and shield of bronze in favour of new-fangled iron weapons, just as the hero of Waterloo preferred the musket long after the superiority of the rifle had been demonstrated to less prejudiced minds. We cannot altogether wonder at it, for in the early days of its manufacture iron was a somewhat uncertain metal, and, when a man's life depended upon the trustworthiness of his sword, the proved weapon, even if antiquated, might well be preferred to the more modern one if the slightest doubt existed as to its reliability.

*RHYS JENKINS, *The Engineer*, 1921, **131**, 116, 502, 546.

Polybius, for example, tells us that the defeat of the Kelts by the Romans at the battle of Addua, near Milan, 223 B.C., was largely attributable to the fact that the long iron swords of the Kelts were "easily bent and would only give one downward cut with any effect, but that after this the edges got so turned and the blade so bent, that, unless they had time to straighten them with the foot against the ground, they could not deliver a second blow."

The same kind of difficulty faced the warriors in Iceland more than a millenium later. In the Viking sagas, covering the period A.D. 800 to 1100 (approximately), we constantly read of the failure of the iron swords to "bite". In *The Story of the Ere-dwellers**, for example, we are given details of a family squabble which ended in an appeal to arms. "So then befell a great battle", we are told, "and Steinthor was at the head of his own folk, and smote on either hand of him; but the fair-wrought sword bit not whenas it smote armour, and oft he must straighten it under his foot." Such, then, was the state of affairs as late as the eleventh century of our era!

The early metallurgist, to whom chemical analysis and micrographical examination were unknown, was unable to explain the uncertainty of his iron. When, by chance, a good piece of metal was obtained, it was often given a supernatural origin. Thus the sacred sword of Attila (A.D. 395 to 453) was believed to have been found by a shepherd, inverted in the ground, and was handed to that "Scourge of God" as a token of Heaven's approval. It is interesting to note that the name Atli, Etzel or Attila, in the Hun language, is believed to have signified the metal iron†. The divine origin of Arthur's Excalibur is beautifully portrayed by Tennyson in *The Passing of Arthur*. One can sympathise with bold Sir Bedivere who hesitated to consign so beautiful a weapon to the misty waters of the mere.

When a sword had once been proved to be reliable, its value was priceless. Upon the death of its owner it was not usually buried in the warrior's grave, but was appropriated by his conqueror or by his next of kin for future use. Thus the weapons became christened with suggestive names and developed a sort of pedigree. Numerous examples are quoted in the Icelandic Sagas, and similar tales are associated with the famous swords of the Japanese Samurai.

---

*Translated by Morris and Magnússon (Quaritch, 1892), p. 120.
†BRION, "Attila, The Scourge of God", translated by Ward (Cassell, 1929).

Cast iron

At first the iron was always produced by direct reduction although even in Roman times it would appear that cast iron was sometimes produced by accident through overheating of the furnaces (p. 269); but this would be regarded as unfortunate as in those days there was no use for this brittle product. As the size of the furnaces increased, however, the iron remained for a longer time in contact with the fuel and the temperature tended to rise, ultimately reaching that at which carbon and iron combine, yielding cast iron. This accidental production of cast iron became increasingly frequent until ultimately it became, designedly, the only product, as it is to-day. We do not know when cast iron first became important metallurgically. It is recorded that in 1340 a blast furnace designed as such was erected near Namur in Belgium and there were blast furnaces in England before 1490; in 1497 one Simon Ballard cast large quantities of iron shot in Ashdown Forest in Sussex. But of course cast iron was known in England much earlier than this, certainly by 1350 in Sussex.

It is held that the introduction of the blast furnace proper, as apart from the ordinary furnace really intended to produce wrought iron direct, led to Sussex becoming the premier iron producing district in England; the forests yielded ample fuel and the streams provided the necessary mechanical power.

At first cast iron was used exclusively for casting purposes and several Sussex church yards are graced with cast iron tomb stones. Cast iron cannon balls are said to have been made at Memingen in 1388, whilst in 1412 cannon were cast at Lille as the earlier bronze cannon were found too weak to stand the increasingly larger charges the army desired to use. The first cast iron cannon produced in Britain were made at Buxted near Crowborough in Sussex in 1543. According to local legend —

> Master Huggett and his man John
> They did cast the first cannon.

Cast iron guns were used by the Spaniards in their ships at the time of the attempted invasion of Britain in 1588. After a thorough trouncing at the hands of the Royal Navy under Drake, the surviving ships of the Spanish Armada, afraid to return through the English Channel, straggled home round the north of Scotland in pitiable plight. The weather was stormy and most of the vessels, probably already damaged, either foundered at sea or were broken to pieces on the rocks. In 1740 cast iron guns were raised from *The Florida*, one of the Spanish ships that had sunk off the coast of Mull and had thus lain in the sea for 152 years. On scraping away the corroded surface they became too hot to touch. Wilkinson* states that "the inhabitants of Mull, and all who witnessed the phenomenon, were greatly astonished (as may naturally be supposed); and being themselves unable to solve the mystery, they applied to the surgeon of the ship, as being the most scientific man present; he was, however, as much at a loss to account for such unusual appearances as themselves, but said that although they had been buried in the sea nearly 200 years, yet, as they went down in the heat of action, he supposed they had not had sufficient time to cool!"

Actually of course, the iron had undergone oxidation to ferrous oxide which, on coming into contact with the oxygen of the air, rapidly oxidised to ferric oxide, with evolution of heat, the reaction being strongly exothermic.

About this time, also, guns were made of wrought iron bars hooped together, a good example being afforded by Mons Meg in Edinburgh, made in 1455 (p. 274). The *Mary Rose* was fitted with this type of gun; she was a British vessel which sank off Portsmouth in an engagement with the French in 1545. In 1836 her guns were raised after having lain in the water for nearly 300 years. Wilkinson describes them as "formed of iron bars hooped with iron rings, and they were all loaded"; the cannon balls were of cast iron, originally 8 inches in diameter and weighing 70 lb.

In 1822 some cast iron cannon were fished up off Holyhead†; they had belonged to a pirate vessel sunk there a century or so earlier and had oxidised through their whole mass. When raised from the water they were quite soft and could be cut with a knife. On exposure to air they hardened and were used along with other truly metal ones to fire salutes when King George iv passed through Holyhead somewhat later *en route* for Dublin. It was noticed that these old cannon made more noise than any others when fired; it was a marvel they didn't burst.

The fuel problem

Rich though Sussex was in wood its stocks began to show signs of depletion owing to the large amount of charcoal required to keep

---

*Wilkinson, "On the Extra-ordinary Effect produced on Cast Iron by the Action of Sea-water" (London, 1841).

†Rennie, *Min. Proc. Inst. Civil Engineers*, 1845, **4**, 323.

her furnaces ablaze. The shortage of fuel was equally acute elsewhere in Britain and in the first year of Queen Elizabeth's reign (1558) and again in 1584 Acts were passed for the preservation of timber. But iron was badly needed. Attempts were made by Simon Sturtevant, Dodo (Dud) Dudley and others in the seventeenth century to use "Pit-coale, sea-coale, etc, and with the same Fuell to Melt and Fine Imperfect Mettals and Refine perfect Mettals" as we read on the title page of Dud Dudley's "Metallum Martis", dated 1665. To Simon was granted the first patent in 1611.

Dud Dudley, a natural son of Edward, Lord Dudley, was born in 1599 near Birmingham and as a young man studied at Baliol College, Oxford; in 1619 he was called home to take charge of several iron works belonging his father. In his own words —

> Wood and Charcole, growing then scant, and Pit-coles, in great quantities abounding near the Furnace, did induce me to alter my Furnace, and to attempt by my new Invention, the making of Iron with Pit-cole, assuring myself in my Invention, the loss to me could not be greater than others, nor so great, although my success should prove fruitless; But I found such success at first tryal animated me, for at my tryal or blast, I made Iron to profit with Pit-cole and found *Facere est addere Inventioni.*

Dudley took a prominent part in the Civil War as a Royalist and in 1642 he was busy making cast iron cannon at his foundries for use by the King's troops. He died in 1684 at the ripe age of 85, and in the church of St Helen's at Worcester a large monument was erected on the South Wall to his memory.

Dudley's persevering efforts met with a given measure of success, but it was not sufficient to induce others to follow in his footsteps. In the Forest of Dean, charcoal furnaces some 30 feet high were in use and Henry Powle*, writing in 1677, states that, although various attempts had been made to substitute coal for charcoal all had proved abortive. The problem of smelting iron with coal was not really solved until 1735 when Abraham Darby the younger, at Colebrooke Dale, Shropshire, first coked his coal and then reduced his calcined ore; by 1750 coke-fired furnaces were becoming serious rivals of the charcoal ones and eventually superseded them. The Colebrooke Dale Works were very progressive; they appear to have been the first to use a steam engine

---

*POWLE, *Phil. Trans.*, 1676, **12**, No. 137, p. 931.

and they were the first to erect a cast iron bridge, about 1785, over the Severn. By 1790, 81 of the 106 furnaces in the country were coke fed.

The iron industry had reached its zenith in Sussex round 1650 and employed some 50,000 men; it then began to decline, but it was not until 1809 that the last Sussex forge was extinguished. Writing of this Lady Nevill stated, "Ashburnham was closed in 1809, the immediate cause of it being the failure of the foundrymen, through intoxication, to mix chalk with the ore, by reason of which it ceased to flow, and the blasting finally ended."

Meanwhile, however, the iron industry had spread to many other centres. In 1740 England and Wales together possessed 59 furnaces the total annual yield of metal being 17,350 tons; this looks small in comparison with the modern output of the order of 15 million tons of steel.

The essential difference between steel and wrought iron is that the former contains more carbon, which is combined with the iron to form a carbide known to the metallurgist as cementite.

It was already known to the Romans that certain ores yielded what we call steel. The iron ores of Noricum were celebrated for this; but the real reason was unknown. Both Biringuiccio in 1540 and Agricola (p. 50) in 1561 described the making of steel by keeping lumps of wrought iron for several hours immersed in molten cast iron. The process of "cementing" by keeping iron at red heat in charcoal whereby the carbon is absorbed converting the metal into steel, was described by Réaumur (p. 226) in 1722, but it was even then an ancient process. In 1750 Benjamin Huntsman improved it by melting wrought iron with a definite amount of charcoal in fire-clay crucibles, thus paving the way for the pre-eminence of Sheffield in the steel industry. With this "cement" steel tools, shears, razors, springs, etc, were produced, although the chemistry of the process long remained ill-understood. Be it said, however, that long before Benjamin Huntsman saw the light, Sheffield was already famous for her steel. Peter Bates, writing in 1590, gave the schoolmaster sound advice regarding the making of quill pens. "First then be the choice of your pen-knife. A right Sheffield knife is best." The poll tax records of King Richard II (1379) show that the making of knives was an important Sheffield industry even in those days. The miller in Chaucer's Reve's tale (*circa* 1388) bore a Sheffield knife* —

> Ther was no man, for peril, dorste hym touche;
> A Sheffeld thwitel baar he in his hose.

The idea of obtaining wrought iron from cast iron by oxidation of the impurities in the latter was put into practice by T. and G. Granage in 1776, more successfully by Henry Cort in 1784, and still more successfully by Rogers in 1816. The cast iron was heated in a furnace lined by Cort with siliceous material, by Rogers with iron oxide; such a furnace came to be known as a *puddling furnace*; the iron oxide yields up its oxygen to the cast iron converting its carbon into gaseous carbon monoxide which escapes, other impurities being oxidised such as silicon to silica and entering the slag. The carbon monoxide burns with a blue flame as it meets the air, yielding the *puddlers' candles*, as they are called. The escape of the gas causes the appearance of boiling, and the workmen refer to this as the boil. The metal is now pasty, for the melting point of wrought iron is much higher than that of pig iron; it is removed from the furnace, squeezed whilst hot to force out the still molten slag, and rolled to give the product a fibrous structure. This formed a second outlet for the cast iron which had hitherto been used mainly for castings.

It would appear that if the oxygen of iron oxide could effect the purification of cast iron, so might atmospheric oxygen. Accordingly in 1852 Kelly patented a process for forcing air through molten pig iron. In 1856 Henry Bessemer patented a "converter" for this purpose and later bought up Kelly's patent. In this converter air is blown through the molten pig iron, and when the impurities have been sufficiently oxidised, an alloy of iron and manganese, containing also some carbon, is added to carburise the metal and convert it into steel. The manganese helps to remove the sulphur. The liquid steel is then cast into ingots.

Bessemer† was born in 1813 and showed great promise at an early age. When only about twenty years of age he invented the

---

*"The Canterbury Tales". The quotation comes from "The Works of Chaucer", Globe edition (Macmillan, London, 1910). The word "thwitel" (A.S. thwitan, to cut) survives in the modern word "whittle". The citizens of Sheffield, rightly proud of this Chaucerian reference, have recently installed in their cathedral a stained-glass window depicting a scene from "The Canterbury Tales". It was designed and painted by Mr Christopher Webb.

†E. J. LANGE, *Memoirs of the Manchester Literary and Philosophical Society*, 1913, **57**, No. 17.

method of dating stamps by perforation; this was designed to prevent the transfer of Government stamps from old deeds to new ones, a practice which he had been informed caused the Stamp Office an annual loss of revenue of some £100,000. Not having patented his invention, the grateful Government appropriated it without offering any reward until a twinge of conscience some 45 years later led them to make a tardy amend by bestowing upon the now wealthy and celebrated inventor the honour of knighthood.

In 1854 Bessemer invented a rotating projectile for guns but the War Office, with characteristic aloofness, refused to have anything to do with it; Louis Napoleon, later Napoleon II, saw the value of the invention, being himself an authority on artillery, and offered to finance the necessary experiments. A chance remark by Commandant Minié — the inventor of the rifle of that name — that the new projectile would require a better gun than one of cast iron led Bessemer to consider the possibility of improving the then known methods of steel production. This led to his invention of the process already described, an account of which was presented to the British Association at their Cheltenham Meeting in 1856 under the title "The Manufacture of Malleable Iron and Steel without Fuel". Sir Henry lived to the ripe age of 85, passing in 1898 at his residence in Denmark Hill, London.

It so happens that many ores of iron contain phosphorus which, if left in the steel, would render it brittle and unsuitable for most purposes. In 1878 Thomas and Gilchrist showed that by lining the furnace with a basic material such as dolomite (calcium magnesium carbonate) the phosphorus could be made to enter the lining as metallic phosphate. Two birds could thus be killed with one stone. The steel was rendered free from phosphorus and the basic lining became valuable as a fertiliser in virtue of its phosphate content. In this manner arose the familiar basic Bessemer and open hearth processes. The latter, developed in England by Sir William Siemens, has now superseded the basic Bessemer process in most countries. The industry is an enormous one, world production of ingots and castings being of the order of 140 million tons annually.

Uses of iron

According to an ancient Chinese proverb the nation that holds the iron of the world may rule the world. Needless to say uranium and atomic forces had not then been visualised. Kipling put the case in a nutshell —

> Gold is for the mistress, silver for the maid,
> Copper for the craftsman cunning at his trade.
> "Good" said the Baron, sitting in his hall,
> "But iron, cold iron, is master of them all."

Iron is so intimately bound up with every phase of modern civilisation that we cannot hope to do more than mention a few of its more important uses.

Ships

Probably the earliest recorded suggestion that iron might be made to float on water occurs in Holy Writ, 2 *Kings* vi. 6, where we are told that, whilst a beam was being felled, the iron head of an axe wielded by one worker flew off into the Jordan; whereupon Elisha caused it "to swim" evidently by prodding it in some way with a piece of wood sufficiently large to bring it to the surface. This was about 840 B.C. Another reference of interest but much more recent occurs in the sixteenth century prophecy of Mother Shipton (p. 125) who said that —

> Iron in the water shall float
> As easy as a wooden boat.

The earliest use of iron in ships, apart from such minor commodities as nails, etc, appears to have been for naval purposes. According to a work published at Stuttgart in 1866, one Samuel Kieshel visited Stockholm in 1586 and was specially interested in the warships he saw lying in the sea approach to the city. The largest was named *The Great Dragon* and Kieshel describes it as a strong and stable vessel with several decks. He further adds "I have been told that the space between both the ship's boards has been filled with iron so that the shots rebounded and could not easily go through the vessel or inflict damage to it." If this was really the case Sweden must be credited with having possessed the first iron-clads in the world.

In Britain an iron canal boat was launched in 1788, and the first iron sea-going vessel, the *Aaron Mawby*, was built in 1821. Round 1835 the use of armour plate was proposed; at first the ships were built of wood and cased with metal; later the wood was discarded and the vessels built entirely of steel.

On 17th October 1855 the first iron-clad ships went into action in the Black Sea, in the shape of three primitive floating batteries protected with iron armour, against the Russian fortifications at Kinburn which were destroyed in a few hours. This sounded the doom of Britain's wooden walls, for but a few months previously a combined attack by the British and French fleets of wooden battleships had been driven off by fire from the forts at Sebastopol and badly knocked about.

The armed cruiser *Triomphante**, built for the French Navy in 1877, illustrates the gradual transition from the wooden battleships of Nelson's time to the modern all-steel vessels. She was built of wood with an armour belt nearly six inches thick whilst her batteries were protected with iron armour nearly 5 inches thick. She played an important part in the operations in the Min River during the China War of 1884.

Bridges

There are, however, other ways of crossing water than by boat, and many millions of tons of iron in its various forms have been used in the construction of tunnels and of bridges. The first cast iron bridge in the world appears to have been that over the Severn near Colebrooke Dale about 1785. To-day steel is more commonly used, although the year before last (1949) saw the opening of a bridge of aluminium-alloy (p. 164).

The *Forth Bridge*, designed by Sir Benjamin Baker and opened in 1890, is perhaps the most impressive in existence. For centuries the traveller wishing to cross the Forth at its junction with the sea had been dependent on ferry-boats, and many a one had been over-taken by a gale which prevented his ever reaching the other side. In 1805 it was proposed to construct a double tunnel, some 15 feet wide, under the bed of the Forth, one tunnel for the 'comers' and one for the 'goers' as was quaintly explained; but nothing came of it.

In 1873 the Forth Bridge Company was formed with the object of building a bridge designed by Sir Thomas Bouch, but the collapse of the ill-fated Tay Bridge in 1879 shook public confidence and the scheme was abandoned. In 1882 an Act of Parliament authorised the construction of a bridge designed by Mr (later Sir) Benjamin Baker, based on the principle of the cantilever, full advantage being taken of the island of Inchgarvie, a peak of whinstone rock in the middle of the Forth. Some 50,000 tons of

---

*See *The Engineer*, 1890, **49**, 648.

steel were required and the total cost of the bridge approximated to £3,200,000. In order to protect it from corrosion the bridge is continuously painted by "steeplejack painters" as they are called from the dangerous nature of their work. These men are always at work; it takes them some three years to paint the bridge from end to end, and when the job has been completed it is necessary to begin over again. It is estimated that the total surface to be painted amounts to about 135 acres of steel, and during the process trains pass over every few minutes.

Nails and horseshoes

It is remarkable what a wealth of legend and romance has collected round iron nails and horseshoes. Reference has already been made to the legends surrounding the nails used at the Crucifixion of our Lord (p. 263). The earliest type of nail was undoubtedly the wooden peg, which in later years became known as a "tre-nail", that is a nail of wood (tree). Such pegs are used to-day alongside their metal fraternity, and were very frequent in the pegged joints of medieval half-timber work. The discovery of metals paved the way for a metal nail industry and legend states that the Argos which carried Jason and his crew to the Black Sea in search of the Golden Fleece was built of oak and pine joined with bronze nails. The greater strength of iron, once man had learned to produce it in good quality, gave the iron nail the premier position as a means of fastening woodwork, although nails of copper, brass and bronze are still frequently used, sometimes because they are more ornamental in the circumstances and sometimes, too, because they are less susceptible to corrosion.

The smooth wire nail, so commonly used to-day, readily enters wood with the minimum danger to splitting, but for the same reason it may easily come out of the wood again. This led to the invention of a threaded nail or screw. It seems impossible to discover when screws were first used; it cannot have been later than the fourth century for, in the literature of that period an account is given of the chasing of screws by hand. At first they were known as "screw-nails". The screw cutting lathe was known to one Jacques Besson in 1548, but Maudsley was the first to make really accurate screws in 1800 to 1810.

Until about 1750 all nails were hand-made and the smith who forged them was called a "nayler", a word that survives in the modern surname Naylor which, however, is not quite so common as Smith. Leland, when he visited Birmingham in 1538, recorded that "there be many Smithes in the Towne . . . and a grate many Naylors."

In medieval records nails are mentioned under various interesting and curious names, the meanings or origins of which are not always patent. For example "strokhede nayles" are referred to in the Windsor Castle records of 1534. The entry runs: "111 c of vstrok hede nayles tinned for the new Dore in the colege garden wall, price Vjs". The reference to tinning shows that our tin-tacks are not mere modern luxuries. The fact that these nails were intended for doors suggests that they were stud nails, partly constructive and partly decorative, as was common enough in those days. The "five stroke" perhaps refers to the labour involved in making the nail head as these were formed with a "nayle tulle" (nail tool) or matrix in which the head was shaped by hammering. Perhaps the number five also indicated the size of the head, for in other MSS. the prefix VII is sometimes used; if all were of the same size there would be less point in quoting the stroke number. "Strake nails" were used for fixing the strakes or iron plates of cartwheels before the iron band or tyre became common. In the "penny" nail, the prefix stands for pounder and refers to the weight in pounds per thousand. The derogatory expression "Not worth a tenpenny nail" thus meant that the article in question was not even equal in value to a nail, 1000 of which weighed only 10 lb.

"Tyngyl nailles" or "chingil nayles" were made to replace the old wooden "tylepynnes" or oak pegs used for fixing roof shingles before the introduction of nibbed tiles, the nibs keeping them in position on the laths. Other kinds of nails were known in medieval times as spykynges, goletts, haxnailles, sharplinges, flywings or sparabilis (sparrow bills), and traversnailles. Several of these names are difficult to unravel, but the reader will without difficulty recognise the modern forms of brods, takkets and bordnayles.

Animals sometimes take a fancy to nails, and a curious case was recorded in 1938 of a pigeon which built its nest of six-inch nails. Workmen engaged on the erection of scaffolding in front of the Birmingham Art Gallery, were perplexed by the disappearance of their nails during their lunch hour. No boys or other persons appeared to be involved, so a watch was set. It was soon found that the thief was a pigeon whose mate had ensconced herself on top of one of the columns supporting the façade of the Art Gallery. Waiting until the coast was clear, the bird made innumerable flights, bringing back each time a new "stick" for the nest.

Its efforts must have involved a considerable tax on its strength, for the watchers saw the bird labouring for breath after every flight. Nor was the avian labourer helped by the tendency of the nails to roll over the edge of the column head; nearly 2 lb. of nails were afterwards picked up, having been lost by the birds in this way. Eventually, however, the nest was complete, and two eggs were duly laid therein.

Iron nails have frequently been used in the past both for purposes of medicine and necromancy. A favourite remedy for toothache consisted in hammering a nail into a tree and as the iron rusted so would the toothache disappear. This was much less drastic than having the tooth extracted. Warts have been a nuisance for centuries, though it is difficult to understand why such should have been the case as so many infallible remedies have been prescribed from time to time. The mere touching of a wart by a wise man will effect its disappearance provided an iron nail is offered as a reward for the service; but lack of men sufficiently wise may nowadays make this cure somewhat difficult to effect. A simpler remedy hails from the Weald of Kent, namely rub the warts with a piece of raw steak and then bury the latter. As the meat rots so will the wart disappear.

The arabs believed that the soul of a murdered man should be nailed down by driving a nail into the ground where the murder was committed, otherwise the ghost would rise*.

Once each year, namely in October, the Corporation of London and the Sheriffs of Middlesex pay a curious rental to the King for two pieces of land. London's imposing Law Courts are built on one of these plots, the site of an ancient jousting ground; the other plot lies somewhere in Shropshire, but nobody appears to know exactly where.

On the annual rent day the King's Remembrancer goes into the city to represent the Sovereign. He sits in full wig and gown on the bench, with the City Clerk and other leading officials of the Corporation at the table below him. First of all the warrant from the Sheriff and City Remembrancer demanding the payment of the rent for the piece of land in the Strand is read out, calling upon the "tenants and occupiers of a certain tenement called The Forge in the Parish of St Clement Dane's, in the County of Middlesex, to come forth and do their service."

---

*C. J. S. THOMPSON, "The Mysteries and Secrets of Magic" (London, 1927), p. 90.

The site had been granted in 1235 by Henry III to a farrier, one Walter le Brun, for repairing the armour of a Knight Templar wounded in a tournament, on condition that he annually paid six horseshoes and 61 nails as rent, and in course of time it passed into the hands of the city with the same liability.

The Secondary having recited the warrant and stated the facts, the City Solicitor solemnly hands up to the King's Remembrancer the six horseshoes and the 61 nails, counting them one by one in a stern voice. This little account being settled, the Secondary next proceeds to recite the authority for paying his Majesty the sum of one billhook and one hatchet for the piece of land in Shropshire which the Corporation has held from the Crown for more than 700 years. But this time the representative of the Sovereign must be assured that the billhook and hatchet are good sharp implements.

So, before the rent is paid, the City Solicitor places a small chopping block on the table. A clerk hands him a bundle of sticks. Then, having chopped some with the billhook and some with the hatchet, he presents both tools to the King's Remembrancer, who formally accepts them as payment of the Shropshire rent. A written acknowledgment follows later. Actually the Crown only gets the billhook and hatchet each year. The horseshoes and nails are kept to serve as hardy ceremonial annuals.

Who has not heard of Horse-Shoe Corner in Lancaster City where John of Gaunt's horse is said to have cast a shoe, about 1380, on a visit the Duke never actually paid? A horseshoe lies embedded in the middle of the road to perpetuate the legend; it has to be replaced every few years, however, for modern traffic wears it away.

Oakham in Rutland is the tiniest county town in Britain; it possesses an ancient castle; nailed to a wall in which is a remarkable collection of horseshoes. Rutland has exacted by traditional right, accorded to the Ferrers family centuries ago, one horseshoe from every member of the Royal Family and every peer who has crossed its border. The collection contains, amongst others, horseshoes presented by Queen Victoria and by her son, King Edward VII.

Horseshoes are generally regarded as bringers of good luck; but the owner should be careful to hang his specimens with the two ends upwards, otherwise there is a danger that his luck may run out. The shoe nailed to the mast of the Victory at Trafalgar in 1805 was wrong way up. What wonder that Nelson paid the penalty! When, as late as April 1930, the Duchess of Bedford set out on her return flight by aeroplane from South Africa to England, a lady well-wisher handed her a be-ribboned horseshoe for luck; the plane, called *The Spider*, was thus enabled to make a perfect ascent from the Maitland Aerodrome, Cape Town, and the crowd raised a hearty cheer as the Duchess waved her farewell to them.

In northern Scotland it was believed that if a horseshoe were nailed over the stable door, no witch or warlock would dare to enter and steal a horse no matter how badly the animal was required to take them to their conventions.

During their excavations at Wookey Hole, Balch (p. 271) and his collaborators found the shoe of an ox which had apparently been used by the cave-dwellers for burden or draught. It is "of interest to note that the early workman made the holes for the nails in exactly the same form as the farrier of to-day uses for his horse-shoes"*. Evidently the long lapse of time has failed to improve upon the positions of the nails.

Alloys of iron

This chapter could hardly be regarded as complete without some reference, however brief, to the numerous alloys of iron and steel that play such an important part in modern civilisation. One of the best known and most popular of these is *stainless steel*, an alloy containing some 13 per cent of chromium. This beautiful metal has saved the housewife much arduous toil, because it does not rust when exposed to air and water, even in the presence of organic acids like vinegar or the juice of oranges and lemons. Many of us can well remember the unsavoury appearance of the table knife after a meal including lamb and mint-sauce; but that fortunately is a thing of the past. One day a steel manufacturer, a friend of the author, had a lump of his own stainless steel worked up into table knives and proudly exhibited them one evening at dinner, inviting his guests to try them. Beef and pickles were on the menu and, to the manufacturer's disgust, his stainless steel rusted. Confident that his steel was all right he had the pickles analysed; they contained sulphuric acid! Stainless steel is not immune to attack from mineral acids; sea water will also effect its corrosion; such corrosion, however, is invariably localised resulting in deep pitting. The actual loss in weight may be small, but if a tube or a tank, for example, is pitted through, that is, perforated, it may be much

---

*BALCH, *Opus cit.*, p. 87.

289

U

more seriously damaged than if it had lost ten times as much metal through corrosion distributed equally over its entire surface.

Another interesting alloy, known as *invar* (p. 297) contains some 35 per cent of nickel and is particularly valuable for certain purposes such as clock pendulums, because of its negligible expansion with rise of temperature. An alloy containing 40 per cent of nickel expands by a similar amount as glass and may therefore be sealed into glass instead of the more expensive platinum which at one time had to be used; for this reason the alloy is known as *platinite* (p. 297).

Steels containing both chromium and tungsten are known as high speed tool steels and retain their temper at high temperatures — at red heat, indeed, when ordinary carbon steels would soften and be useless. Alloys containing small amounts of chromium and vanadium are very hard and strong; they find application in springs, locomotive wheels, axle-shafts and the like. Manganese steels are also very hard and are used at tramway points and elsewhere where great resistance to wear and tear is essential. Various high tensile steels are now used in large quantities in the construction of fast-going steamers and ocean liners. The hull of the magnificent French liner *Normandie*, for example, was stated to include some 5000 tons of high tensile steel. Unfortunately she was a war loss, being burnt out in New York harbour.

Important alloys of iron with other metals are also discussed in connection with those metals.

Iron for adornment

Iron beads were possibly used by pre-dynastic Egyptians some 4000 B.C. although the evidence is not unassailable (p. 260). Remains of iron finger rings have been found in Palestine dating back some 1000 B.C.

Pliny*, in a lengthy discourse on rings, states that at the time of the Second Punic War (218 to 201 B.C.) rings were in very general use. These were mostly of gold, but Pliny is careful to add that "not even in those days did all the senators possess gold rings, seeing that, in the memory of our grandsires, many personages who had even filled the prætorship wore rings of iron to the end of their lives." In Pliny's own day iron was a much more common commodity, and when slaves wore rings of iron they were allowed to

---

*PLINY, "Natural History". Translated by Bostock and Riley (Bohn, 1857), Book 33, Chapter 6.

encase them with gold. Apparently, however, slaves were not allowed to wear pure gold rings, the use of which was confined to the free.

The wedding rings of the Romans were generally of iron; probably this originated in another Roman custom, namely, the bestowal of a ring as an earnest upon the conclusion of a bargain*. In Rome it was at one time customary to give a newly made bride a ring of pure gold and to send at the same time an iron ring to her parents as a remembrance of modesty and domestic frugality.

It is not impossible that the modern use of iron or steel finger rings to "cure" rheumatism is a relic of those times when iron was supposed to ward off attacks of the evil one.

In modern times steel has been used even in this country for jewellery for the production of which both Birmingham and Wolverhampton were at one time famous (Plate 3, opp. p. 274). Missen referred to the good quality of the Birmingham ware in 1690, and in the succeeding century Boulton and Watt were engaged in its manufacture. Thackeray tells us that when King George IV (1820 to 1830) made his first appearance at a Court Ball "his hat was ornamented with two rows of steel beads, five thousand in number, with a button and loop of the same metal, and cocked in a new military style."

With the introduction of numerous alloys resembling gold, steel jewellery gradually became less popular. But primitive races still love to adorn themselves with iron rings and bangles. Kaffir bangles, for example, are made of malleable iron in the shape of a horseshoe, so that African chiefs, no matter how fat they may be, can get them on their arms and legs. When they have got them on the ends are forced together; they are nickel-plated, so that they scintillate in the African sun.

Cobalt

Certain natural arsenides of cobalt were known, many centuries ago, to be associated with silver ores in Saxony, although their chemical composition was not understood. They were probably what are to-day called *smaltite*, $CoAs_2$, and *cobaltite*, $CoAsS$, but were then recognised under the general name *kobold*, from the Greek *kobalos*, a subterranean gnome or malicious sprite, the word being akin to our "goblin". The miners were a superstitious folk (p. 18) and, as the mineral was believed to be poisonous, its presence in the mines was attributed to the malice of the little devils inhabiting

*WILLIAM JONES, "Finger Ring Lore" (London, 1877), p. 303.

the underworld, from whose pestilential machinations it was customary to pray for deliverance on the Sabbath in the churches. Goethe mentioned these kobolds or sprites in "Faust".

Up to 1540 the mineral was regarded as useless, but Scheurer then found that it would impart a beautiful blue colour to glass — a discovery that gave it a commercial value; he sold his secret to England, and from that time on till the present cobalt compounds have been used in the European glass industry. One great advantage lies in the fact that the colour is but little affected by the composition of the glass, 0·1 per cent of the metal being ample to produce an intense blue colour, whilst a pale blue tint results even with 0·01 of cobalt.

Cobalt compounds had been used in very early times for colouring glass, though of course nothing was then known of their real composition. Thus, cobalt blue glass or "fine lapis of Babylon" figured in the tribute sent by the ancient city of Assur in Assyra, some 1480 B.C. to Thothmes I, the Egyptian king, after his conquest of Syria and Palestine. Metallic cobalt was present (0·54 per cent) in the nickel-bronze coin of the Bactrian king Euthydemos, 235 B.C., but its inclusion was undoubtedly a matter of accident and not one of design.

In 1735 the cobalt ore used by the glass maker was examined by Georg Brandt, a Swede, born at Riddarhytta in Vestmanland in 1694, and not to be confused with Hennig Brand, the Hamburg merchant, who obtained phosphorus from urine in 1669 (p. 76). Brandt isolated a new metal from the mineral in impure form in 1742 and called it *cobalt*. That it was really a new metal was confirmed by Bergman in 1790 and by Tassaert in 1799. The real study of the chemistry of cobalt compounds began with the researches of Thénard in 1802 and of Proust in 1806.

A few years ago almost the only commercial uses of cobalt lay in its compounds; but two important fields have suggested themselves, namely, electroplating and coinage on account of its hardness and resistance to oxidation. Several alloys of cobalt are now marketed such as *stellite* (p. 245), used for stainless cutlery, surgical instruments, and some parts of motor cars. It is an alloy of cobalt, chromium, and a little tungsten. *Cochrome*, analogous to *nichrome*, contains cobalt and chromium, and is used for the windings of electric fires and furnaces; it is extremely resistant to atmospheric corrosion, even at elevated temperatures. A 35 per cent cobalt steel is used in loud-speaker magnets and for short bar magnets, a high magnetism being possible with this alloy. An alloy containing 75 Fe, 35 Co, 2 Cr, 5 W and 0·9 C was until comparatively recently the most highly magnetic material known. It has now been superseded by Ni-Fe-Al alloys, some of which also contain cobalt.

Cobalt is the best binder for tungsten carbides and similar excessively hard materials welded on to steel for cutting purposes.

Nickel

The early history of nickel is closely interwoven with the "Doctrine of Signatures" to which reference was made when dealing with the search for gold in gold-coloured urine, which search led to the discovery of phosphorus in 1669 (p. 76). According to this doctrine Nature has implanted her signature upon all things, great and small, animate and inanimate. This enables the observant and initiated to ascertain to what good ends Nature's gifts may be properly used. Thus, a plant with leaves curiously spotted reminds one of the lungs; this is Nature's way of indicating, to those endowed with eyes to see, that an infusion of this plant would prove a remedy for lung trouble — whence its name *lung wort* or, as the botanist has it, *pulmonaria*. Colas, writing in 1657, says, of the "Heart trefoil", that it is so called "not only because the leaf is triangular like the heart of a man, but also because each leafe doth contain the perfect icon (image) of an heart, and that in its proper colour. It defendeth the heart against the noisome vapour of the spleen."

In a similar manner minerals were held to indicate by their shapes, colours, or some other outstanding physical properties, the specific uses to which they are specially adapted. Thus yellow arsenic sulphide, like urine, was supposed by virtue of its colour, to contain gold — whence its name *orpiment* or *auri pigmentum*, the pigment of gold (p. 81).

Few minerals resemble copper in appearance; one of the best known and most important of these was known to German miners and was used to colour glass green. Although repeatedly worked for copper, that metal could never be extracted from it; the doctrine of signatures had broken down. Not that Nature herself was at fault; it was the Devil who had deliberately tinted the mineral in order to mislead the poor miner. So the mineral was called Kupfer-nickel, that is *false* copper, *pseudo* copper, or, more literally, *Old Nick's* copper.

The term Old Nick is sometimes regarded as a perverted form of St Nicholas, the patron saint of children, thieves, and fishermen.

The reference to fishermen might be due to its connection with the Anglo-Saxon *Nicor*, a water sprite. Anyhow, Old Nick was a disreputable fellow, and Saxe referred to his bad behaviour when he wrote —

Don't swear by the Styx
It's one of Old Nick's
Most abominable tricks
To get men into a terrible fix.

In 1751 Axel Frederick Cronstedt, the Swedish mineralogist, who introduced the blowpipe into analysis, turned his attention to kupfer nickel or niccolite, as we generally term it to-day. Cronstedt was regarded by his illustrious compatriot, Berzelius, as "the founder of the chemical system of mineralogy". He observed that, although the mineral dissolved in acid yielding a green solution, no copper was deposited on metallic iron placed within it. This surprised him for he was familiar with the old alchemical trick of converting iron into copper with the aid of copper sulphate solution. He therefore calcined a portion of the green deposit on the surface of some weathered niccolite, reduced the resulting oxide with charcoal and obtained a whitish metal, that certainly was not copper. For this new element he suggested the very appropriate name of *nickel*.

At first chemists were disinclined to accept the view that nickel was a new element. Cronstedt's specimen was impure and many believed that it was merely a more or less unholy mixture of cobalt, arsenic, iron, and possibly copper. But in 1775 Torbern Bergman, Cronstedt's famous Swedish contemporary, confirmed the existence of nickel, of which he prepared a fairly pure sample, and showed that no alloy of copper, iron, cobalt, and arsenic would behave like it.

"Natural" alloys of nickel have long been used by man, being reduced by reduction of naturally occurring mixed ores, the introduction of the nickel being at first purely accidental. Thus ancient bronze implements from pre-iron age civilisation have been found to contain from 2 to 4 per cent of nickel. Reference has already been made to the coin of the Bactrian king[*], Euthydemos II, dating back to 235 B.C., analysis of which showed copper 77·6, nickel 20·0, with cobalt 0·54, and iron 1·0. It has been conjectured that the alloy was originally obtained in ingot form from China

---

[*]CHARLETON, *J. Roy. Soc. Arts*, 1894, **42**, 496.

possibly carried by camel trade to the Mediterranean, for it is known that nickel-copper alloys were made from nickeliferous copper ores in very early times in Yunan and Szechuan. These alloys were known as *Pei-tung*, that is, white copper, or *Pack-tong*, incorrectly rendered as Pack-fong. They contained copper, nickel and zinc and were used for gongs and other musical instruments.

As soon as refined nickel became commercially available the Chinese alloys were made in England and Germany, the latter country making one in particular, called *Argentan*, which became a popular substitute for silver — whence the general term "German silver" (see table, p. 297).

Nickel coins*

In 1850 the Swiss Federal Government decided to use German silver as the basis of their coinage, on the ground that it was hard and durable, and was thus resistant to abrasion and difficult to counterfeit. The first attempts were not very successful as it was desired to make the coins worth their face value, and accordingly some 5 to 15 per cent of silver was added, according to the value of the coin. They were intensely hard, the coining dies broke, and the impression obtained on the coin itself was shallow. Similar difficulties were encountered with our own coinage after World War I (1914 to 1918), as already explained (p. 118) and we ought not to have fallen into the same error. After experimenting with several alloys, the Swiss, in 1881, decided to use pure nickel — the first time in history that the pure metal had been used for coins. It could not have been used much earlier because it was only in 1879 that Fleitmann showed the brittleness of commercial nickel could be removed by addition of a small amount of magnesium; it thus became possible now to roll the metal. This, Fleitmann did; he also rolled sheets of nickel both upon iron and steel much as silver was rolled on copper in the manufacture of Sheffield Plate. He thus became the pioneer in the development of nickel-clad steel.

In 1855 the Belgians decided to reform their low currency coins and, after experimenting with a number of alloys, were the first to employ one containing copper 75 and nickel 25. In 1857 the U.S.A. replaced their cumbrous copper cent pieces by an alloy of copper 88 and nickel 22, the latter metal then costing $2 per pound and was admittedly added to raise the intrinsic value of the coins. Later, in

*See *Report of the Royal Ontario Nickel Commission*, Toronto, 1917.

1865, the U.S.A. adopted the Belgian alloy, and Germany followed suit in 1873. We in Britain are now replacing our silver coins with a copper-nickel alloy (p. 106).

It is estimated that up to the end of 1912 some 900 million pure nickel coins had been issued in the old and new worlds, together with some 4500 million coins of nickel bronze*. It is easy to distinguish between the two, since nickel coins are readily attracted by a magnet, whereas the alloys are not.

Miscellaneous alloys

As nickel and copper mix in all proportions yielding uniform solid solutions, the nickel increasing both the hardness and electrical resistance of the alloys, mixtures of many different compositions are marketed bearing special names.

Cupronickels contain from 15 to 20 per cent of nickel, the remainder being copper. They can be cold-worked; for example they can be cold-rolled from 1 inch down to 0·05 inch without annealing being necessary. They have been extensively used for bullet jackets. The 25 Ni, 75 Cu alloy used in coinage has already been mentioned. A 30 Ni, 70 Cu alloy is used for condenser tubes. Another useful alloy, sometimes known as *constantan*, has 40 Ni and 60 Cu. Owing to its high electrical resistance and low resistance temperature coefficient it is used for standard electrical resistances.

In 1905 Ambrose Monell, President of the International Nickel Company, suggested smelting mixed copper and nickel ores together to produce a natural alloy containing small quantities of a few other elements as well. The registered trade name of this alloy is *monel metal* and it contains from 60 to 72 per cent Ni, the remainder being copper with iron up to 6·5 per cent and small quantities of Mn, Si and Al. The U.S. Government Specification, issued in July 1910 for the rolled metal, was 60 Ni, 36 Cu, 3·5 Fe and 0·5 Al, but no lead. The alloy looks like nickel, is non-magnetic and resistant to corrosion; it retains its high tensile strength at elevated temperatures. It is used for locomotive fireboxes, propellers, turbine blades, laundry fittings, kitchen ware, etc. One recent use is for aircraft fittings where steel, being magnetic, might influence the instruments.

Numerous other nickel alloys are now marketed, including many grades of *nickel-silver*, which are essentially ternary alloys of copper, nickel, and zinc.

---

*Bulletin Imperial Institute, 1916, **14**, 228.

The manufacture of nickel silver in Europe was begun in Berlin in 1824 and the fancy names given are legion. Different grades are recognised in the trade, the first three in the accompanying table are three of many recognised in the trade in Birmingham and Sheffield. Nickel-silver to which a little tungsten has been added is known as *platinoid*. *Argozoil* contains, in addition to the three usual elements about 2 per cent each of lead and tin, whilst *manganin* has up to 12 per cent of manganese. Nichrome has many interesting features; it has a high electrical resistance and is used for electrical heating appliances; it is also very resistant to acid attack and is thus suitable, amongst other uses, for pickling baskets.

	Ni	Cu	Zn	Miscellaneous
White Metal	24	54	22	—
Arguzoid	20·5	48·5	31	—
Electrum	26	51·5	22·5	—
Argentan	20	55	25	
Honda Metal	31·5	—	—	Fe 63·5, Co 5
Nichrome	60	—	—	Fe 15, Cr 14
Platinoid	14	60	24	W 1 to 2

Alloys of nickel and iron are also of great economic importance. Ordinary nickel steel, containing some 3 to 5 per cent of nickel, is hard and tough, and is suitable for naval armour, burglar-proof safes, and for parts of machinery that are subject to special wear and tear. A 3·5 nickel steel was used in Segrave's Golden Arrow.

Steels with 7 to 35 per cent Ni, often with a little Cr are heat and corrosion resistant; they are used in chemical apparatus, domestic and marine fittings, turbine blades and in the food industry. A 13 per cent nickel steel is extremely hard and can hardly be cut or drilled. With 24 per cent of Ni magnetic power is lost and with 24 to 32 of Ni the alloy offers a high resistance to the passage of an electric current, for which reason it finds application in heating coils. With 36 of Ni the alloy, known as *invar*, has an extremely low coefficient of expansion with rise of temperature. *Platinite*, with 46 of nickel expands comparably with glass and may thus replace the more expensive platinum for sealing into glass ware. *Permalloy* is used in cables, yielding a more rapid service in virtue of its high permeability.

Towards the close of the 80's of last century, Samuel J. Ritchie, who was interested in the Sudbury nickel ores, wrote to Krupps suggesting the use of an alloy of nickel and iron for ordnance. Krupps without hesitation rejected the idea as absurd. Meanwhile, however, the French had developed chrome steel projectiles that were making havoc with the naval armour plate, and the problem arose as to how this was to be countered.

In 1889 James Riley* of Glasgow drew attention to the various special properties of nickel steels. This interested, amongst others, the American Naval Authorities, who, in 1891, purchased plain steel plates from British and French manufacturers and nickel steel plates from Le Creusot works of Schneider in France. On testing these, the last named proved much more resistant to projectile attack than the others. The results attracted world wide attention and the introduction of alloy steels for naval armour plate dates from this time.

Honda metal, a ternary alloy prepared by Professor Honda of Japan, has a lower thermal coefficient of expansion even than silica. Its composition is given in the table on p. 297.

Nickel added in small amount to cast iron increases its strength and resistance to corrosion; it also enhances the ease of casting and machining. Such alloys are used in Diesel engines, valves, pumps, etc.

Nickel plating

Already in 1839 Jordan was depositing copper electrolytically from sulphate solutions and establishing the art of electrotyping. In 1842 Boetger had pointed out that dense, lustrous deposits of nickel could be obtained electrolytically in similar manner from solutions of nickel salts but it was not until about 1870 that the art of nickel plating was developed for, prior to that date, there was a difficulty in obtaining suitable nickel anodes at reasonable cost. Once that difficulty had been solved the nickel plating industry rapidly progressed and many hundreds of tons of nickel are used annually in this country for this purpose alone. It yields a hard coat, takes a good polish and does not readily tarnish; it looks well and is ornate. One can always detect nickel plate by moistening with a drop of acid, absorbing the drop on filter paper, adding ammonium hydroxide, then acetic acid and dimethyl glyoxime. The characteristic red colour of the nickel derivative is developed.

---

*RILEY, *J. Iron Steel Inst.*, 1889, I, 45.

Nickel is used in the manufacture of cooking utensils and table "crockery" or "silver"; for this it is particularly useful, as it is remarkably resistant to corrosion and will withstand rough usage, such as that encountered in hotels, cafés, and restaurants. In a finely divided condition nickel is used as a catalyst for many reactions; for example, the "hardening" of oils is an important industry, unsaturated liquid oils being "hardened" or rendered solid by the absorption of hydrogen with the aid of a nickel catalyst.

Occurrence

Nickel is much more plentiful in the Earth's crust than lead and tin as indicated in the table on p. 7. The world production of nickel is normally of the order of 100,000 tons annually.

For a time the world was combed for supplies of nickel ores and ores containing as little as 1 per cent nickel were profitably worked. For many years the pyrrhotite-chalcopyrite deposits of Norway were the main source of nickel, the industry reaching its height during 1870 to 1877.

In 1774 Captain Cook discovered New Caledonia, an island in the S. Pacific Ocean and once used as a French convict station. In 1865 Garnier found a nickel ore there near the capital Noumeia. It is a silicate, $(Ni, Mg)SiO_3.Aq.$ and exists in two varieties; one is light green and is known as garnierite, the other is dark green and called noumeite. In 1874 it was proved present in large quantity and by 1875 some 300 tons had been exported; the export rate increased until New Caledonia's output exceeded that of Norway, and the island became the chief producer of nickel; it maintained its lead until 1905.

An area of fewer than 1000 sq. miles in the Sudbury District of Ontario now entered the scene. Already in 1856 a Government Surveyor had reported the presence of ores there, but it was not until 1883, when the Canadian Pacific Railway was being extended westward from Sudbury, that the discovery assumed industrial importance. The first attraction was copper; later the nickel content was noted and a nickel industry developed, which by 1905 succeeded in swamping that of New Caledonia. It is likely to maintain its foremost position long into the future as the area contains many millions of tons of ore.

CHAPTER 22

THE PLATINUM METALS

THIS group comprises platinum, ruthenium, rhodium, palladium, osmium and iridium.

Platinum

Platinum was the first of the so-called *platinum metals* to be discovered, and its history reads like a Jules Verne novel. Platinum occurs in nature, sometimes in a fairly pure state, but more usually alloyed with its congeners in the eighth vertical group of the Periodic Table. Generally, it appears as grains or scales, but occasionally irregular lumps or nuggets have been found, ranging in weight from anything up to some 20 lb. The largest nugget ever found weighed 21 lb. Troy, or 7837 grams, and was deposited in the Demidoff Museum at Leningrad. Platinum does not appear to have been used or prized by primitive man to any extent, certainly not like gold; possibly because its appearance is far less attractive. In 1901 Berthelot stated, however, that a Theban (Egypt) casket of about 700 B.C., covered with inscriptions, had a portion of one of its characters made of an alloy of platinum. It was too small for a complete analysis, but from its behaviour towards *aqua regia* it was thought to be native metal, possibly from the alluvial deposits of Nubia or the upper regions of the Nile Valley.

It is said that in 1557 Scaliger referred to a metal, found in Mexico and Colombia, that could not be melted in existing Spanish furnaces. This is usually regarded as a reference to platinum, which is found in these regions. In 1741, Charles Wood, a metallurgist, sent his relative, Dr Brownrigg, a specimen of a new metal which he had found in Cartagena, Colombia. Nine years later this was handed over to the Royal Society. "I take the freedom to inclose to you," wrote Dr Brownrigg, on 5th December 1750, "an account of a semi-metal called *Platina di Pinto*; which, so far as I know, hath not been taken notice of by any writer on minerals."

The story now returns to South America. In 1735, Don Antonio de Ulloa was one of two officers selected by the French and Spanish Governments to take charge of a scientific expedition to Peru. Whilst out there, Ulloa came across native platinum and included an account of it in his log. On his return to Europe in 1744 on a French ship, the latter was captured by the British. Ulloa was treated with the greatest courtesy by the British naval officers and given a safe passage, with his records, to England. We were not at war with Spain at the time. The Admiralty returned his papers and his log was published in 1748. The Spaniards called platinum *platina del Pinto*, that is, "little silver of the R. Pinto". At the time the metal had no commercial value and was frequently used by the Spaniards to adulterate South American gold. So the Spanish Government closed the mines and ordered the metal to be thrown into the sea. The British frequently referred to it as "frog gold", and as late as 1874 its market value was a mere 25s. per oz. Troy. Platinum was found in the Urals in 1819 and five years later (1824) Russia began to export the metal. For very many years that was the main source of the commercial product. At the present time, platinum is being obtained in ever-increasing quantity during the refining of nickel by the International Nickel Co. of Canada. Prior to 1929 the nickel produced by this company contained traces of platinum metals originally present in the ores used, but in that year electrolytic refining of nickel was introduced whereby the platinum metals were obtained in a rich anode sludge. Owing to the large tonnage of the nickeliferous ores worked — over six million tons in 1937 — the actual amounts of the recovered platinum metals are appreciable. There is one part of the metal in two million parts of ore, which is approximately the same as of radium in pitchblende.

Platinum was difficult to work; but William Hyde Wollaston, who began as a medical practitioner at Bury St Edmunds, famous for his researches in metallurgy, mineralogy and optics, found that the metal becomes malleable when the spongy form is strongly compressed. It then may be annealed and hammered. His discovery brought him a fortune of some £30,000, so he was able to "retire" in 1800 at the age of 34 and devote himself to scientific pursuits. We shall meet him again presently. Incidentally, it may be mentioned that Wollaston drew gossamer threads of platinum by enclosing in silver, extending, and removing the silver with acid. These threads he made red hot with an electric current from a voltaic cell constructed in a tailor's thimble! We may thus regard Wollaston as the inventor of the first electric glow lamp.

Thomas Cock manufactured platinum by Wollaston's process, and Wollaston was associated with him for some time. In 1805, platinum crucibles could be bought for 17s. 6d. per oz., and wire

301

at 16s. per oz. Cock was a relative of Percival Norton Johnson, who began a metallurgical business in Hatton Garden in 1817. A few years later he was joined by George Matthey, and thus was founded the world-famous firm of Johnson, Matthey & Co. Ltd. which is "still going strong".

Brownrigg referred to platinum as a *semi*-metal, and the interest of chemists was rapidly engaged. One has only to refer to early issues of certain well-known scientific journals to realise what an immense amount of research was carried out by famous chemists at the close of the eighteenth and beginning of the nineteenth century. Such names as Berzelius, Berthollet, Bonsdorff, Descotils, Pelletier, Tennant, Klaus, Osann, Vauquelin, and others, constantly recur. It was not long before it was realised that native platinum was far from the pure metal and contained elements, alloyed with it in varying proportions, that were entirely new to science. In those days there was no rule to guide chemists as to the greatest possible number of elements such as we possess to-day in the Atomic number — the product of the brilliant work of Moseley in 1913. There thus appeared to lie before each and every investigator the possibility that he might discover a new element. Alas that such a possibility should be so remote to-day!

Palladium and rhodium

In 1803 Wollaston* dissolved crude platinum in aqua regia, and, after evaporating off the excess acid, obtained a yellow precipitate by the dropwise addition of mercuric cyanide solution. It was a lucky experiment, for only one of the platinum metals is precipitable in this way. On ignition of the precipitated cyanide a white metal remained which Wollaston called *palladium* in honour of the minor planet *Pallas*, discovered the previous year by Olbers.

Wollaston's discovery succeeded in raising the usual crop of sceptics, as witness such titles as "Reward of Twenty Pounds for the Artificial Production of Palladium" and "Enquiry concerning the Nature of a Metallic Substance lately sold in London as a New Metal, under the Title of Palladium", which appeared in Nicholson's famous Journal in 1804.

Following up his discovery of palladium, Wollaston dissolved some native platinum in aqua regia, removed platinum as ammonium hexachlorplatinate and palladium as cyanide. Evaporation of the filtrate with acid effected the decomposition of excess of the

---

*WOLLASTON, *Phil. Trans.*, 1804, p. 419; 1805, p. 316.

mercury cyanide and a dark red double chloride of sodium and a new metal remained. To this new metal Wollaston gave the name *rhodium* from the Greek *rhodon* rose, because of the beautiful rose colour of aqueous solutions of its salts. The double salt, probably $Na_3RhCl_6 18H_2O$, was reduced in hydrogen, the sodium chloride leached away, and rhodium obtained as a powder.

Iridium and osmium

But Wollaston was not the only chemist who was tackling the mysteries of native platinum. In the same year (1803) the Wensleydale Yorkshireman, Smithson Tennant*, a pupil of Black at Edinburgh, also dissolved the metal in dilute aqua regia. Despite his happy-go-lucky temperament he did happen to ponder over the insoluble black residue which had hitherto been regarded as merely graphite, and which we now know to have been osmiridium. He found that by alternate action of acid and alkali it was possible to effect its separation into two distinct metals. One of these he named *iridium*, from the Greek *iris* rainbow, because it yielded salts of various colours — green, red, violet. The other, on heating, yielded a volatile oxide which he at first called *ptène*, from the Greek *ptenos*, winged; but he was persuaded against that very awkward term and called it *osmium*, from the Greek *osmé* a smell, in recognition of the unpleasant odour of the volatile tetroxide, OsO_4, produced when the metal is heated in air. The vapour is very penetrating, intensely poisonous, producing temporary blindness and other unpleasant symptoms. Osmium thus reminds us of the halogen (p. 49) which Balard first called *muride* but accepted its alteration to bromine from the Greek *brómos* a stench.

Poor Tennant came to an untimely end shortly after his election to the Chair of Chemistry in Cambridge. Ever fond of horseflesh, he was riding over a drawbridge at Boulogne, when the bridge moved and he fell into the ditch, with his horse on top of him. When extricated he was fast dying.

In 1922 the extraction of gold by the amalgamation process was discarded on the Rand in favour of the cyanide process and a preliminary concentration on blankets and corduroy introduced. This recovers the osmiridium together with coarse gold particles that are not readily dissolved in the subsequent cyaniding. This is comparable with the sheep-skin method of the ancients used in the recovery of gold from river gravels, which is generally believed to

*TENNANT, *Phil. Trans.*, 1804, p. 411.

have given rise to the legend of the golden fleece. The Rand gold mines are now the main source of osmiridium; only small quantities are present, amounting to about 1 oz. in 1200 tons or roughly 1 part in 30 million.

Ruthenium

Ruthenium was the last of the platinum metals to be discovered and for it we are indebted to the Russian chemist Karl Karlovich Klaus*. It owes its name to Osann who, in 1828, thought he had obtained three new metals from crude metal from the Urals; he christened them *pluranium, polinium, and ruthenium*, the last named being derived from Ruthenia, a name of Russia. The first two supposed elements, however, were not new elements but the existence of one new element in Osann's "ruthenium" was confirmed by Klaus, who retained for it the name ruthenium. In 1842 Klaus obtained 20 lb. of platinum residues from the laboratory of the Russian Government Mint in what was then known as St Petersburg. He separated osmiridium by its insolubility in aqua regia, fused with potassium hydroxide and nitrate, and extracted the melt with water, thereby obtaining an orange-coloured solution of potassium osmate, K_2OsO_4, and ruthenate, K_2RuO_4. Addition of nitric acid effected the precipitation of osmium di-oxide and ruthenium oxide from which the osmium was separated by distillation with aqua regia; addition of ammonium chloride to the residue yielded what was supposed to be ammonium hexachlorruthenate, $(NH_4)RuCl_6$, but was most probably the nitrosyl derivative, $K_2RuCl_5.NO$, from which the new metal was obtained by ignition.

Uses of the platinum metals

Although ruthenium appears to have no industrial applications all the other platinum metals are used to a considerable extent.

A good deal of platinum is used in jewellery, often alloyed with iridium to increase its hardness. It is valued as a setting for diamonds the brilliance of which is developed by the white colour of the metal.

Platinum is largely used in the chemical industry as a catalyst in various processes. Every chemist thinks immediately of the "contact" process of the sulphuric acid industry and the classic researches of Knietsch in 1901. A healthy stimulus to the investigation of platinum catalysts was afforded by the placing on the market

---

*KLAUS, *Annalen*, 1845, **56**, 257; 1846, **59**, 234. *Pogg. Annalen*, 1845, **64**, 192; **65**, 200. OSANN, *ibid*., 1828, **14**, 329; 1845, **64**, 197.

of a vanadium catalyst; but the palm still goes to the former as they give an efficient conversion of SO_2 to SO_3 over a wide range of SO_2-concentration in the initial gases. Platinised asbestos is a favourite, but platinised silica gel was introduced into factory use in 1926, and possesses an undoubted advantage in being immune to arsenical poisoning.

Platinum is unusually ductile; it can be drawn into wire of diameter 0·00005 inch; one ounce of metal could thus be drawn out for several hundred miles. Its coefficient of linear expansion from 0° to 100° C is 0·0000089, which is closely similar to that for ordinary glass; for this reason platinum wire is used in the construction of electrical and other apparatus in which it is necessary to pass wire through glass and leave a perfectly air-tight and hermetically sealed joint.

World production of platinum in 1938 was 460,000 oz. Troy and two years later it is believed to have exceeded 600,000 oz.

Rhodio-platinum, an alloy containing 10 of rhodium, is widely used, in the form of gauze, in the catalytic oxidation of ammonia to nitric acid — a process that has largely supplanted natural nitrates as a source of nitric acid. Its conversion ratio is higher than with platinum alone. Thermocouples of platinum and rhodio-platinum, that can be immersed direct in molten steel in open hearth furnaces, have recently been designed; the junction is encased in a silica sheath, covered by a steel tube; the latter melts, but the silica sheath lasts for several immersions. Rhodio-platinum, as also alloys of platinum and gold (30 : 70) and platinum, gold and palladium (20 : 70 : 10) are used in making spinnerets for the production of rayon.

As rhodium is very resistant to tarnish and remains white even in concentrated solutions of alkali sulphides, it is now in demand for electroplating. Although a very costly metal, exceedingly thin coats suffice so that the process is not too expensive. It is claimed that a coat, 0·0001 in. in thickness, on silver can withstand boiling aqua regia for 30 minutes without appreciable damage. A new secret process for rendering silver untarnishable, known as rhodanising, can be applied to old and new silver alike (1936).

Rhodium-plated reflectors, on account of their resistance to heat and oxidation, are particularly suited for searchlight and cinema projectors. Rhodium black has been used for producing a black colour in the decoration of pottery.

On account of its hardness and extreme incorrodibility iridium is used for pivots, surgical tools, etc. Alloyed with platinum it is used in electrical contacts used under severe conditions as, for example, in aircraft; in constructing chemical apparatus, a classical instance being the U-tube and electrodes used by Moissan in 1886 for the isolation of fluorine from the electrolysis of potassium hydrogen fluoride. An alloy containing 10 of iridium and 90 of platinum was used in preparing the *International Prototype Metre* and the corresponding *Kilogram* (pp. 307, 309).

Iridium black like rhodium black has been used in producing black colours in the decoration of porcelain.

For crucibles an alloy of platinum and rhodium, with 3 to 5 per cent of the latter, is recommended for high temperature work. Iridium stiffens platinum but increases its volatility above 900° C whereas rhodium not only stiffens the platinum but also reduces its volatility. Iridio-platinum is used successfully in sparking-plug electrodes of aero-engines, best all-round results being obtained with 20 per cent iridium.

Osmium is used in the fountain pen industry being the most important component of "iridium" tips. Alloys of extreme hardness containing osmium are finding increasing application. It has been used in the filaments of electric lamps on account of its infusibility which closely approaches that of tungsten; its melting point being 2700° C (tungsten, melting point 3382° C). Osmium is also used in electroplating as, for example, for searchlight reflectors.

Palladium is now being used more in industry than hitherto, often as a substitute for platinum. Sometimes medals are struck in it. Alloyed with gold it is used as a substitute for platinum. Gold with 20 per cent palladium is completely white and is sometimes used in expensive jewellery under the name "white gold".

On account of its resistance to corrosion it has been used for astronomical and dental purposes.

Standards of length and mass

The original standard metre and kilogram were constructed by Borda in platinum. The *metre* owes its origin to the French Republic of 1795. It was decided that the metre should be a physical constant and, as a convenient length, one ten-millionth (10^{-7}) of the Earth's quadrant was selected, or more precisely that of the distance between the N. Pole and the Equator measured over the surface of the Earth along the meridian passing through Paris. It was thought that by this means if ever the standard were lost it could be replaced. The actual measurements were carried out by Delambre and Méchain between Barcelona and Dunkirk, and Borda was entrusted with the task of constructing the standard metre.

It was soon realised, however, that, if the metre were defined as above, every time a more accurate determination was made all the copies in general use would require altering, which would be almost fatal to scientific progress beside causing a great deal of inconvenience to trade. The metre was therefore converted into a purely arbitrary unit like the British yard and was defined as the distance between the ends of Borda's platinum rod.

According to more recent measurements the mean meridian quadrant measures 10,002,100 metres.

The *International Prototype Metre* is a copy of the original Borda standard or *Metre des Archives*; it is made of an alloy of Pt 90 and Ir 10 per cent, this alloy being hard, durable, very resistant to corrosion and possessed of a low thermal coefficient of expansion. The metre is here the distance between the centres of two lines engraved upon the standard, when measured at 0° C.

Platinum-iridium copies of this metre, called the *National Prototype Metres*, were made at the same time and distributed about 1889 to various Governments, the British copy being housed at the Standards Department of the Board of Trade.

In ancient times in Britain three barley corns were taken as the measure of one inch. The earliest recorded standard of length in Britain was the *gird* or *yard*, decreed by the Saxon King Edgar (959 to 975); it was kept at Winchester and is believed to have represented two cubits, the cubit being the average length of the fore-arm and one of the earliest known standards of length recorded in ancient history.

From time to time new standards were prepared approximating very closely to the old ones, the last standard being housed, down to 1834, in the House of Commons. It was destroyed, however, in the fire of 1834, when the Houses were burned down, the fine old Westminster Hall fortunately escaping.

By 1845 a new standard had been prepared by taking the mean length of the most authoritative measures constituting the best primary approach to the lost standard, no official duplicates or copies ever having been made or recognised. The new *Imperial yard* was defined as the distance between two fine lines cut in gold plugs let into a bronze bar, measurements being made at 62° F.

The composition of the alloy was Cu : Sn : Zn as 16 : 2·5 : 1. Four official copies were made and housed in different places, the standard being kept at the Standards Department of the Board of Trade in accordance with the Weights and Measures Act of 1878.

Copper alloys are now known to be unsuited for standard lengths and in 1902 an iridio-platinum (10 : 90) copy was made.

The metre was recognised by the British Parliament in 1897, and the legal equivalents established by Order in Council of May 1898 are —

$$1 \text{ metre} = 1 \cdot 0936143 \text{ yards}$$
$$1 \text{ yard} = 0 \cdot 914399 \text{ metre}$$

Both the metre and yard have now been measured in terms of the wavelength of the red cadmium spectral line, λ_r, in vacuo with the following results —

$$1 \text{ metre} = 1,552,734 \cdot 44 \lambda_r$$
$$1 \text{ yard} = 1,419,818 \cdot 24 \lambda_r$$

It would thus be possible to replace the standards with great accuracy in the event of loss or destruction of the standards themselves and their copies.

Ordinary cadmium consists of several isotopes and ideal monochromatic light is obtainable from a single isotope only. Even greater accuracy may therefore be expected when light from one single isotope is available. Cadmium is difficult to separate into isotopes but, by the bombardment of metallic gold with neutrons in an atomic pile, one of the isotopes of mercury (At. wt. 198) has been prepared. Thus —

$$Au (197) + n \rightarrow Hg (198) + e$$

an electron e being evolved, which is an inversion of the alchemists' dream of transmutation. Hg (198) gives a pure monochromatic green light and in time this should be available for standard length measurements. Preliminary measurements of this line indicate (1950) the metre to equal 1,831,249·2λ in standard air. On the Continent the krypton isotope 84 is being similarly studied.

The metric standard of mass is the *kilogram*, a lump of platinum prepared by Borda to represent the mass of a cubic decimetre of water at the temperature of its maximum density, namely 4° C. It is called the *Kilogram des Archives*.

This kilogram was prepared at the close of the eighteenth century with the very greatest care, but during succeeding years methods of measurement became increasingly refined and by 1872 it was realised that the experimental error in the determination was greater than was permissible for accurate work. So instead of defining the kilogram as the mass of 1000 cc. of water it was decided to make the mass of that particular lump of platinum the arbitrary unit. The *International Prototype Kilogram* is the mass of a cylinder of iridio-platinum (10 : 90), similar in composition to the alloy used for the metre and for the same reasons; it is an exact copy of the original Borda standard. Copies of this have been prepared and distributed to various Governments as *National Prototype Kilograms*. The British copy is kept at the Standards Office.

Ever since Saxon times the unit of weight in Britain has been the *pound*, but that pound has varied considerably in value from time to time. In 1533 Henry VIII instituted the pound Troy as the legal unit. This had been introduced from the French city of Troyes towards the close of the reign of Edward III (*d.* 1377) and was apparently widely known and used even before it became official. The standard Troy pound appears to have been renewed from time to time and that used from 1758 onwards was destroyed in the fire at the House of Commons in 1834, having been housed there along with the standard yard.

A commission was accordingly appointed to consider the whole question of standard weights and measures; it was decided to construct a Troy lb. in platinum as close in weight as possible to the lost standard by averaging reliable copies. The difference between the two must have been extremely small.

As the old Troy lb. was equivalent to 5760 grains the new grain was defined as one 5760th of the new standard Troy lb.

At this time the Troy lb. was less popular among business men than the heavier Avoirdupois pound which had been in use more or less from the time of Edward III. It was equivalent to 7000 grains. Advantage was accordingly taken to change the legal standard from Troy to Avoirdupois and a cylinder of platinum was prepared equal in weight to exactly 1 lb. Troy × 7000 ÷ 5760. A pound weight was thus obtained equivalent to 7000 of the new grains. By Act of Parliament (1878) the weight *in vacuo* of this cylinder became the standard pound from which all other weights and all measures having reference to weight were to be derived. The cylinder was marked "P.S. 1844 1 lb." The letters P.S. mean Parliamentary Standard.

The connection between the kilogram and pound is defined legally (1898) as —

$$1 \text{ kilogram} = 2 \cdot 2046223 \text{ pounds}$$
$$1 \text{ pound} \quad = 0 \cdot 45359243 \text{ kilogram}$$

Thus, both the kilogram and the pound are purely arbitrary units.

CHAPTER 23

THE RADIOELEMENTS AND THE ACTINIDE SERIES

THESE include elements of atomic numbers 84 upwards. Elements of higher At. No. than uranium are frequently termed *transuranic*, and six of these are now known. When they were studied it was observed that they bore a closer resemblance to uranium than to the elements of Group VIII — the platinum metals. It appeared, therefore, that these elements formed part of a new series resembling the rare earth elements, Nos. 57 to 71. This suggested that the electronic arrangements might be analogous, the O shell now filling up in a similar manner to the N shell in the former. Actinium thus resembles lanthanum, thorium resembles cerium, and so on. It was therefore proposed by Seaborg that the rare earth elements be termed the *lanthanide series*, and the radioelements from actinium onwards the *actinide series*.

The electronic arrangement is shown in the following table, in the final column of which are given the symbols of the corresponding rare earth metals. Elements 97 and 98 (p. 327) have not yet been (1950) officially recognised and are not included in the table.

Shell	K	L	M	N	O	P	Q	
Maximum No. of electrons	2	8	18	32	50	72	98	
89 Actinium	2	8	18	32	18	8 + 1	2	La
90 Thorium	2	8	18	32	18 + 1	8 + 1	2	Ce
91 Protactinium	2	8	18	32	18 + 2	8 + 1	2	Pr
92 Uranium	2	8	18	32	18 + 3	8 + 1	2	Nd
93 Neptunium	2	8	18	32	18 + 4	8 + 1	2	(61)
94 Plutonium	2	8	18	32	18 + 5	8 + 1	2	Sm
95 Americium	2	8	18	32	18 + 6	8 + 1	2	Eu
96 Curium	2	8	18	32	18 + 7	8 + 1	2	Gd

Uranium

In 1789 Klaproth was investigating a mineral which, from its black, shining appearance, was known as *pitch-blende*. It was thought

311

to be an ore of zinc and iron, but since, on dissolution in nitric acid and neutralising with caustic potash, a precipitate is obtained soluble in excess of the latter reagent, Klaproth rightly conjectured that he was dealing with a new element. To this he gave the name *uranium* in recognition of Herschel's discovery of the new planet Uranus in 1781. It constitutes about 4 ppm of the earth's crust.

By igniting a paste of the oxide with oil and charcoal, Klaproth obtained a black, metallic-like powder which he regarded as uranium itself. In 1841, however, Peligot showed that it was an oxide. He analysed the chloride, UCl_4, and his results added up to 110 per cent. This impossible result was due to the fact that the "uranium" he had weighed was not really the element but the very stable oxide, UO_2, which was not reducible either with hydrogen or carbon. He therefore reduced the chloride with metallic potassium in a closed platinum crucible and, after removing the potassium chloride by leaching with water, was rewarded by finding a residue of metallic uranium, the properties of which were different from those of the oxide hitherto regarded as the element.

More than a century passed between the recognition of the presence of a new element in pitch-blende by Klaproth in 1789, and the discovery that this element possesses extraordinary physical properties, the examination of which led to revolutionary ideas on the structure of matter.

It came about in this wise. In 1896, Antoine Henri Becquerel was studying the fluorescence shown by uranic salts such as potassium uranyl sulphate, $K_2SO_4.UO_2SO_4.2H_2O$, and made the interesting observation that these would affect a wrapped photographic plate, even in the dark. This appeared to rule out the possibility of fluorescence being the cause, and further support came from the activity of uranous salts, which similarly affected the photographic plate, although they were not fluorescent. It appeared, therefore, that an entirely new type of radiation was being emitted, capable of passing through black paper and affecting a photographic plate.

The scientific world, at this time, was all agog with Röntgen's discovery of 1895 of a new set of rays, the so-called X or Röntgen rays, emanating from the glass walls of tubes where bombardment by cathode rays occurs. The time was therefore ripe for Becquerel's results and scientists were not slow to turn them to good account.

Shortly before this Marie Sklodowska, daughter of a science master in Warsaw, had gone to the Sorbonne in Paris and worked in the laboratory of Pierre Curie. With the wilfulness of her species, she neglected *Punch's* advice to those about to be married — and, in 1895, changed her name to Curie. This, as afterwards transpired, was a distinct advantage for scientific nomenclature. The two were happy though poor; Pierre swept the floor and Marie cooked the meals. She still found time for science. Interested in Becquerel's discovery, Mme Curie began to test all sorts of substances for "rays" and was not long in discovering that thorium compounds were also active.

It was soon realised that this radioactivity is an atomic property with an intensity directly proportional to the concentration of the element yielding it and entirely independent of the state of chemical combination of that element. Not only do the rays affect a photographic plate, but they induce ionisation in air and thus assist the discharge of an electroscope. Hence a radioelement can be detected electroscopically no matter what chemical process it undergoes. This enormously simplifies the method of detection which is both rapid and delicate.

Radium

Mme Curie noticed that certain pitch-blendes show greater activity than corresponds to their uranium content, and concluded that this was due to the presence of an unknown element, much more active than uranium itself, but present in such minute quantities that it had escaped detection by the ordinary methods of analysis. Upon request the Austrian Government very generously placed a ton of pitch-blende residues from their state "Dollar Mine" at Joachimstal, at the disposal of Mme Curie. This, with the collaboration of her husband, she fractionated according to accepted qualitative methods of analysis, each precipitate being tested electroscopically for radioactivity and rejected when inert. In this way the radio precipitates were concentrated, and two radio-substances eventually separated in 1898. One of these was precipitated with bismuth and was named *polonium*, in honour of Poland, Mme Curie's native land; the other was precipitated with the barium and was christened *radium*, because of its great activity*.

For many years radium was only known in the form of its salts. These were purified by fractionation; for four years Mme Curie

---

*Full references are given to this early work in FRIEND'S "Textbook of Inorganic Chemistry", Vol. III, Part I, by M. S. BURR (Griffin, 1925).

carried on this dangerous task and in 1903 presented her results to the Paris Faculty of Science with a view to her doctorate. Poor Pierre's hands were crippled by the activity of the rays, whereas Marie escaped injury — a striking tribute to the knightly chivalry of her husband, who evidently bore the brunt of the exposure. The happy pair leaped into fame; the same year, the Nobel Prize was shared between them and pecuniary embarrassments were now at an end. Pierre's fame was short-lived. In 1906 he went out one day to lunch with some friends; Marie waited in vain for his return; he had been run over and mortally injured by a dray*.

This cruel blow did not prevent Mme Curie from carrying on her research. She learned to cultivate a sublimely detached attitude towards things in general, as her maid once discovered to her consternation. She had entered the laboratory exclaiming, "Madame, madame, I have swallowed a pin!" Madame attempted to soothe her, saying, "There, there, don't cry, there's a good girl; here is another pin for you."

To perpetuate the name of Curie, the quantity of emanation in equilibrium with one gram of radium was termed a *curie*. This is an inconveniently large amount and the *milli-micro curie* is frequently used as a practical unit. It is the quantity of emanation in equilibrium with one millionth of a milligram of radium. Since one-fiftieth of this can be detected with a sensitive electroscope, this method of detecting the presence of radio-elements is extraordinarily sensitive — more so even than the spectroscope. The above definition of the curie has now been superseded. In July 1950 the Joint Commission on Standards, Units and Constants of Radioactivity defined the curie as the quantity of any radioactive nuclide in which the number of disintegrations per second is 3.700×10^{10}.

The radium content of the Earth's crust is estimated as 1.4×10^{-12} per cent†.

In 1904 an amalgam of radium was obtained by Coehn‡ who electrolysed a solution of radium bromide in methyl alcohol using a silver anode and an amalgamated zinc cathode. It was not until 1910 that Mme Curie and Debierne§ isolated the pure metal by

---

*EVE CURIE, "Madame Curie". Translated by V. Sheean (New York, 1943).
†G. BERG, "Das Vorkommen der Chemischen Elemente auf der Erde" (Berlin, 1932), p. 113.
‡COEHN, *Ber.*, 1904, **37**, 811.
§CURIE and DEBIERNE, *Compt. rend.*, 1910, **151**, 523.

distillation of the amalgam in a current of hydrogen. The same year Ebler* obtained it by thermal decomposition of the azide, $Ra(N_3)_2$.

Radium is a brilliant white metal, melting at 700° C, and manifesting luminescence, thereby differing from the other alkaline earth metals.

Radium is continuously disintegrating; the process is subatomic and can neither be accelerated nor retarded by any means at our disposal. Radium is a member of the *Uranium series* and may be found in all minerals containing this latter element. The scheme in Fig. 8 shows the various stages of the disintegration of uranium,

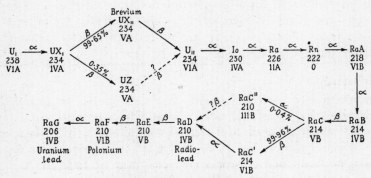

Fig. 8 — The uranium series

The arrows are marked to indicate whether the disintegration takes place by α- or β-emission

the ultimate product being *radium G* or *uranium lead* (p. 324). The atomic weights are given beneath the symbols and the vertical groups in the Periodic Table to which the elements belong.

It is customary to express the stability of a radioelement in terms of its *half-life*, by which is meant the time that would be required for one half of a given mass of the element to undergo natural disintegration. Thus the period of half-life or half-change of radium is 1600 years. If therefore we have to-day a gram of radium, in 1600 years there will be only half a gram left, and in a further 1600 years the amount will have fallen to 0·25 gm. and so on.

During the disintegration of radium, as indeed of uranium, many new transitional elements are formed, some of purely

*EBLER, *Ber.*, 1910, **43**, 2613.

ephemeral existence, like *radium C*, whose period of half-life is estimated at 10^{-6} second, and *brevium*, $1 \cdot 14$ minutes, whereas *radium D* has a life of some 16 years. Polonium is the penultimate disintegration product of radium, and is also called *radium F*; its period of half-life is $136 \cdot 5$ days; when it loses an α-particle it is converted into radium G or uranium lead. In its chemical properties polonium resembles tellurium and early preparations were sold as *radio-tellurium*. Old radon tubes are a useful source.

Radium itself has no commercial applications. Its compounds are used mainly for medical purposes and as a source of radon; these absorb some 85 per cent of the world's output: 10 per cent is used for rendering dials of instruments and other objects luminous, the remaining 5 per cent being used for scientific and miscellaneous purposes*. One mg of radium emits $22 \cdot 2 \times 10^8$ α-particles per min. Its half-life is 1610 years.

Atomic energy

Decomposition of a radioelement, whether natural or induced by bombardment is invariably accompanied by liberation of energy. When, for example, a radium salt is confined in a thick lead vessel almost all the evolved energy is converted into heat, some 25 gm-calories per hour being produced per gram of radium. For this heat to serve any useful economic purpose we should require vastly greater quantities of radium than we could ever hope to obtain.

The position is even worse with uranium, $U(238)$, the half-life period of which is 4,500 million years. During that period a gram of the metal would, it is true, evolve an enormous amount of energy, equivalent to 3×10^{12} gm-calories. This could raise 30,000 tons of water from freezing to boiling point, or afford hot baths for more than one million people — a matter of supreme indifference to those politicians who do not bathe.

But this energy is evolved over so long a period that the quantity available at any one moment is too small to be of economic value. It has been calculated that 10 million tons of uranium would be required beneath the boilers of the *Queen Mary* (81,235 tons) to propel that noble vessel across the Atlantic at full speed. This it could continue to do for many million years without renewal.

But that is of no use to us. No ship could possibly carry so vast a load of fuel; and even if it could the radioactivity would be so

---

*See Jennings and Russ, "Radon" (Murray, 1948).

intense that no human freight could accompany it. If, however, we could hurry up the rate of disintegration, something economically useful might be achieved. If, for example, we could induce uranium to reduce its period of half-life from 4,500 million years to six months, its energy would be liberated some 9000 million times as rapidly and a matter of 2 lb. would suffice to take the *Queen Mary* across the Atlantic at full speed; refuelling after each journey would require less than 1 oz. of uranium. This would enormously reduce the fuel space and increase that for cargo. At present this cannot be done. No means has yet been discovered of accelerating the natural decomposition of uranium or indeed of any other radio-element for economic use in this way.

We can often hasten a chemical reaction with rise of temperature. On the average it is found that if the temperature is raised by $10°$ C the rate of reaction is doubled. By raising the temperature through $100°$ C therefore, the reaction would, if it followed the rule, proceed 2^{10} or 1000 times as rapidly; raised through $1000°$ C its rate would be roughly 10^{30} or one pentillion times as rapid. Experiments were accordingly tried with uranium, but no influence whatever was observed by raising its temperature to $2500°$ C.

There is no doubt, however, that if we could obtain a sufficiently high temperature the rate of disintegration would be increased. In the interior of the sun, for example, which approximates to 20 million $°C$, matter as we know it cannot exist; even atoms are disrupted.

But although we cannot accelerate the natural radio-decomposition of uranium, we can effect an entirely different type of decomposition by bombarding its nucleus with suitable projectiles moving with appropriate speeds. A useful projectile is the neutron, which is a minute mass of neutral matter entirely devoid of electrical charges. On account of its neutrality and small size, its diameter being 10^{-12} cm, it possesses unique penetrating power. It can pass through the planetary space surrounding the nucleus of an atom without disturbing the electrons. Its existence, first suggested as possible by Lord Rutherford in 1920, was confirmed by Chadwick in 1932.

The results obtained by the bombardment of uranium with neutrons depend both on the isotopic form of uranium used and the speed of the neutrons.

Isotopy of uranium

Ordinary uranium is a mixture of three isotopes, all of which are radioactive. Thus —

Isotope	Per cent in natural metal	Emission	Half-life (years)
U(238)	99·294*	α	4.56×10^9
U(235)	0·70	α	7.1×10^8
U(234)	0·006	α	2.7×10^5

*By difference

Although identical in their chemical behaviour these isotopes respond differently towards neutron bombardment. At speeds between those of fast and thermal (relatively slow), neutrons are captured by U(238) without fission, producing a very active isotope U(239), which loses an electron producing a new element *neptunium*, Np, which in turn loses an electron yielding *plutonium*,

$$\underset{\text{(Intermediate)}}{^{238}_{92}U + n} \longrightarrow {^{239}_{92}U} \xrightarrow{\text{Emits } \beta} {^{239}_{93}Np} \xrightarrow{\text{Emits } \beta} {^{239}_{94}Pu} \xrightarrow{\text{Emits } \alpha} {^{235}_{92}U}$$

Half life — 4·56 × 10⁹ yrs.　　　　23 mins.　　2·3 days　　2·4 × 10⁴ yrs.　　7·1 × 10⁸ yrs.

(a) Formation of transuranic elements, Np and Pu, and U(235)

$$\underset{\text{(Thermal)}}{^{235}_{92}U + n} \longrightarrow \underset{\substack{\text{Critical energy} \\ \text{for stability} \\ \text{exceeded}}}{^{236}_{92}U} \longrightarrow {^{86}_{36}Kr} + \underset{\text{(Fast)}}{^{147}_{56}Ba} + 3n$$

(b) Fission of U(235) after thermal-neutron capture

Fig. 9 — Neutron bombardment of uranium

Pu, which is radioactive, ejecting α-particles and yielding U(235); this decay is relatively slow. The scheme may be written as in Fig. 9(a).

Thermal neutrons have relatively little action on U(238) but can effect the fission of U(235). This is illustrated in Fig. 9(b). Krypton and barium are not always formed; many different elements have been identified. The fission is accompanied by the liberation of an enormous amount of energy, and this is the principle of the atomic bomb. It will be noticed that these artificial disintegrations yield very different products from the natural processes as shown on p. 315.

The uranium bomb

The high speed neutrons liberated by fission of U(235) mostly escape or are neutralised by foreign bodies during natural disintegration. As, however, usually one to three secondary high speed neutrons are liberated for each fruitful collision it is clear that, if sufficient of these could be slowed down to thermal velocities and themselves allowed to combine fruitfully with further U(235) atoms, the process might be made continuous or chain-wise. This is shown diagrammatically in Fig. 10.

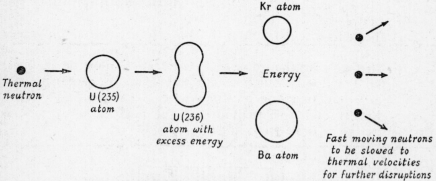

Fig. 10 — The initiation of a chain reaction

Owing to the rapidity with which fission occurs (about 10^{-12} second) when once the neutron has been absorbed, if one could ensure that even only a few more of the evolved neutrons than those absorbed in producing them could collide fruitfully, the number of collisions would increase with terrific speed leading to an explosion of unprecedented violence.

Let us consider how this can be done.

(i) It is first necessary to increase the proportion of U(235) in the metal; in Nature it constitutes less than one per cent. As U(235) is merely an isotope of U(238) and hence possesses identical chemical properties, its separation presents unusual difficulties. One of the ways in which the difficulty has been overcome lies in the fractional thermal diffusion of the fluorides $U(238)F_6$ and $U(235)F_6$, there being only one form of fluorine. The process is lengthy.

(ii) A neutron liberated in the middle of a mass of uranium has little chance of escape; one produced near the surface has obviously a better chance. Hence the average opportunity for a neutron to escape without fruitful collision is proportional to the surface area of the generating material, whereas the chance of capture is a volume effect. For spherical masses the area is $\propto r^2$ but the volume is $\propto r^3$; hence the larger the lumps the less the chance of escape. There is thus a critical size for a mass of U(235) below which rapid disintegration will not occur, but above which, owing to neutrons normally present in consequence of natural decay, rapid disintegration will occur spontaneously. What that critical mass may be has not been disclosed; it probably lies between 20 and 40 lb.

(iii) To effect a maximum fission capture the high speed secondary neutrons must be slowed down. This can be effected with the aid of *moderators*. These must be of such a kind as will function without actually capturing the neutrons. Graphite is largely used.

(iv) Finally both the uranium and the moderator must be as free as possible from impurities.

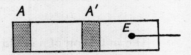

Fig. 11—The atomic bomb

Having prepared the material the next step is to construct the bomb. This presents great mechanical difficulties which, however, have been solved to a certain extent.

The principle consists in assembling lumps of U(235), suitably moderated and of size well below the critical so that they remain stable, apart from natural radio-disintegration. When an explosion is required these lumps must be made to coalesce mechanically with great rapidity and completeness when spontaneous disintegration will immediately occur. An arrangement like that shown in Fig. 11 might be expected to fulfil the above conditions. A,A′ are two lumps of U(235) in a steel tube. When the explosive charge E is fired, A′ rapidly coalesces with A; the combined mass is above the critical size and disintegration occurs immediately.

A trial bomb based on the above principles was fired in New Mexico on 16th July 1945. It was mounted on a tall steel tower. As detonation occurred there was an intense flash and a huge dome of fire ascended heavenwards. The temperatures attained were of the order of those attained in the centre of the sun; the steel tower disappeared and in its place was a shallow crater surfaced with fused grains of sand. The Frontispiece shows photographs taken at two different intervals after detonation.

President Truman has stated that the bomb which devastated Hiroshima on 6th August 1945, was equivalent in its explosive power to more than 20,000 tons of T.N.T. It has been estimated that the total cost involved in the production of this type of bomb was of the order of £700 million.

The atomic pile

The uranium bomb is of relatively little economic value; its energy is liberated as much too rapidly as that of uranium is liberated too slowly in natural radio disintegration. If the liberation of that energy could be controlled at will, it would be of unprecedented value to the human race. For example, it has been calculated that, assuming 100 per cent efficiency, 1 lb. of U(235) would suffice to keep an 18,000 h.p. engine running for 100 years. Even a mere 10 per cent efficiency would be of inestimable value. But there are enormous difficulties that have not yet been surmounted, although scientists have now been tackling the problems for several years.

The nearest approach as yet to the solution lies in the atomic pile. This usually comprises rods of uranium surrounded by some suitable moderator such as graphite. The so-called GLEEP pile at Harwell commenced operations in 1947; the larger BEPO or British Experimental Pile, with O for euphony, began operations in July 1948. It is air-cooled, the warmed air being used to warm the buildings. Its moderator consists of several hundred tons of graphite, the ratio of carbon to uranium being about 10 to 1. The first French atomic pile began work in December 1948.

At present, owing to the extreme susceptibility of uranium to corrosion it is not possible to use the evolved heat for steam raising purposes. But the pile has many other uses including the production of new elements, such as plutonium; the manufacture of radio-compounds for greenhouses, etc, or as tracers for engineering, chemical and medical purposes; and for research into the production of complex substances.

Thorium

In 1898 both Mme Curie and Gerhardt Carl Schmidt, professor of physics at the University of Münster, independently discovered the radioactivity of thorium, observing it to be less active photo-graphically than uranium, but equally active electroscopically, this latter indicating an equal ionising power. The interested reader may easily demonstrate the photographic activity of thorium compounds by laying a gas mantle on a wrapped photographic plate and leaving it undisturbed for two or three weeks. Upon developing the plate an image of the mantle is obtained.

The changes undergone by thorium during its spontaneous disintegration to lead are indicated in Fig. 12, which gives the type of "particle" evolved, the recognised symbol for the product, its atomic weight and the vertical group in the Periodic Table to which it belongs.

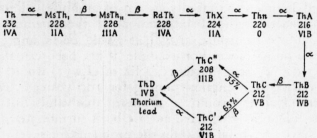

Fig. 12 — The thorium series

The first product of disintegration is *mesothorium* I, discovered by Hahn in 1907. It is isotopic with radium and is used as a substitute for certain radium preparations. As large quantities of thorium minerals are now worked up in connection with the gas-mantle industry, and mesothorium is a by-product, it has assumed commercial importance. It is separated from thorium in monazite being precipitated along with barium as sulphate. *Thorium X*, discovered by Rutherford and Soddy in 1902, is another isotope of radium. *Radiothorium*, RdTh, is an active isotope of thorium and cannot be separated from it directly; it has to be obtained from mesothorium I by disintegration if required free from isotopes.

The final product is *thorium D* or *thorium lead*. Several isotopes of thorium are known. Fast neutrons can cause fission with Th(232) as with U(238) and Np(237)

Actinium

Actinium was discovered in pitch-blende by André Debierne in 1899, a friend of the Curie family and later associated with Mme Curie in the isolation of metallic radium in 1910. He found actinium was precipitated along with the rare earths in fractionating pitch-blende; in 1902 it was re-discovered by Geisel who named it *emanium*. It resembles the rare earth metals, particularly lanthanum, and when the double magnesium nitrates of actiniferous earths of the cerium group are fractionated, it concentrates in the neodymium and samarium fractions.

Actinium is a member of a third radioactive series, known as the *actinium series*, which originates in *actino-uranium*, an isotope of uranium I with a half-life period of 4×10^8 years. It occurs in all uranium minerals in a constant ratio to UI whatever the age.

Until last year (1950) compounds of actinium have not been obtained in anything like a state of purity. This is partly because of

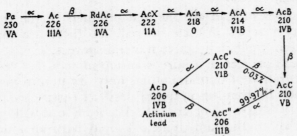

Fig. 13 — The actinium series

rarity, only 0·15 mg of actinium occurring per ton of pitch-blende; also it is invariably associated with rare earth elements, usually those of the lanthanum end, from which it is extremely difficult to separate. Of the known isotopes, only Ac(227) has a sufficiently long life for macro-separation. Hagemann* has succeeded in synthesising actinium bromide by neutron irradiation of radium bromide; thus

$$Ra(226) + n \rightarrow Ra(227) \rightarrow Ac(227) + \beta$$

Although the metal was not isolated, micro quantities of pure Ac_2O_3, AcF_3, $AcCl_3$, etc. were obtained and shown to be isomorphous with the corresponding lanthanum and cerium derivatives.

The immediate parent of actinium is *protactinium* or *ekatantalum*, discovered independently by Hahn and by Soddy in 1917; it occupies the position between thorium and uranium left vacant by Mendeléeff in his Periodic Table of 1869. It loses an α-particle yielding actinium. At one time the actinium series was regarded as a branch of the uranium series. In old minerals the

---

*HAGEMANN and co-workers, *J. Amer. Chem. Soc.*, 1950, **72**, 768, 771.

U/Ac ratio was found to be constant, but the amount of actinium present was nevertheless less than would be expected if it were a direct disintegration product of uranium. This was the reason for assuming it to lie in a separate chain. By the Group Displacement Law protactinium should belong to Group v and thus resemble tantalum. It was this consideration that led to its discovery.

The changes undergone by protactinium during its spontaneous disintegration to *actinium lead* are indicated in Fig. 13, which gives the type of radiation evolved, the recognised symbol for the product, its atomic weight and the vertical group in the Periodic Table to which it belongs.

Atomic weight of lead

Three isotopes of lead are the end products of the three natural disintegration series just considered. As these are inactive they accumulate in their radioactive mineral sources.

If the lead present in a pure uranium mineral has resulted from the disintegration of uranium atoms only, its atomic weight should approximate to that of uranium less 8 α-particles, that is, to $238 \cdot 14 - 8 \times 4 \cdot 002$, or $206 \cdot 12$. Actinium lead will be the same. But lead from a thorium mineral should have an atomic weight equal to that of thorium less 6 α-particles, that is $232 \cdot 12 - 6 \times 4 \cdot 002$, or $208 \cdot 11$. Hence the atomic weight of lead may be expected to vary with its source.

Experiment has shown this to be the case. Ceylonese thorite was found to contain $0 \cdot 39$ per cent of lead oxide presumably derived from thorium by natural disintegration during past ages. The atomic weight of the lead was found by Soddy and Hyman in 1914 to be $208 \cdot 4$.

On the other hand several investigators have obtained a value of approximately $206 \cdot 0$ for lead extracted from pure uranium minerals. Mention may be made of the value $206 \cdot 06$ obtained by Hönigschmidt and Horovitz in 1915 for lead from a sample of Norwegian bröggerite, a variety of uraninite from Norway; and $206 \cdot 00$ found by Baxter in 1933 for lead from Katanga pitch-blende. The atomic weight of ordinary lead is $207 \cdot 22$.

Radon

In 1900 Rutherford[*] observed that thorium compounds impart a temporary activity to the surrounding air, this activity being

---

[*]RUTHERFORD, *Phil. Mag.*, 1900, (5), **49**, 1.

retained for a short time after the removal of the thorium compound, but rapidly diminishing in strength, its half-life being less than one minute. He showed that the emanation was a gas that could be condensed at or about the temperature of liquid air. The gas is now known as *thoron*; it is chemically inert, belonging to Group O and is one of the isotopes occupying the place of element 86.

Rutherford sought for a similar gaseous emanation from radium compounds, but the quantity of these at his disposal was too small. Within a few months, however, Dorn* detected the presence of the gas and three years later Debierne† found that actinium behaved likewise. The three emanations are now known as *thoron* of half-life 54 secs., *radon* 3·825 days, and *actinon* 3·9 secs.

Of these radon alone is of medical importance, the other two isotopes being too short lived. The medical use‡ of radon in the U.K. began in 1914. Radon capsules are used in the treatment of deafness where due to blocking of the Eustachian tube. This occurs with airmen when flying at great heights or when changing their altitudes rapidly, as for example, during dive-bombing. As radon is soluble in petroleum jelly a radio-ointment is prepared that has been used in the treatment of necrosis and radiation injuries. Radon "seeds" and "needles" are also used. The seeds are short lengths of capillary glass tubing filled with radon which may be inserted into growths such as, for example, occur in cancer of the tongue. Needles are generally larger. Being a chemically inert gas, radon readily diffuses into most tissues and is used in biological research. It is also used as a tracer element in the study of gas flow.

Trans-uranium elements

Neptunium was the first of these to be synthesised§; it was obtained in traces by bombardment of U(238) with neutrons (see Fig. 9(*a*), p. 318). Its chemical properties are not in general like those of rhenium or the other elements of Group VII. It yields no volatile oxide corresponding to Re_2O_7. It functions with valencies 3, 4, 5 and 6 and in its higher stages of oxidation it tends to resemble uranium. Several isotopes are known including 237, 238 and 239. It was named after the planet Neptune discovered in 1846.

---

*DORN, *Abh. Naturforsch. Ges. Halle-a-S.*, 1900.
†DEBIERNE, *Compt. rend.*, 1903, **136**, 446, 671; 1904, **138**, 411; 1904, **139**, 538.
‡JENNINGS and RUSS, *Opus cit.*
§McMILLAN and co-workers, *Physical Review*, 1939, **55**, 519; 1940, **57**, 1185.

Plutonium was synthesised by Seaborg in 1940. It has been detected both in pitch-blende, $UO_2.2UO_3$, and in carnotite, $K_2(UO_2)_2(VO_4)_2.8H_2O$, to the extent of about 1 in 10^{14}. Probably the natural element is the isotope 239 formed by non-fission absorption by U(238) of some of the neutrons always present, possibly resulting from spontaneous fission of U(238). Although it has a longer life than radium, namely $2 \cdot 1 \times 10^4$ years (as against 1600) each mg emits 160 million α-particles per minute so that it is dangerous to handle. It functions with valencies of 3, 4, 5 and 6 and generally resembles neptunium and uranium, being more stable than the former in its lower stages of oxidation. Several isotopes are known including 236, 238 and 239. Slow neutrons cause fission with 239Pu as with 235U.

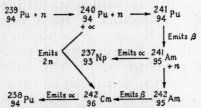

Fig. 14 — The transuranic elements

Production of plutonium was begun in Chicago in 1942 in an atomic pile. The bomb that devastated Nagasaki in Japan on 9th August 1945 contained plutonium.

The name plutonium was suggested for barium by E. D. Clarke, Professor of Mineralogy at Cambridge, 1808-1822, and was used in this sense by Thomas Thomson in his "System of Chemistry" in 1817.

In 1945 the synthesis of elements 95 and 96 was announced. No. 95 corresponds to europium in the lanthanide series (p. 177) and was hence appropriately named *americium*. No. 96 corresponds to gadolinium, named after the Finnish mineralogist Gadolin. It was therefore felt that it was the turn of the Curies to be honoured, and the new element was named *curium*. Several isotopes of the two elements are known.

Both elements are dangerous to handle. Am(241) with a half-life of 500 years evolves 7×10^9 α-particles per minute per mg, and Cm(242) with a half-life of 5 months evolves 10^{13}. The relation between these elements and plutonium is illustrated in Fig. 14.

Neptunium, plutonium and americium metals have been isolated by reduction of their fluorides with barium at 1200° C. Like uranium they are base metals and do not resemble the platinum group. The metal curium has not yet been described.

From the Radiation Laboratory of the University of California* comes news of the syntheses of two more elements, Nos. 97 and 98.

No. 97 has been obtained, by irradiation of americium (96) with helium ions accelerated in the cyclotron, as a nuclide of half-life 4·6 hours and probable atomic weight 243. It decays by electron capture. For it, the name *berkelium*, Bk, has been suggested.

No. 98 has been similarly synthesised by irradiation of curium (96); its half-life is only 45 min. and its atomic weight probably 244. The name *californium*, Cf, has been suggested.

---

*Office of Public Information, University of California; released 17th March 1950. See also PANETH, *Nature*, 1950, 165, 748.

NAME INDEX

337

x

SUBJECT INDEX